A New Start at the Beach Hotel

Francesca Capaldi has enjoyed writing since she was a child, largely influenced by a Welsh mother who was good at improvised story telling. She is a member of the RNA and the Society of Women Writers and Journalists. Francesca currently lives in Kent with her family and a cat called Lando Calrissian.

Also by Francesca Capaldi

Wartime in the Valleys

Heartbreak in the Valleys
War in the Valleys
Hope in the Valleys
Trouble in the Valleys

The Beach Hotel Series

A New Start at the Beach Hotel

A New Start at the Beach Hotel

Francesca Capaldi

hera

First published in the United Kingdom in 2023 by

Hera Books
Unit 9 (Canelo), 5th Floor
Cargo Works, 1-2 Hatfields
London SE1 9PG
United Kingdom

A CIP catalogue record for this book is available from the British Library.

Print ISBN 978 1 80436 133 7
Ebook ISBN 978 1 80436 132 0

Printed and bound in Great Britain by Clays Ltd, Elcograf S.p.A.

1

Dedicated to my history teacher, Miss English, at Maud Allen/The Littlehampton School, who played a big part in kindling my love of history. Gone many years now, but never forgotten.

Prologue

22 June 1914, the Sussex Downs

Edie Moore closed the front door on her life as it was, and stood at the top of the scrubbed steps. She placed the carpetbag down to re-pin her straw hat, which had tipped slightly sideways on her inexpertly tied knot of mid-brown hair. The sigh that followed came up from her boots to the lacework neck of her blouse, before she exhaled it into the cool dawn air.

Ahead of her lay one of the Sussex Downs, covered in wild flowers, sloping to a verdant plain. The wide expanse led ultimately to the distant English Channel that glinted in the sunlight. She'd always loved that view, especially this early in the morning, with the pale blue and pink sky spreading from east to south, crossing the sea. The scene before her was completed by the birds chattering about the new day.

New day. New start.

'Right, Edie, this is not getting you anywhere,' she whispered to herself. She needed to escape before people awoke and someone discovered her here.

The door opened behind her. Edie's stomach twisted painfully as she closed her eyes. To have to face someone now and get into such trouble, after all her planning, would be disastrous. She turned slowly. Relief flooded her as she realised it was Jenny in her starched white apron.

'Oh, thank goodness. I thought it might be—'

'Do you have to go? Lady Moreland will surely forgive you.' Jenny's mouth tipped down at the edges.

'Lady Moreland is unlikely to do any such thing, and you know it. She is unforgiving and always has been. It has become impossible here. If I were you, I'd leave too.'

'But I won't get a reference. What are you going to do?'

Edie didn't want to confess her plans, nor that a sympathetic soul, in the guise of Lady Evelyn Stansfield, had given her a reference when she'd heard of her dilemma.

'I'll be fine. Thank you so much for sorting out the clothes.' She looked down at the grey serge skirt that Jenny had taken in for her, along with the cream blouse and her blue jacket. They would suffice.

'It was the least I could do. What about young Mr Moreland? He was looking for you yesterday, while you were out. Seemed quite keen to find you. Shouldn't you wait until he returns?'

Edie looked up at the white Georgian edifice of Downland House, in which she'd spent eight of her twenty-four years. She shook her head, pressing her lips together. 'No, I won't wait. It's his fault I'm in this mess in the first place.'

An anger bubbled up from deep inside her. Freddie Moreland was a liability who would get into trouble one way or another. Besides, if they got wind of what was happening and found her, goodness knows what would happen next. She shivered.

'Better get inside now, Jenny. You don't want to get into trouble with Mrs Garrett.'

The housekeeper was a harridan, the way she bossed the poor staff around. Edie had a brief regret at leaving Jenny at her mercy. But no, she couldn't take the under housemaid with her.

'Goodbye, Jenny. Take care.'

The maid raised her arm and waved vaguely, the sadness inhabiting her face once more. She stepped back inside and closed the door.

Edie took a last look at the house before picking up her bag and stepping nimbly down the ten steps to her new life.

Chapter One

22 June 1914

A mixture of nerves and excitement filled Edie as the gas towers came into view. She had visited Littlehampton a few times as a child. The towers had always signalled the approach of the railway station.

She got up, the only person in her compartment, and peered outside as the train chugged past a long terrace of small houses. The whistle tooted and the brakes squealed as she was lifting down her carpetbag and umbrella, the deceleration almost knocking her off her feet. She clutched at the velvet upholstery to steady herself, giggling despite her scare.

Why she'd headed to Littlehampton, she wasn't sure. Happy childhood memories, perhaps. She wanted somewhere far enough from Downland House that she was unlikely to bump into the family, but close enough to be familiar. A small village wouldn't suit, yet neither did she want to be anywhere too large. There were shops here, and businesses requiring staff, and plenty of middle- and upper-class families in Beach Town needing servants. The prospect was daunting, yet the freedom was exhilarating. Oh, how she'd longed for that freedom all the time she'd lived in Downland House!

The train clattered to a halt. She let herself out of the compartment and into the corridor, but struggled with opening the door on to the platform. A young porter came to her rescue, smiling and tipping his hat slightly as she stepped out.

'Welcome to Littlehampton, miss, or welcome back. Though I knows all me regulars, and I don't reckon I've seen you hereabouts before.'

'Thank you. It has been rather a long time since I last visited. I wonder if you could point me in the direction of an eating establishment? I believe it must be time for luncheon.'

He looked at her with some confusion. 'Governess, are you?'

She wondered how he'd jumped to that conclusion, then realised: her somewhat genteel enunciation. She must rein it in. It might be fit for the likes of Downland House, but here, in her new position in life… 'Not exactly. Just my little joke. Though I am here to find a position of some sort.'

'Well now, let me carry your luggage out to the front and I'll answer your questions.' He took the bag and led the way down the platform towards a brick building. 'First of all, I recommend the Cypress Temperance Restaurant for a good dinner.'

Dinner. Of course. Not luncheon.

'Out of the station you turn left, go straight down Terminus Road, through High Street and just after the turning to East Street, it'll be on your left. As for a job, you could have a look at the *Littlehampton Gazette*. There's a newsagent on High Street. You could pick one up there.'

As they walked she unclipped her crocodile skin handbag, something Freddie had given her and which, in hindsight, she should have left behind. She rummaged around in it for her purse to extract a coin. By the time she'd found one, they'd reached the curved forecourt at the front of the station. One carriage stood ready awaiting newly arrived passengers, while another announced its arrival by the clip-clop of the horses' hooves. She wouldn't be needing their services.

She turned towards the porter, taking her bag from him. 'Thank you so much for your help.' She offered the threepenny piece, the silver glinting in the sun as she handed it over.

The porter put his hand up and shook his head. 'For you, miss, it's on the house.'

'Thank you. That's most kind of you.'

'Good luck with your job hunting.'

He'd barely finished the sentence when a much older, stouter porter appeared at the entrance. 'Stubbs! There are passengers awaiting your services. I think you're done with that – young *lady*.'

Stubbs raised his eyes so only she could see, turning on his heel to do as he was bid. 'Coming, Mr Mills.'

Edie walked round the pavement, holding in her resentment at the older porter's words. His assumption that she was beneath their attentions had her biting the inside of her cheek. It was bad enough that the working classes were looked down on by those who perceived themselves to be above them, but for one of their own class to do so... Perhaps if she'd been a man, it would have been a different matter.

The town was busy, mostly with women walking singly and in pairs, some with parasols, taking it easy, others with baskets bustling to get past. There was chatter and laughter, and the odd shout of a vendor. A motor car chugged by, sounding its horn at a horse and cart ahead that was carrying crates of vegetables. The windows in High Street were packed with all manner of goods. She wished she could visit all the establishments, never having had the opportunity to shop in this way. Maybe she would, after she'd eaten. Her one concession was to stop briefly to examine the window of a clothes shop, noting its busy display. This might be the perfect place to pick up some suitable clothing. She couldn't wear the same thing every day.

At that thought, doubt crept into her brain. How would she get her laundry done? Where would her meals come from? None of these questions had concerned her, living at Downland House.

Her stroll at last brought her to the Cypress, just where Mr Stubbs had described it. At least one problem would be solved for now. She entered the restaurant.

–

By mid-afternoon Edie was walking down Pier Road, towards the coast, watching as the River Arun rushed towards the sea. Memories of those long-ago visits entertained her as she went. Along the Arun's sloping banks sat fishing boats, nets and floats, the briny odour tickling her nose. The chug and splash of a paddle steamer alerted her to the vehicle's journey towards the river mouth. On the other side of the road that faced the river there was a hotchpotch of single- and double-storey cottages, one of which had become the Harbour Tea Rooms.

She knew from past visits that there were many lodging houses on South Terrace, a road that faced the beach, round the corner from Pier Road. But first she would take a rest at the tea rooms.

You're just stalling, Edie, putting off the inevitable.

'I know,' she whispered to herself.

She'd never thought of herself as timid, but thrown into a new life, all by herself, she started to wonder what on earth had possessed her. She'd always known the people around her, had rarely had to ask favours of strangers.

About to cross the road, she stopped in her tracks. She turned to survey the circular Oyster Pond ahead, on the edge of which were young boys sailing toy yachts, some accompanied by nursemaids. Beyond them was the square of coastguard buildings and cottages, including the imposing windmill by the river. It was a pleasant day and, even though only a Monday, the area was quite busy. Staring at the vista for some moments, she tried to settle on the best course of action.

Edie tapped her umbrella on the ground firmly, as if creating a full stop. No more dithering. It was necessary to secure a room and not put it off a moment longer.

She took a deep breath and crossed the road diagonally, skirting past the Nelson Hotel on the corner. Taking the bend with purpose, she marched towards the tall red-brick edifices of South Terrace.

The first row of lodging houses all displayed the same sign: NO VACANCIES. It was June, the holiday season, so why had she thought it would be otherwise? Doubt assailed her and she was tempted to march straight back to the tea rooms, or further, back on the train to Brighton and beyond.

No. This road was long, with endless places to stay. She'd get a room somewhere. Despite these words of encouragement, her throat constricted with the pressure of the endeavour, rooting her to the spot.

It was the family coming towards her that brought her into the present once more. The father was gesturing boldly with a walking stick that seemed to be for show. He was pronouncing pompously on some subject or other. Seeing her in their way, he poked her with the stick before she had time to move. Her response was swift.

'How dare you, sir. Who do you think you are?'

The man, clearly taken aback by her genteel pronunciation, was lost for words. He shuffled his family around her, their amazed gazes suggesting that people seldom questioned him.

His parting shot was mumbled. 'Airs and graces above her station.'

If she'd had any doubts before about carrying on with her plan, they'd now vanished. Men like him – they made her blood boil. Oh, and she'd come across a good many in her time. It was another good reason to quit Downland House. It was the fury from this encounter that propelled her on, across the side road to the next row of houses.

Passing each house, she became increasingly agitated by the number of NO VACANCIES signs, her steps becoming more rapid.

Resigned to crossing the road yet again to the next row, she almost missed the VACANCIES sign at the second to last house. She gazed up at the second floor of the building, to its sharp gable, then down to the iron balcony on the first floor. The ground floor was a little above street level. There was also a basement, accessible from the front. Every floor, apart from the second, had a bay window. The sign announced 'Channel View'. She ran up the steps to the front door before she had time to change her mind, knocking boldly once she'd reached the top.

She'd almost given up on anyone answering when she saw an outline beyond the glass. The door was flung open to reveal a small woman with a long beak of a nose and small hazel eyes. Her red hair was tied into a tight bun, the colour contrasting with her violet dress. The skirt was bell-shaped, while the bodice had voluminous sleeves that peaked at the shoulders. Her outfit was straight out of Queen Victoria's last years.

She looked Edie up and down, her eyes narrowed. 'Can I help you?'

Edie decided to speak once more in a cultured voice, thus hopefully persuading the woman that she was at least educated.

'Good afternoon, madam. I see that you have vacancies, and I was wondering if there might be a room I could rent.'

The woman was a little bemused. 'I do have rooms available, though I normally prefer a letter to be sent to me first, plus some references. And I usually rent long-term to those with means.'

Edie's heart sank. Of course. But then she remembered the letter.

She put down her bag and umbrella and unclipped her handbag. She pulled out the envelope and handed it to her prospective landlady. 'This is my job reference, but it might help you decide.'

The woman removed the paper from the envelope and scanned the lines quickly. By the end she was smiling.

'Well, Lady Evelyn Stansfield has certainly sung your praises. I'm aware of Her Ladyship, of course, with all her good works with the poor and unfortunates in Sussex.' She handed the letter back and stood to one side. 'I'm Mrs Hadley, the proprietress of this establishment. Pleased to meet you, Miss Moore. Do come in.'

Edie tucked the envelope back into her bag, picked up her belongings and stepped over the threshold, grateful to Lady Evelyn once more for helping her in her hour of need. Without her help she could never have escaped her inevitable fate. The hall was spotless, with a small table on which stood a bronze statuette of a woman.

She followed Mrs Hadley up the stairs to the first floor as the landlady chatted about rent and rules. At the top she waited for Edie before saying, 'I have a room free on the first floor at the front, or the second floor, right at the back. Which would you prefer? The front faces the sea, though you can't see much past the cottages and coastguard station.'

'The first floor would be lovely, thank you, Mrs Hadley.'

'My tenant, Miss Brownlow, is also on this floor. The other one, Miss Nye, is upstairs. I have my bedroom at the back on the ground floor. That way I can keep an ear out for unauthorised guests. I have strict rules about that. Female friends are allowed to call only between the hours of nine in the morning and six in the evening. Male callers are strictly forbidden.'

They entered the room. The old-fashioned wallpaper was dark. Within there was a fireplace, double bed, small wardrobe, two-drawer chest, bedside table, washstand and a single dining chair. There was a whiff of neglect and lavender. She peeped out through the lace curtains of the bay window that overlooked the common, spotting the Oyster Pond on the right. Despite what the landlady had said, she could spy the sea to the left of the coastguard buildings.

'It's splendid, Mrs Hadley.'

The landlady beamed. 'I'll leave you to unpack. Dinner's at six thirty and breakfast at seven in the morning. Both are taken in the dining room, the first room on the right when you come through the front door.' She started to turn but halted part way. 'Oh, I really should ask for a week's rent in advance. If you have it with you.'

'Of course.' Edie removed her purse from her handbag and took out the required amount.

'Most obliged.'

As the landlady went to leave once more, it was Edie who halted her this time. 'Mrs Hadley, I wonder. Do you know of any jobs around and about? I should like to secure some work as soon as possible.'

The landlady screwed up her lips to one side, perhaps regretting taking in someone without work.

'I do have enough money to tide me over for a few weeks,' Edie clarified, 'but the sooner I get a job, the better.'

'I haven't heard of any governess work recently—'

'It doesn't have to be that,' Edie interrupted. 'Anything where I could earn enough to pay my way would do.'

'I will ask around for you then.'

'Even an office job of some kind would be fine.'

Mrs Hadley shook her head. 'Not likely to be much of them jobs for a woman. You know how it is. Most office work is done by men, for us poor women don't have the wherewithal to cope with it.' She tapped her head twice.

At first Edie thought she was being serious, but quickly realised the landlady was mocking the general attitude to women's capabilities.

'I see what you mean, Mrs Hadley.'

'But I'll listen out all the same.' She stood staring at Edie as if waiting for any further questions.

To fill the silence Edie said, 'I'm so pleased to have found somewhere on South Terrace. I holidayed here as a child and young woman.' She immediately regretted sharing that information, hoping that Mrs Hadley would not interrogate her on this matter.

She need not have worried. Mrs Hadley sniffed and pinched in her lips before stating, 'This is Empress Maud Road. South Terrace is the other side of Granville Road.'

Edie had forgotten this peculiarity, for although the name at this end was indeed different, the houses of the promenade road were numbered from one end to the other consecutively. Clearly there was some source of pride in the separate names.

'Of course. So silly of me. I'd better let you go,' said Edie. 'I dare say you have need to prepare dinner for the guests, and Mr Hadley, of course.'

Mrs Hadley pulled her mouth into a wide non-smile. 'I'm afraid he's no longer with us.' It was said in a manner that did not suggest regret at the situation, though the landlady struck her as someone who would be loath to show emotion.

'I am sorry to hear that. I would not have mentioned him had I known.'

'No, no, it's fine. You weren't to know. As you say, I have dinner to prepare.' She beat a hasty retreat.

After she left, Edie sank onto the bed. Trust her to make such a faux pas when she hadn't been here five minutes.

Now to unpack and decide what to do with the rest of the day.

And the rest of her life.

Chapter Two

At six twenty-eight precisely, according to the small carriage clock on the mantelpiece in her room, Edie headed downstairs. In the hall she sniffed a brief hint of roasted meat. The dining room had the same view as her own, albeit from the floor below. There were five tables, each with two chairs. On each of the tables was a lace cloth and a cruet set. Three of them were also laid with cutlery.

She was delighted to see two other women in the room. One was sitting in the corner furthest from the window, while the other sat admiring the view. Both looked to be middle class of some sort. They were unlikely to be interested in her though.

This was confirmed by the woman sitting in the corner, dressed in a high-necked blouse. Her dark hair was swept up and finished in a knot on top of her head. She looked over at the new guest, her face neutral, and gave a brief nod of acknowledgement, then turned away. Edie had changed into the plain navy-blue skirt and white blouse she'd bought on a trip back to High Street that afternoon, hoping to look more presentable.

However, it was a different matter with the woman by the window who, having noticed Edie, smiled and beckoned her over. Edie noticed her eau de Nil blouse with a V-neck. It was most attractive, and went beautifully with her mid-auburn hair that was plaited and coiled upon her head. Her eyes were a deep blue.

'Do join me.' The woman grinned in welcome.

'Thank you.'

Outside, the sun was muscling through the clouds, creating a bright spot over the pond.

Edie's new companion leant in close to whisper, 'Don't worry about Miss Nye. She's most unfriendly. Can barely bring herself to say hello.'

Edie mouthed, 'Oh,' before introducing herself. 'I'm Edie Moore. How do you do?' She held out her hand.

'And I'm Pamela Brownlow. How do you do?'

They shook hands.

Edie had a moment of panic as she anticipated Miss Brownlow asking about her reasons for being here, and possibly her life generally. She took two deep breaths. This had all been worked out on the train, so she must stop worrying. But she must also stick to her story.

'Do you live in Littlehampton, or are you just visiting?'

'Visiting, though I intend to stay a while and am looking for work here,' Edie replied.

'Have you visited the town before?'

'I have, but not for a number of years. Yourself?'

Miss Brownlow lifted the napkin from the table, unfolding it before placing it on her lap. 'I've been living here nearly six months. Ah, here is Mrs Hadley with dinner.'

Sure enough, the landlady had entered, skilfully carrying three plates, for which Edie was grateful. They had been dangerously close to revealing their places of origin.

Mrs Hadley put one plate down in front of Miss Nye, who at least showed appreciation of it to the landlady. The remaining plates were brought over to them.

'There is a table laid up for you over there, Miss Moore. You don't have to sit with Miss Brownlow.' She seemed put out.

'That's fine, Mrs Hadley,' Miss Brownlow replied. 'We're happy to become acquainted.'

'Miss Brownlow is a teacher in Arundel.' Mrs Hadley's expression was as proud as if she'd been her own daughter.

'Perhaps she knows of a position for you, considering your last—'

'I fear not,' Miss Brownlow interrupted. 'We have sufficient teachers… in fact, one too many. The headmistress needs to dismiss one of us as it is. Not me, luckily.' She gave, what seemed to Edie, a forced smile.

Mrs Hadley nodded solemnly. 'Such a shame. Now, eat up your meals before they get cold.' She left the room.

Edie surveyed the lamb chop, carrots and mashed potato. 'This looks delicious.'

'You sound surprised.'

Edie half laughed. 'I'm not sure what I expected, Miss Brownlow.'

Her companion picked up the salt pot, sprinkling the condiment liberally over her food. 'Call me Pamela. We're friends now.'

She was pleased to make a chum so quickly. 'And please, call me Edie.'

Both took up their cutlery and started their meal. Edie's new life had begun well. All she needed now was a job. That she would tackle tomorrow.

-

It had been a long day, walking up and down the streets of Beach Town, asking in various businesses whether there were any jobs going. These had included two grocery stores, a greengrocer and a post office. She'd done her best to imitate Jenny at Downland House, so she would appear more appropriate for the jobs. Mentioning that she'd been good at arithmetic at school, so would be able to add up people's bills quickly, had made no difference. They'd had no vacancies. The butcher she'd spoken to had looked at her in astonishment, as if to question what contribution she could possibly make to their business. She'd even tried the dairy farm on the edge of town, mentioning that she'd worked with animals, albeit horses. They'd declined her request for work without any explanation.

In the antique dealer's and the fancy repository, with its gifts and arts and crafts merchandise, her accent had become more middle class. She hoped. But there were no jobs on offer in those places either. Or so they said. The public houses she'd passed by, except for the New Inn on Norfolk Road, which was also a hotel. But with no luck.

Tomorrow she would try in the town, though Mrs Hadley had tutted when she'd suggested it yesterday during dinner. She'd talked of 'Town people' not being 'genteel folk' like 'Beach people'. Edie found this ironic, given Mrs Hadley's rather affected accent, that suggested she too was originally from further down society. Still, you couldn't always tell, as she well knew.

Walking the length of Norfolk Road, with its mixture of large, gentrified houses and simpler terraces, Edie emerged onto the eastern end of South Terrace. Here she was among the hotchpotch of Georgian buildings, some tall and stark, others balconied and more homely. The first spits of rain wet her face and she put her umbrella up.

Now what? In the distance, to the west, was the Beach Hotel, imposing and impressive. She crossed the road to the common and set off towards it.

Had she made a mistake leaving Downland House? Yet how could she have stayed there after the recent trouble? And there was that threat to get her locked up. Maybe an idle threat, but you could never quite tell. The strain of this impossible situation made her head ache. The day was gloomy, a lot cooler than yesterday. But the breeze that wafted around her was welcome in her troubled state.

Things would work out. She was strong, determined. Awkward, her mother no doubt would have said, but it would hold her in good stead in her new situation.

Reaching the Beach Hotel, she stood and admired it. It contained three distinct sections, with a large canopy in the middle for the entrance. The brickwork was a rusty red and there were many smaller and larger gables scattered about the roof. On the right-hand side, both the terrace on the ground floor and the balcony on the first floor curved around the building, with wooden props that looked like tree branches. There were numerous windows. It was rather rambling and infinitely more interesting than the staid Georgian Downland House. Around the hotel and large grounds was a stone wall. Attached on the left side was a single-storey public house with a short clock tower.

She'd often wondered what it was like inside, on those long-ago visits here with Miss Langley and Nanny Street. The young nurse with them had yearned to be sent somewhere 'posh' like this, as she'd put it. It was, after all, one of the premier hotels on the South Coast. Nanny Street had replied that their lodgings on South Terrace were cosy enough, and that they should be glad to be sent on this holiday by Lady Moreland at all.

About to move off, she halted to gaze at the hotel. 'What have I got to lose?'

She pushed open the nearest of two gates and headed across the courtyard to the entrance, passing under an open brick porch. After one more brief hesitation as she closed her umbrella, she opened one of the double wood and glass doors and went inside. She emitted a small gasp. It was even lovelier than she had imagined. The foyer was elegant with its cream walls, crystal chandelier and marble floor.

Gathered around a painting on the wall were three women, arty types, with colourful dresses and turbans. They were pointing to the painting and were obviously discussing it. How she would have loved to stop and chat to them, having never had much of a chance to engage with such people in her old life.

Standing in the middle of the foyer, as if waiting for somebody, was an old matriarchal type, hair done up elaborately and fussily, with a large hat pinned on top of it. Her lips were pinched in as she considered a door on the far side. In her hand was a silver walking cane with a fancy globe-shaped pommel on the top. She tapped it impatiently on the floor.

Oh yes, this character was familiar, though she'd never met this particular one.

Through the door she was examining came a slightly younger, more plainly attired woman.

'Cecelia, about time,' called the matriarch. 'Come along now.'

'Yes, Lady Blackmore.' The woman hurried in short, dainty steps towards her.

Edie almost laughed. Lady Blackmore's sort she would *not* miss from her old life. But would there be a job here where she could avoid such people?

She headed towards the dark oak reception desk. Here stood a tall woman, her blonde hair coiled elegantly on top of her head. She was looking down at a large book, writing on the top line. As Edie approached the woman looked up, smiling.

'Good afternoon, how may I help you?'

Now, what tone of voice to employ? Educated, but not upper class, would be best. More like the governess, Miss Langley. Freddie had always said what a good imitator she was, especially when mimicking the pompous rhetoric of many of the guests of Downland House, along with the more petulant staff.

'Good afternoon. I was wondering whether you might have any positions of work available here?'

The woman shut the book before looking Edie over a couple of times, perusing her not unkindly, but enquiringly. 'It just so happens we have the post of bookkeeper vacant, a live-in job if you require that, with a reduction in wages, of course. Have you any appropriate experience?'

'I confess I do not. However, I was educated to sixteen years of age, have a very good head for figures and am a quick learner.'

'I can offer you an interview, if you have a reference, though there are four other people applying for the job.'

That being the case, she had little chance of success. Still, as she'd told herself before entering, what had she to lose?

'I do have a reference, and I would like to take up your offer of an interview, thank you.'

'The manager will be interviewing tomorrow morning, if you'd like to return then. Let's say...' She considered a loose piece of paper on the desk. 'Eleven thirty? Then you can be the fifth interviewee.'

'Thank you, I very much appreciate that, um...'

'Mrs Bygrove. Helen Bygrove. My husband is the manager here. And you are Edie Moore, I gather from your reference.'

'That's right.'

'Pleased to make your acquaintance, Miss Moore.'

'Likewise.'

Mrs Bygrove wrote Edie's name on the paper. The other names she spied on the sheet were surprisingly all women.

'Until tomorrow then,' said the manager's wife.

Edie understood she was being dismissed and took her leave.

Out in the fresh air again she sucked in a deep breath. It was a start, even if she didn't get the job. The rain had stopped but the sky was no less overcast. The murkiness did not dampen her spirits. With a dash more optimism coursing through her blood, she crossed the common to the promenade, continuing her journey towards the river.

There were few people about today. The bathing tents sat unused, while the unridden donkeys looked forlorn. Passing the coastguards' cottages and the pier, she rounded the corner to stroll by the Arun. Floating downriver was a ship, its sails billowing in the breeze. She watched it for a while, wondering where it was heading, wishing she could sail away too.

Turning back to regard the old windmill she remembered from years gone by, she was surprised to see a couple of new buildings in front of it. One was a tea room, but the larger was called the Kursaal, and seemed to be some kind of seaside theatre. This hadn't been here the last time she'd visited. It advertised two shows a day with 'Nathaniel Janus's Pierrots', whose programme included singing, sketches and burlesques. She'd never attended such a show and experienced a tingle of excitement. Booking for one of the evenings would give her something to do other than sit in her room.

She stepped inside cautiously.

There was a faint odour of fresh paint. At the small window of a ticket booth sat a young woman serving a couple, chatting as she described the shows. On her head was a white beret with a red pompom. Edie listened in as she explored the poster on the wall, wondering whether she should spend her money on it. As she pondered, a middle-aged man skulked through a side door, examining his nails. She noticed briefly that he was tatty, before returning to the poster.

The couple, having purchased tickets, left. She checked her purse. No, she'd need to buy a couple more items of clothing. Reluctantly she returned the purse to her handbag. As she pushed the outside door open once more, she heard a piercing scream from the direction of the ticket booth. She shot back inside. Behind the glass, the young ticket seller seemed to be struggling with someone. She screamed once more before disappearing.

The skulking male Edie had seen only minutes before ran from a door in the booth, a cash box in his hand.

The man turned towards her, his face contorted with rage, making what might have been a handsome visage into an ugly one. He had dark, unruly hair and scruffy, baggy clothes. Around his neck was a red kerchief and a chain with a medallion. She raised her umbrella above her head, emitting a high-pitched shriek as she charged towards him. She had no plan – just her fury. The thief looked set to tackle her when through another door hurried a man in a nautical outfit: white trousers, a double-breasted jacket with brass buttons and a captain's hat.

The thief twisted abruptly and made his way through a back door, vanishing from sight.

One of them should perhaps have followed him, Edie considered as she hurried towards the booth, but the ticket seller was clearly their priority. The young woman stumbled from the booth to the floor. The man in the nautical outfit got to her first.

'Brenda, Brenda, you all right, love?' He lifted the head and shoulders of what was little more than a girl, Edie realised, now that she could see her better. On her head was a burgeoning bruise.

'Oh, Mr Janus, sir, I'm sorry. Did he get away?'

'Don't worry about that now, girl. It isn't you that should be sorry. Are you badly hurt?'

'Just a little dazed.' She lifted herself up to a sitting position, her long navy skirt covered in dust and cobwebs.

'Did you get a good look at him?'

Brenda shook her head mournfully. 'I'm afraid I didn't.'

'I did,' Edie piped up.

'Would you be able to give a description to the police?' asked Mr Janus.

She paused briefly, wondering if this would give her away somehow. But surely not. 'Yes, of course.'

The man helped the poor girl up and placed her on the chair. 'Thank you, by the way, for being willing to tackle him. A foolhardy act, I shouldn't wonder, though your bravery is appreciated. Perhaps I could get the *Gazette* to feature it.'

She felt as faint as young Brenda looked. 'Please, I don't look for congratulation, and I like to keep myself to myself.'

'Fair enough. But if I can ever do you a favour in return, I will. I'm Nathaniel Janus, owner of this establishment.'

'Edie Moore.' She hesitated. 'I don't suppose you have a job vacancy of any kind?'

Mr Janus chuckled. 'Only for a player in my Pierrot troupe. But for one so unassuming, I doubt it would suit.'

'You're probably right.' Edie wished she had the courage to entertain people. It indeed seemed a merry way of life.

'Now, if you could do me one favour more and take care of Brenda here, I'll go to the coastguard station and telephone the police.'

'Of course.'

Mr Joseph left. Edie leant on the counter and listened to Brenda's version of events.

–

By the time Edie got through the front door of her lodgings, she was exhausted. It was only ten minutes until dinner time. With this in mind she ran up the stairs to her room, expecting at any moment for someone to appeal to her to be 'more ladylike and less like an elephant'. She tidied her hair and washed her face in the china bowl provided with the pitcher, despite there being a sink in the bathroom. Her skirt was sandy on the bottom from walking on the beach, and dusty elsewhere from kneeling next to Brenda, causing her to brush at it vigorously. What a day.

Finally, she was satisfied that she passed muster and headed downstairs.

In the dining room there was talk of the to-do at the Kursaal, the rumour of which had made its way to Mrs Hadley via a neighbour who'd recently returned from a walk.

'Did you hear of this on your travels, Miss Moore?' asked the landlady.

'I did indeed, as I was the patron present when it happened. I haven't long given my statement to the police. It seems the Kursaal may not be the first establishment in the town this man has raided.'

'My goodness, what a thing to happen when you've only just arrived. And Brenda Jones, the attendant, is she all right?'

'Mr Janus fetched a doctor and all seemed fine. She is shaken, of course, poor girl. Luckily I was able to give the police a good description.'

'Do tell,' trilled Pamela, her fingers laced together and placed on the table.

'Let's see.' Edie pictured the scene, describing the man as she had done to the police. 'He was tall, the thief, with dark wavy hair. Very dark eyes and pale skin. His nose was large, lips full. His dirty shirt was half undone, revealing a good deal of chest hair.' She tutted at the memory of this uncouthness. 'His baggy, patched trousers were held up with a rope belt. He wore no hat. He had on some kind of medallion and a neckerchief. And his accent, it might have been a Hampshire one.' The footman at Downland House had been from Southampton and there was certainly a similarity in their voices.

Edie brought her mind back to the present, regarding her hostess. She was staring into the void and had gone quite pale. The fingers of her hands were gripped together.

'Are you all right, Mrs Hadley?'

'What? Oh, yes. What a dreadful man. I was thinking how easily you could have got hurt, and Brenda, too.'

'Well, Edie,' said Pamela, demanding her attention. She blinked several times, mouth opened slightly, before continuing. 'That certainly is a detailed description. How observant you are. But if you had time to take in so much, then so did he. I would watch your back, for he knows you can identify him.'

It seemed more a threat than a warning, but no doubt it was Pamela being dramatic, as seemed her manner.

'If I were him, I'd keep *well* away,' said Mrs Hadley. She puckered her lips, causing deep lines to appear in the skin above. 'Anyway, it's dinner time, so enough of this talk. I must serve your meal.' She backed away, a grin revealing large teeth, but the good humour did not reach her eyes.

Edie looked over at Miss Nye, whose manner was stiff. The young woman glanced in her direction, briefly widening her eyes and raising her brow in a kind of appeal. It was over so quickly she was convinced she'd imagined it.

'Sit down,' said Pamela. Edie's attention was drawn back to her new friend, who indicated the seat opposite her. 'Give me more details of your adventure.'

She sat, determined now not to relate all that had happened, particularly her pursuit of the thief with her umbrella. After dinner she would retreat to her room and not walk out by the river again as she'd planned. Who knew if he might still be about?

Tomorrow's interview at the Beach Hotel, which she had also decided not to mention, could not come quickly enough.

–

Edie entered the Beach Hotel at twenty-five minutes past eleven, according to the grandfather clock in the reception hall. At the desk today was a man who looked to be in his forties. His hair was long on top, parted in the middle. The three-piece suit he was wearing was smart and modern, grey with a blue tie. Could this be Mr Bygrove?

He looked up. 'Can I help you?' His manner was crisp but polite.

'I'm Miss Moore. I've come for the eleven thirty interview for bookkeeper.'

He became at once brusque. 'Then why have you entered by the front door, may I ask? You were instructed in the letter to enter via the servants' entrance, at the side of the hotel.'

This was a terrible start, and she was already at a disadvantage.

'I'm so sorry, but Mrs Bygrove informed me in person yesterday about the interview, so I've had no letter.'

He huffed impatiently. 'Go out of the entrance and turn right, then right again and go through the gate. Knock on the door on the right, not the one on the left. You'd better hurry if you're an eleven thirty. Mr Bygrove will not tolerate tardiness.'

'Thank you very much.'

Not the manager then, but a trumped-up desk clerk. She'd come across a few servants like him during her years at Downland House. She hurried off in the direction he'd indicated.

Entering through the gate in the side wall, she found herself in a small courtyard. She knocked at the appropriate door. A very tall man with dark brown hair answered, almost certainly a porter. He was dressed in a mid-blue uniform and circular hat with a peak and was around her own age. His eyes were bright blue and crinkled with curiosity.

'Can I help you, miss?'

'I'm Edie Moore, here for the bookkeeper's interview.'

'Another one, eh? Come in.' He opened the door into what was clearly a scullery. 'I'll show you the way.'

They passed through a stillroom where a maid was making jam, judging by the aroma. She breathed in the fragrance. Raspberry. Her favourite. She followed him through two further doors, finding herself in a short dark corridor.

The porter pointed to the door on the left. 'That's Mr Bygrove's office. If you'd like to wait here till he calls you.'

'Thank you for your kindness.'

The man knitted his eyebrows. 'Me, miss? Just my job, isn't it?' He treated her to a wink before going back the way he'd come.

Goodness, thought Edie. She wasn't sure whether she was offended or flattered. The porter certainly had a presence with those large gleaming eyes and mischievous grin. She experienced a small shiver of delight, immediately reproving herself for being so silly.

She surveyed the corridor. There wasn't even a chair to sit on. Instead, she leant against the wall next to the door, weary from little sleep the previous night. There was a vague murmur of voices, though nothing she could make out. Tipping her head back, she yawned. Her heart thumped against her ribs. This was even more nerve-racking than the evenings of her visits to the suffragist meetings and her fear of discovery. That hadn't worked out well, and no doubt neither would this.

The louder voices and the clicking of the door handle caused her to straighten her back and neaten her skirt. A youngish woman emerged. She turned to bid the man in the doorway farewell before walking away.

The man noticed her now, appraising her with squinting eyes. 'You must be the Moore woman.'

The Moore Woman? This wasn't a good start.

'Miss Edie Moore, sir, yes. How do you do?'

'Come in.'

She followed him into a tiny dim office, lit only by a high row of windows, relieved to see Mrs Bygrove sitting a foot or so from the dark oak desk. The manager's wife smiled at her, easing her nerves a little.

The man sat and pointed at the chair opposite. 'Sit.'

Edie did as she was bid.

'I would not have chosen to interview someone without bookkeeping experience, but since my wife had already invited you to come...' He gave Mrs Bygrove a stern glance. 'So, Miss Moore, my wife tells me you've had but one job, as a governess.'

She took the envelope from her bag and handed it to him, wondering how many times she'd have to do this before she secured work. 'My reference.'

'How old are you?'

'Twenty-four, sir.'

He placed a pair of spectacles on his nose, then perused the letter as he asked, 'And why did you leave your last position?'

'My charge went to boarding school.'

'So why are you not applying for a governess's job?'

She had anticipated this question. 'I didn't want to become attached to another child, only to lose contact with them.'

Mr Bygrove looked over his glasses at her. 'I see. My wife informs me you were in education until sixteen years of age. Where?'

She hadn't predicted this question. How she wished Lady Evelyn had not written such a thing on her reference. She recalled the local blacksmith in the nearby village, sending his daughter to a grammar school. It gave her an idea.

'The grammar school, sir.'

This was becoming too easy, and that worried her. Reality mixed in with untruths. Where would it end?

He handed her back the reference. 'Your father had money enough for that, did he? What's his trade?'

'He sells timber, sir.' This was at least the truth.

'Very well. We will inform you in the next day or so whether you've been successful. Leave your address with my wife.' He left the chair and then the room without a goodbye.

Mrs Bygrove came to the desk and leant over it. 'Here, you can write your address on this.' She pushed a piece of paper and a fountain pen towards her.

Edie wrote down Mrs Hadley's address, almost certain it would make no difference. Unless the other candidates were particularly dreadful or unqualified, she was highly unlikely to get the job.

'Here you are, Mrs Bygrove.'

'Thank you… Ah, you're just up the road. I know of Mrs Hadley. There was an incident at her boarding house a year or so back, a lot of shouting and screaming. I don't know the details, probably a troublesome boarder, but I know word got round and the poor woman lost custom. I hope it's picked up for her.'

That might explain why there were only two other guests. It was therefore surprising that she should not have been particularly enthusiastic about Edie's initial arrival at the house. Perhaps the incident had made her more cautious about whom she took in.

'It all seems perfectly decent now,' she said by way of politely defending Mrs Hadley, who had, after all, solved one problem for her. 'I presume I'll have to leave via the servants' entrance.'

Mrs Bygrove looked heavenward and tutted. 'I suppose you had better, as it's what Douglas has instructed, though you are quite presentable.'

Edie appreciated the compliment, given the length of time it had taken her to pin her hair up neatly that morning. At one point she had swept the pins from the chest of drawers to the floor in frustration.

She rose from the chair. 'Thank you once more for adding me to the interviewing list. Farewell.'

'Farewell, Miss Moore, and good luck.'

Good luck with getting a job, as this one is not for you, is what Edie added in her head.

She left the office and made her way back to the servants' entrance and out into the sunshine.

Chapter Three

Edie sat with her head leaning out of her open bedroom window, peering west towards the river, admiring the mauve and cerise sky of the dying day. She hadn't yet bothered to light her gas lamp. It was nearly ten o'clock and Edie was tired, but she couldn't pull herself away from this natural work of art. Outside it was silent, not even the distant waves or the few walkers adding any sound to the still evening.

That morning, Mrs Hadley had come up with an idea on her work situation. There were many private schools in Littlehampton, she'd told her, educating the children of the upper echelons. Had she tried any of them?

She'd been reluctant to put this idea into action at first. But an increasing lack of choice persuaded her it was worth a try. After obtaining a list and rough map from her landlady, she'd set off on her quest, visiting first the schools in Beach Town. All had claimed to be fully staffed, or were not sufficiently impressed with her single reference as a governess and apparent lack of training. There were also schools in the town, some private, some not. She'd try them tomorrow, though held out little hope of success.

She pulled her head in, sat back down in the seat she'd brought to the window and placed her elbows on the ledge. This was the calmest she'd felt since leaving Downland House, and she intended to take full advantage of it before going to bed.

After a couple of minutes, she found herself drifting off, lulled by the fresh evening air and the muted colours. The call of a single gull wove its way into her half-dreams. She sighed with contentment. Work would turn up if she put in the effort to find it. There was still a little money left that she'd saved that would tide her over in the meantime.

And there was always the pearl necklace as a last resort. A very last resort.

She was lost in this notion when voices roused her from her reverie. She leant her head out of the window, making out two people in the gloom. One spoke in a loud whisper, the other shushing them into silence. It wasn't Mrs Hadley, for she retired to bed before ten o'clock each night.

Worried they might be up to no good, she went out into the corridor. Mrs Hadley kept a gas ceiling light burning here in the night, to allow guests to see their way to the modern bathroom and water closet she was so proud of. Edie knelt near the top of the stairs, peeping around the newel post. If it were thieves, what could she do anyway? Alert Mrs Hadley, whose bedroom was at the top of the house, without being detected?

It was soon clear that it was Pamela, who seemed to have brought a friend home. She recalled Mrs Hadley's strict rules about this. Guessing that Pamela and her friend would come upstairs, Edie rose and was about to creep back to her bedroom when her foot got caught in her skirt. She tumbled to the floor, grabbing the newel post to prevent herself from falling onto the stairs.

When she managed to look up again, Pamela was flat against the wall, her eyes wide with panic. Behind her was not a female friend, as she'd assumed, but a young man. He too looked troubled.

'What on earth are you doing?' Pamela hissed. 'You scared the life out of me.'

'I thought you might be thieves.'

Pamela looked back at the man, saying, 'This is my… my young man, Jim.'

He removed his flat cap, dipping his head. 'How do.' He was blond, his hair cut short at the sides and long on top, parted on one side. He had only a waistcoat over his shirt, no jacket.

'Please don't tell Mrs Hadley. You know her rules. But how is one to court?' She grinned coyly. Jim looked down at his feet and rubbed his neck, looking decidedly uncomfortable.

'No, of course not,' said Edie. 'You're lucky she sleeps so soundly.'

'Aren't I just? So much for her listening out for offenders. Now off to bed with you.'

Edie moved away from the stairs, allowing her friend, who had grabbed her young man's hand, to pull him up the stairs and into the bedroom at the back. She stared at the door, feeling quite shocked. Surely they wouldn't be…? No, they probably just wanted to be out of the way of prying eyes to canoodle. Still, she felt uneasy about Pamela's deception, which had now become her own, and hoped most fervently that Mrs Hadley never found out.

–

Edie sat at the table nearest the window looking out at the near-empty street. White clouds were skittering across the sky, showing tantalising glimpses of blue. She hoped for a sunny day to lift her spirits, so downtrodden was she by her lack of luck in securing a job. Still, who knew what today might bring? She might, just might, even get the job at the hotel.

'Looks like it could be a fine morning, if the clouds blow over.'

The voice brought Edie out of her trance. She was surprised to find she was being addressed by Miss Nye, on her usual table by the wall. The young woman had bid her good morning when she'd arrived at breakfast. Her greetings were always polite, but she had certainly never engaged her in any other kind of conversation before.

'Indeed. Let's hope so.'

Miss Nye's lips tipped up into what was the nearest to a smile she'd given so far, but the conversation seemed to be at an end. Edie certainly didn't know what to add to it.

Miss Brownlow had not yet appeared at breakfast, despite it now being almost ten past seven. She assumed the sweetheart, Jim, had already left. It could be that Pamela was tired from her activities last night. She felt the scarlet of embarrassment creep up her neck to her face. Staying out late was what had initially been on her mind, but she thought once more of how there were other activities she could have been engaged in.

There were footsteps up the stairs from the basement, announcing Mrs Hadley's pending arrival with the breakfast. Sure enough, she was through the dining room door a few seconds later, holding aloft two plates from which Edie could detect the savoury aroma of bacon.

The housekeeper wrinkled her nose. 'Miss Brownlow still hasn't appeared?' She took the first plate to Miss Nye. 'Well, I'm very clear about times for meals, and if she doesn't turn up soon, she may well have to go without.' Next, she brought Edie her plate. Apart from the bacon there was an egg and some fried mushrooms.

'I dare say she's overslept.' It was the only thing Edie could think of to say.

Mrs Hadley placed her hands on her slim hips. 'Well, if she's after catching the omnibus up to Arundel at eight fifteen, she'd better look lively. Not that it's any of my business, but if she gets the sack for being tardy, where's her rent coming from, hm? Eat up, ladies, and I'll bring the toast.'

As she was about to leave, another footfall was heard, this time coming down from the first floor. Pamela appeared in the doorway, beaming at all present. The teal skirt and pale blue muslin blouse she wore looked crisp and new. She was bright and chirpy, not at all like someone who'd been up half the night.

'Good morning, all.'

'About time.' Mrs Hadley wagged her finger. 'One minute more and you'd have been too late for breakfast. You know my rules. I've got other things to be getting on with.'

'I'm so sorry, Mrs Hadley. I had *such* a disturbed night.'

'Not the first one, from what you've said before. Perhaps you should get to bed earlier, Miss Brownlow, not reading them penny dreadfuls into the night, or whatever it is you do.'

'But they're *so* entertaining.'

The landlady left the room muttering, 'Entertaining, indeed.'

Pamela giggled as she took her place next to Edie. 'My goodness, she's such a fusspot. It's only just gone a quarter past seven.'

As she poured herself a cup of tea from the china pot, an unknown figure, not much more than a girl, climbed the outside steps with an envelope in her hand. Next, they heard the letter box clatter.

Pamela rose. 'I wonder what that is.'

'I would leave it for Mrs Hadley,' said Miss Nye, as if talking to a schoolgirl. 'You know she likes to sort out the post.'

Pamela walked to the door regardless. 'This isn't post, it has been delivered by hand.'

Edie looked over to the other woman, but she was back to eating her breakfast.

Pamela soon returned, holding aloft a small envelope. 'It's for you, Edie.' She presented the letter with a flourish.

There was only one missive she was likely to get here. A small flame of hope burned deep inside. She took the envelope and opened it. The flame was extinguished.

Pamela, still standing, leant over to look. 'Well, what is it then?'

Edie folded the letter up and placed it in her pocket. 'Just a note from the Beach Hotel, telling me I haven't got the job of bookkeeper I applied for.'

'Bookkeeper. Goodness, you don't look mousy enough to be one of those.' She glanced over at Miss Nye, as if to demonstrate what 'mousy' looked like. 'Never mind, I'm sure you'll find something today. If not, maybe *I* could find you something.'

'Would you? That would be very kind.' Even as the words left her mouth, she remembered that Pamela had already said that there were no jobs at her school. So what was she likely to find for her?

About to ask, she decided against it. Her new friend was no doubt trying to be encouraging, so she'd leave it at that.

–

Edie had little success at the schools in the town she'd tried. The following day, she had a similar lack of luck at the shops in High Street and Surrey Street. It seemed her glowing reference from Lady Evelyn Stansfield might even be held against her, making her appear too educated to do well in a humble shop. Yet without it she had no reference at all. Some of the shops, including the International Stores, had made it clear they did not hire women.

Heading back up Pier Road, she quickly diverted to the quay which led off it. She crunched across the pebbles towards the river's edge. Lining the river here, and the opposite bank, were timber mills and shipbuilding workshops that loomed over the water. She wondered briefly if these establishments employed women in any capacity. Moreland and Buckley, which she had visited once with her father and brother, employed no women whatsoever. It was what had struck her the most about the visit as a twelve-year-old.

She came to a halt on the short, pebbly beach, in front of a public house called The Britannia, among lobster pots and tangled nets. On the top storey of the simple building was a sign announcing 'G. S. Constable & Sons', which was the huge brewery in the town. There was a strong tang of stale fish which made her wrinkle her nose. A small tug passed by, creating waves that lapped gently onto the shore nearby. It would be on its way to guide a ship into the harbour.

She'd had no luncheon, determined to finish her quest for work before eating, and was feeling decidedly peckish. She turned from the water, set on visiting the Harbour Tea Rooms in Pier Road.

She'd almost reached the side of the public house when she heard a high-pitched laugh. Glancing round the corner guardedly, in the direction of the sound, she spotted a man in his thirties, a fisherman by the look of his baggy clothes and long beard. He was clutching the arm of a dark-haired woman, who put her arms around his shoulders and whispered something in his ear. Next, she hitched up her skirt to show him the edge of her stocking suspenders.

Edie looked away abruptly, her face flaming. She looked back hesitantly as a younger man approached them, taking money from the older one.

No, surely not. It was Jim, Pamela's sweetheart.

A man with an apron tied round his middle came out of the public house, gesticulating in a way that suggested he wanted them away from the premises. They disappeared around the other corner, still arguing.

Edie went back the way she'd come. Should she tell Pamela? She'd only seen Jim in a dim light and could be mistaken. Or he might be a relative of Jim's, and have a likeness.

For now, she'd return to her plan of visiting the tea rooms and put the whole sordid scene behind her.

-

Edie was finding it hard to drop off tonight, despite the fresh air wafting through the window and the calming sound of a high tide's waves. The stress of not finding a job, something she thought would be simple, had given her a blinding headache. It had eased a little with lying down but was not conducive to sleep.

Earlier she'd heard Pamela's door open and close. Either she'd gone to the bathroom, or she'd gone to let her sweetheart in.

She didn't hear her again, but she might have been extra quiet if she were with Jim. She recalled the incident on the quay. The more she thought of it, the more she was convinced she was mistaken.

Returning her thoughts to her situation, she considered her options. If the worst came to the worst, she could return to Downland House, couldn't she? Under what conditions, though, and with what penalties? Could they really lock her away for what she'd done, unable to see anyone for years, as they'd threatened? Or was it just an idle threat?

It was no good; she needed to get up and walk about, instead of fidgeting in the bed. A trip to the bathroom to rinse her aching temples was what she needed. As it was at the back of the house, next to Pamela's bedroom, she crept along the landing so as not to disturb her. What a strange mood she'd been in at dinner that evening; a little snappy. Edie didn't wish to irritate her further.

She was standing at the sink in the dark, holding the cold water in her hands to her face, when she heard a tinkling sound, like glass breaking. There'd been some trouble with a group of boys from the farms recently. They'd been seen smashing the windows of a couple of shops on Norfolk Road. She opened the curtain to look out, but it was too dark at the back of the house to see anything.

About to leave the bathroom, she heard a door open and close on the ground floor. Creeping halfway down the stairs, Edie spied the landlady before the woman headed towards the flight down to the basement floor, holding up her oil lamp as she went. Mrs Hadley had perhaps broken something in her bedroom and was fetching a dustpan and brush. Edie crept back upstairs.

She hadn't quite reached her room when there was an almighty scream.

Without fully thinking through the consequences, Edie ran back along the landing, banging on Pamela's door before rushing down the stairs. It occurred to her as she went that she was in her nightie, so not exactly decent. But it covered everything her day clothes did. Apart from her feet. And she could do nothing about that now.

As she reached the hall, she heard Mrs Hadley shouting at someone in her living quarters in the basement, her voice shrill. Edie could just make out the bronze statuette on the tall occasional table. She grabbed it before proceeding down the next set of stairs, taking the steps carefully in the dim light.

There was a piercing screech before the back door into the garden slammed. Then there was silence.

By the light of the lamp, she noticed upturned furniture in Mrs Hadley's sitting room. There were drawers emptied across the floor, their contents spread wide. Where was Mrs Hadley? Had she been the one leaving?

The door clattered open once more. Edie expected the landlady to return with a tale of pursuing some villain or other. She watched the door from the kitchen, ready to greet her. But it wasn't Mrs Hadley who appeared in the doorway.

It was the thief she'd encountered at the Kursaal two days previously.

On seeing her, he scarpered. She had no stomach to tackle him this time. She placed the statuette on the drawers and picked her way to the button-back armchair nearest the stairs and perched there, wondering what to do. Where was Mrs Hadley?

It was when she bent to pick up a piece of broken china that she saw it.

A leg.

She leapt out of the chair and stumbled backwards, hesitating before creeping slowly forward once more.

At this moment Miss Nye appeared at the bottom of the stairs. 'What on earth has happened here?'

Edie could not find the words to reply. Instead, she pointed behind a Chesterfield that had seen better days. The other woman walked over, standing next to her to look down at the same spot.

Behind the settee Mrs Hadley was lying on her back on the floor, eyes open wide in shock, a knife sticking straight up from her chest.

Chapter Four

The police – a detective inspector, a sergeant and two constables – had not arrived at the house until five past eight in the morning, claiming a break-in on High Street had taken up their time. As they'd stepped in there'd been a murmur of complaint from the older officer, Sergeant Gardner, about having had no breakfast.

'Ah, it's you,' he said. 'You were at the Kursaal when young Brenda was attacked.'

'Yes, that's right,' Edie sighed, closing the front door. 'Hello again.'

Detective Inspector Davis and the sergeant went to the dining room and sat down at the window table, while the younger constables were sent to search among the debris downstairs. The detective held a small notebook in which he was making notes as Edie recalled the night's events. He was reasonably tall with tanned skin, his black hair combed back beneath a homburg hat. Under an unbuttoned fawn trench coat he wore a dark green sack suit, despite the warm morning.

'So, Miss Nye entered the scene as you found Mrs Hadley lying on the floor.'

'That's right.' Recalling the spectacle of the dead woman created in her a vague nausea, along with a desire to cry.

'And you reckon the man you saw was the same one you'd seen at the Kursaal two days before.'

'Yes, yes, I do.' A gull keened outside, like a harbinger of doom, distracting her briefly from the probing questions.

'And you think the other tenant, Miss Brownlow, must have gone out last night?'

'Yes, she wasn't in her room when I knocked, though I'd heard her earlier. She has a sweetheart: Jim.' She'd not wanted to reveal this fact, but what did it matter now? Pamela could no longer get into trouble with Mrs Hadley. 'It could be that she was with him.'

'I have to inform you that, having searched Miss Brownlow's room, we've found it empty of her possessions.'

Edie looked back at Davis, wondering what connection he was making. 'You mean, she's packed up and gone?'

'Precisely.'

'She must have run off with her sweetheart, then.'

The sergeant laughed, earning a glare from the detective.

'Why is that so amusing?' she asked.

The detective leant back in the chair, squeezing his lips together. 'It has come to our—'

Miss Nye entered the room with a tray of tea things, including a plate of biscuits, placing it on the table next to where they were questioning Edie. 'I thought you might appreciate this, given your lack of breakfast.' She started to pour.

Gardner rubbed his hands together. 'We would that.'

'Thank you,' said the detective. 'As I was saying, it's come to our attention that Miss Brownlow was… how can I put this delicately?'

'She were a whore, sir.' The sergeant was clearly not so squeamish.

Davis gave him a disapproving sideways glance. 'Thank you, *Sergeant*. There are ladies present. She was a "lady of the night". Were you aware of this?'

Goodness gracious, was he suggesting this was a disreputable establishment and they were all – *ladies of the night*? 'Most certainly not!'

'Neither did I,' said her fellow boarder. 'Though I suspected from the beginning that she was not telling the truth. I tried to warn Mrs Hadley when she moved in, but she'd clearly taken a shine to the woman's silver tongue and insincere smiles.'

The detective raised his eyebrows. 'You didn't take to her then?'

'No.' Miss Nye placed cups and saucers in front of the three of them, passed the biscuits round, then stepped back. 'Particularly after I discovered her claim to be a teacher at a school in Arundel to be false. I am myself a teacher at East Street School.'

The detective nodded to show he knew the school.

'I asked around, and it came to light that there is no Miss Brownlow at that school in Arundel.'

Inspector Davis half smiled. 'You should be a detective, Miss Nye.' He folded his notebook and placed it in his pocket. 'It seems to me perfectly obvious what has occurred here. Miss Brownlow was short of funds. She raided Mrs Hadley's rooms for money, believing her to be out of earshot upstairs. The landlady caught her red-handed. Miss Brownlow stabbed her then ran away, having already packed.'

Edie could not believe he'd come to this conclusion. 'Wouldn't I have seen her go past me to get her things? And Miss Nye here?'

'This Jim fellow must already have taken her things, and she escaped the back way,' said Davis. 'Or, yes, more likely Jim killed Mrs Hadley and Miss Brownlow had already left. Either way, she's an accomplice.'

'But what of the broken glass? What of the man I saw at the Kursaal?'

'You'd had a shock, miss,' Gardner said, helping himself to another biscuit. 'And you was still shaken from the previous incident. You simply mistook one man for the other. You was probably half asleep.'

Edie sat bolt upright. 'I hadn't even been to sleep. I had a blinding headache, so—'

'There you are then,' said Detective Davis. 'The headache, together with the lack of sleep, must have made your mind play tricks on you. Miss Brownlow, and this Jim, are clearly the perpetrators of the crime.'

Gardner nodded his head while sipping at his tea, spilling it in his saucer in consequence.

'But Jim was blond and the Kursaal thief was swarthy.'

'It was dark,' said Davis.

Could she have been mistaken? 'So Pamela and her sweetheart had planned this all along?'

'Sweetheart? More likely her pimp.'

'*Sergeant!*' Davis frowned.

'Sorry, sir.'

'What about the trouble last year,' Edie persisted, 'when the police were called?'

'I wasn't here then,' said the detective. 'Sergeant?'

'I do vaguely remember something, though I didn't attend. I believe Mrs Hadley didn't wish to pursue it. I suppose that might have been this Jim too.'

Edie remembered an article she'd read in a newspaper recently. 'And what about fingerprinting?'

Davis sighed. 'Everyone's an expert. We will, of course, test the prints on the knife, but on initial inspection they seem smeared, so I'm not sure how much use they'll be.'

Any further argument from her was stalled by the arrival of a motor ambulance. From the cab at the front two men in blue uniforms alighted.

'Now, if you'll excuse us, we need to get the body moved to the mortuary.' Davis and the sergeant left the room.

Miss Nye sat in the detective's discarded seat and poured herself a cup of tea. 'The body in the mortuary: that's all she's been reduced to. It's so sad.'

'It does seem rather harsh and final.' Edie drank her tea, placing the cup on the tray when she'd finished. 'So, that is why you were so unfriendly towards Miss Brownlow. I did wonder what she had done to upset you.'

'Yes, but as I said, I didn't trust her from the beginning. There was something shifty about her. I'm quite perceptive when it comes to people.' She looked Edie in the eyes.

What did this woman make of her, she wondered? 'That is indeed a good skill to have in life, Miss Nye.'

'It is. But of course, not everyone who has something to hide is evil. We all have our own reasons for keeping secrets.' She smiled warmly. 'Please, call me Julia.'

Julia. She'd been sure she was a Constance or a Hope, or owned a name equally virtuous. 'And I'm Edie, as you probably know.'

'Yes, since Miss Brownlow used it so frequently. One of her tricks, I fear, to become familiar with you. She'd given up on me.'

'Whatever would she want with me?'

Julia left the question unanswered as they heard the heavy footsteps of men struggling on the basement stairs. They must be bringing Mrs Hadley up. An impulse to cry came over Edie again. She'd only known the woman four days, but she'd been a decent sort, and didn't deserve to die in the manner she had. She removed her handkerchief from her skirt pocket, recalling how Miss Langley had made the beautiful lace on it. She wiped her wet eyes.

Julia took her free hand, giving it a little squeeze. 'It is indeed a tragedy. However, now we must look to our own needs, for I doubt we'll be able to stay here. And would we want to? But being June, all the boarding and lodging houses along here will be full. A lot of children come this month, with their nurses and governesses.'

She certainly knew about those.

'Not to mention the many single and widowed ladies, and the families, who come for the sea air,' Julia added.

In all the hubbub the stark fact of their lack of lodgings had not even occurred to her. 'My goodness, I suppose you're right. Did Mrs Hadley own the house, do you know? She did refer to herself as the proprietress.'

'I very much doubt it. I always assumed she was simply the housekeeper but used the title to impress. These establishments are often owned by the gentry and landowners, or by successful businessmen. Take the land where the windmill, the cottages and the Kursaal sit, for instance: they belong to the Duke of Norfolk, as does much of Littlehampton. He owns the castle in Arundel, too.'

She knew the latter, of course, but said nothing of it. 'Wouldn't the owner of this house install a new housekeeper?' Another thought occurred to her. 'Did Mrs Hadley have any family we need to inform? I know her husband had passed on.'

'I'm sure the police will deal with it.' Julia lowered her voice to a whisper. 'But I suppose it wouldn't hurt to check her rooms for papers. After the police have gone.'

Out of the window they observed the two ambulancemen placing a stretcher into the vehicle. Both women stood, eyes downcast.

Detective Inspector Davis popped his head round the door. 'We'll be going now.'

'Will you inform the owners of the house of what has happened?' Miss Nye asked.

The detective stepped in for a moment. 'Mrs Hadley apparently *was* the owner.'

The two women looked at each other, confused.

'My thoughts exactly,' said Davis. 'We found papers on the floor to indicate the fact. We'll check it out, of course, but there you have it. I think you can both sit tight for now, until we find out who the property is to pass on to.'

He left and was soon visible on the pavement, talking to the sergeant as the ambulance drew away.

Edie sat back down. 'I think Davis is wrong about the murderer being either Jim or Miss Brownlow. In fact, I'm sure of it.'

Julia leant against the windowsill. 'I agree. The detective is rather too fond of his own deductions. A shame, for he is rather handsome and clearly quite intelligent.'

Edie was seeing a different side to Miss Nye today. 'My goodness, Julia, do you really think so?'

'I do.' She sighed. 'It's such a shame we haven't met under different circumstances.' She looked round at the clock on the mantelpiece. 'I must leave for school in ten minutes.'

'It's odd that Mrs Hadley mentioned Pamela was a teacher, but not you.'

Julia half smiled. 'That's because she thought Miss Brownlow was at a private school, and I'm at a common elementary school.'

'Ah, I see.' Edie paused a moment. 'There is something else about Jim I maybe should have mentioned.'

'Oh, what's that?'

Edie told her about seeing him at the Britannia public house with another woman who was likely to be a *woman of the night*, as the detective had put it.

'So the sergeant could be right. This Jim was maybe her, you know... what the sergeant said.' Julia looked down at the table as she said it.

'It seems possible.'

Julia shook her head. 'In a way, I feel sorry for her.'

'Who, Pamela?' Edie was somewhat surprised at this change in attitude.

'Yes. I mean, who is to say she wasn't being controlled by this man, this Jim. Some women probably have no choice, in order to survive. I still can't say I liked her, but then, I've never been in her shoes.'

'I suppose you could be right. Though Jim looked a little – weak – to be the controlling sort. Could he be working for someone else?'

'I don't suppose we'll ever know.'

Outside, a woman came towards the detective, engaging him in conversation for a few moments.

'It's Mrs Bygrove,' said Edie with surprise.

'Who?'

'The wife of the manager of the Beach Hotel. I saw her when I went for the post of bookkeeper.' She felt the disappointment of not being given the job all over again.

'She's coming up the steps.'

Edie hurried to see the partly opened door pushed wider. 'Hello, is anyone there?'

'Mrs Bygrove—'

'Oh my goodness, you poor thing. Inspector Davis has just told me about Mrs Hadley. How dreadful. Are you all right?'

'Not really. I found the body and it was, oh, awful.' She swayed, caught by Mrs Bygrove before she lost her balance.

Julia was in the hall by this time and helped the other woman guide Edie into the dining room. 'Sit quietly for a while, until you feel better.'

They fell silent, the other two staring out of the window, like she was. People were already walking around outside, parasols up, taking the air, grand men strutting along the river in lightweight suits and boaters, as if nothing had happened. 'It looks to be such an ordinary day.'

'It does,' Mrs Bygrove agreed. 'How are you generally, Miss Moore? Have you secured a job?'

Edie slumped, knotting her hands together. 'No, I haven't. And now I need to move lodgings, and I believe they're hard to find in June.'

'Then I may be able to solve both your problems. I was on my way to tell you of a post that became available just yesterday. Our youngest chambermaid, Norah, has been found to be… with child. She left last night under the insistence of her parents to marry the lad. She's only just sixteen.'

'Well I never.' It was hard to know what else to say.

'It's not as well paid as a bookkeeper, that's true, but it is live-in and it may tide you over in the meantime.'

'Will I need to interview for it?'

'No. Douglas is keen to fill the post as soon as possible, so when I suggested you, he was happy to agree.'

'I don't know what to say.' After all her failed efforts to secure work, she didn't experience the relief she'd anticipated. *Chambermaid*. However, she did feel a deep well of gratitude to Mrs Bygrove for her kindness. 'Oh, but Julia, I don't want to leave you here alone.'

'Nonsense. You mustn't turn it down on my account. I'm sure I'll find somewhere. If nothing else, there is always a settee in the headmistress's parlour, which has got a teacher or two out of bother in the past.'

'You're a teacher?' said Mrs Bygrove. 'In that case, I might be able to help you also. My cousin has a vacant room above her shop in Norfolk Road. She prefers professional boarders. She was going to advertise today, but if you go to see her, and tell her I sent you, she might take you on. Especially if she hears of your plight with Mrs Hadley. She has a soft heart.' Mrs Bygrove smiled warmly. 'Eleanor Wright is her name.'

Julia looked as taken aback as Edie had felt when offered the job at the hotel. 'Why, that is immensely kind of you to help me when you don't even know me.'

'What's the point of life if you can't help a fellow human being?'

'Thank you.' She stood and filled the tray. 'I'll take these downstairs to wash.'

When she'd left the room, Edie said, 'Can I ask you, Mrs Bygrove, why you picked me for the job, out of the three remaining candidates for the bookkeeping post?'

'The other three were specifically looking for bookkeeping jobs, so probably not suitable. And you, well, you struck me as having… potential.'

'I see.' *Having potential* sounded initially like a compliment. But having potential for what? For being good at cleaning up people's mess? That didn't sound like such a compliment.

'Besides, I liked you the best.' Mrs Bygrove gave her a friendly smile.

'Oh. Thank you… I wonder, could I ask you a favour?'

'Go ahead.'

'At the hotel, could we keep my former role as a governess under wraps, for now at least. I don't won't anybody to form a prejudice against me before I've even started.'

'Of course. I've not said anything, and nor shall I.'

'Thank you.'

'Goodness, what a day.' Mrs Bygrove held up a newspaper she'd been clutching under her arm, displaying the front page. 'Look at this. Archduke Franz Ferdinand, the heir to the Austro-Hungarian empire, was shot and killed yesterday by an assassin. And his wife. Who knows what this could lead to?'

Edie glanced at the date on the newspaper: *29 June 1914*. It would be the beginning of another chapter in her life. She only hoped it would be an improvement on last night.

–

Edie arrived on the path outside the hotel and looked up at its imposing structure. Such a building would not have intimidated her two weeks ago. But now? In order to cope, she'd taken on the full mantle of humility expected of a chambermaid. Yet she knew nothing of the proper methods of cleaning and tidying.

She'd arrived a little later than expected, having gone to Mrs Wright's first. Julia had been teaching all day, and she wanted to secure the room for her. Mrs Bygrove had already been to recommend Julia, so all was set. Edie had returned to the guest house to await her friend's return to help her move.

Now, standing outside the Beach Hotel, she took several deep breaths against the rising tide of panic. It was this or go back. But back to what? There were few choices. Return to the tyranny of Downland House. Go back to being bossed around by her parents. Risk being punished for doing the things that other, freer women could do.

Her answer to all of those was a firm *no*. It would have to be this. She diverted left to the servants' entrance, only to be faced unexpectedly by the young porter she'd met on her first visit, as he appeared from around the edge of the building in his uniform. She stepped back with a jump, then felt immediately idiotic.

'Oh my goodness, where did you spring from?' In the unguarded moment, her voice had taken on its refined tone once more. She must be careful about that.

'The garden. Just delivering something to Major Thomas, one of our long-term guests.' He said this in his version of a posh accent, treating her to the same cheeky grin he'd displayed the first day she'd met him. In his own voice, he said, 'More to the point, what are you doing here? And with luggage.' His head indicated the carpetbag. 'Thought you didn't get the bookkeeper's job.'

'I didn't. Mrs Bygrove has offered me the chambermaid's post.'

'Ah, yes, dear little Norah Daniels. Gone to marry the dairy farmer's son, she has. Don't think they're too pleased, but there ya go. Wouldn't have you down for chambermaid material. Even bookkeeper seems a bit lowly for you.'

She wasn't sure whether this was a flattering remark, a statement of fact or, indeed, an attempt to belittle her in some bizarre fashion. It was her brother's way to declare things like this, double-edged compliments set up to confuse people.

'Why do you say that?'

'Heading more to middle class, you are, I'd say.'

She grinned, lowering her head before gazing up into his eyes. He didn't look away like many young men she'd met. He struck her as a straightforward kind of chap, the sort to speak his mind. With the dimples and impish smile, he had an agreeable countenance. 'Well, um… Oh, I don't know your name.'

'Cobbett. Charlie Cobbett. At your service.' He performed a short bow.

'Well, Mr Cobbett, that just goes to show how wrong a person can be. About class, I mean.'

He pushed his lips out as his head did an odd side-to-side nod. 'It has been known for me to be wrong, very occasionally.' He tipped his head back and laughed, indicating he was joking.

She joined in, feeling the first genuine scrap of joy she'd experienced since arriving in Littlehampton.

'Now, enough of this "Mr Cobbett" business. If you're to work here, I'm Charlie from now on.' He clapped his feet together and leant over slightly, offering his hand.

She took it. 'I'm Edith, Edie, as you already know, of course.'

'How d'ya do, Edith Edie. Right, let's have ya bag and I'll take you in to Mrs B. Mr Bygrove's out today at the golf links over the other side of the river, taking advantage of a quieter Monday. Or so he said.' He took the bag. 'You're lucky – you've arrived in time for early supper.'

He led her through the door on the left this time, to the kitchen. It was busy with the activity of half a dozen people. At the range was a woman in her fifties, tall and solid, placing a kettle on the hob. At the long, chunky table was a man, even taller and broader, chopping carrots swiftly and expertly. He looked up briefly as they passed through, his face solemn.

When they reached the narrow corridor that led round to the office, Charlie said, 'The tall pair are Mrs Norris and her son, Joseph. They're the cooks. He's meant to be head chef, but it's his ma what calls the shots.'

Mrs Bygrove came round the corner, a large ledger in her hand. 'You're here, Edie. Wonderful. I see you're taking care of our new staff member, Charlie.'

'Met her on the way in, Mrs Bygrove. Was just bringing her to you.'

'Perhaps you'd like to show her up to the staff quarters. She's sharing with Lili. You can drop your bag off, Edie, then Charlie can take you to meet Mrs Leggett, the housekeeper. She'll introduce you to Lili and the other staff at supper, no doubt.'

'Very well, Mrs Bygrove.'

'There are twenty-two live-in members of staff, though Vera, the nursemaid, has her meals with my children.'

Her children. She wasn't sure why she was surprised by that. She imagined Mr Bygrove would be a stern father. Poor lambs.

'And Charlie, we have Lord and Lady Lane arriving tomorrow, along with Miss Royston and her charges, the Leroy children. They've particularly requested your services to settle them in.'

'Nice to be appreciated. Especially since Lord Lane is such a good tipper.' He winked and clicked his tongue twice.

The manager's wife gave him a look, part chastisement, part affection. 'Well, Edie. I'm so very glad you could join our staff. I'm sure you'll be an asset.'

She carried on past them and on to the kitchen. Mrs Bygrove certainly seemed pleased to have her there. Goodness knows why she had such confidence in her when she barely knew her. Edie only hoped she wouldn't let her down.

'Come on then,' said Charlie, doing an about-turn. 'Ya room's at the top of the house, up the back stairs. We're all up there, on the second floor, out of the way of their nibses, though the women staff are on one corridor and the men on the other. The Bygroves have rooms on the first floor, which we pass on the way.'

'I see.' So they had back stairs here, too. It made sense, given the status of the guests they had staying.

Ten minutes later they were back downstairs, in the servants' dining room, where they found only the housekeeper. The scratched wooden table almost filled the space, with a fireplace on the long side that was clean and clear of fuel. There was one large window, but since it overlooked the narrow courtyard, the light in there wasn't good. The table was laid with knives and forks and plain white plates.

'Here's your new recruit, Mrs Leggett.' Charlie pointed his hand towards Edie.

The housekeeper's black dress was out of fashion by a good few years, with its extra-long skirt and puffy upper sleeves. She looked Edie up and down. 'You don't look very hardy.'

'That's not fair, now, is it,' said the porter. 'Give her a chance.'

'That's enough of your cheek, Mr Cobbett.'

He lifted his eyes heavenward, tramping towards the door, before treating Edie to a brief grin. 'Just going to see if the grub's ready.'

When he was gone, the housekeeper pointed to a place on the bench, several yards away from her and on the opposite side, indicating Edie should sit.

'Now listen to me, girl, and listen well. I don't tolerate any shirkers in my staff. I'm in charge of the maids and they do as I tell them, do you understand?'

Edie nodded, questioning what she'd got herself into. This Mrs Leggett was bossy, like the housekeeper at Downland House.

'First thing in the morning there are chores in the hotel itself before the guests rise, where you'll help the housemaids, if necessary. Then you'll be allocated a set number of rooms. When guests have gone to breakfast, or otherwise left their rooms, you'll start by opening the windows—'

She was interrupted at this juncture by Mrs Bygrove. With her were two young women. The one about her own age had black curly hair pulled up into a bun. She was slim, almost like a child, with dark brown eyes. If Mrs Leggett thought her 'not very hardy', what did she make of this girl? She gave Edie a welcoming smile. The other, a little younger, had thick, pale brown hair and slate-grey eyes that looked annoyed about something. Both had on a black dress covered with a long white apron, the bib of which had lace edges. On their heads were small frilly white caps.

'Ah, you've met Mrs Leggett,' said the manager's wife. 'This is Lili,' she pointed to the black-haired maid, 'and this is Fanny Bullen.'

The housekeeper stood stiffly, her hands folded one over the other against her body. 'I am just informing Miss Moore of her duties.'

'I think it would be a good idea if she worked the first few days with Lili, in the rooms they'd both be allocated. That way she can learn as she's going along and ask Lili for any advice she needs.'

Fanny humphed and exclaimed under her breath, but loud enough for Edie to hear, ''S not fair.'

Mrs Leggett pulled herself up to her full height. 'I see. It's not what I would have recommended, but then, you are the manager's wife, I suppose.'

Edie expected Mrs Bygrove to reprimand the housekeeper, but instead she said, 'I think it's best.'

'Very well, Mrs Bygrove,' was imparted through stiff lips.

The manager's wife left them to it.

Lili placed herself down next to Edie, saying in a light tone, 'I hope you'll enjoy your time here. It's hard work, it is, but I do love it, with all the fancy folk what come here. Not that we do get to see them much as we have to be invisible, see, but very occasionally I get to serve afternoon tea in the conservatory.' She appeared inordinately pleased about this.

'Is that a Welsh accent?' said Edie.

'It most certainly is!' Lili seemed delighted with the deduction. 'I'm Liliwen Probert, and I'm from the Rhymney Valley.'

'I've been to Cardiff a couple of times, and to the Brecon Beacons.'

'They're not too far from Dorcalon, where I'm from.'

Charlie returned with two dishes full of boiled potatoes, placing them in the middle of the table. Others followed behind him. He sat himself at one end, next to a dark-haired young man in the same uniform and with an Irish accent, who she gathered was called Lorcan. Other staff entered, bearing various dishes. Edie's stomach rumbled as she caught the aroma of herbs and meat. On the table now was a salver of sliced ham, a dish of carrots and another of peas. She glanced at Charlie, who looked over at the same time to wink and grin at her. She returned the smile, then turned away, embarrassed.

Charlie clapped his hands together, silencing everybody at what was now a full table. 'Let's have some introductions for our latest member. This is Edie Moore, the new chambermaid.'

Lili stood, pointing around the table at those seated, calling out the names of the various maids, the hotel nurse, the book-keeper, storekeeper and another porter.

Gertie Green, another chambermaid, was introduced last. She and Fanny, sitting next to her, giggled at who knew what, until Gertie said, 'So you were at the lodgings of that lady what died.' She eyed her up and down as if she were responsible, fiddling with a stray strand of her wavy, bright auburn hair.

'I'm afraid I was.' Edie kept it short, not wanting to discuss the matter or be the centre of attention.

'And they say it was one of them lodgers what done it.'

Edie sighed. It was inevitable they'd want to know. If she got it over and done with now, maybe she could forget it.

'Come on, Edie,' said Fanny, 'tell us about that woman's murder.'

'Mrs Hadley was her name,' said the housekeeper. 'And we don't need to hear any details, thank you very much.'

The housekeeper was indeed in a foul mood today. Or it could be her general demeanour. Time would tell. Now to bring this subject to a close.

'The only thing I'll say is that I do not believe Miss Brownlow, the lodger in question, was responsible, nor her sweetheart, Jim, although they have disappeared. No, I saw another man. A man I'd seen the day before, attempting a robbery.'

As soon as she'd mentioned the latter crime, she regretted it. There was a gasp of astonishment around the table. Now they'd want to know all about that.

Gertie gripped her hands together in front of her. 'Oh, do tell us.'

Mrs Leggett stood. 'That is enough. We are going to have our dinner with no talk of murders and thefts.' She glared at Edie, whose fault she clearly thought this was.

Gertie and Fanny giggled once more.

'But first, we'll say grace.' The housekeeper sat and placed her palms together. 'For what we are about to receive, may the Lord make us truly thankful.'

There was a murmur of 'Amen' from everyone.

Edie helped herself to the ham as the tray was passed round.

A poke in the elbow from Hetty, the maid in charge of the stillroom, brought her out of her daydream.

'Here, you gonna pass that round, or what?'

'Sorry. Here you are.'

Hetty took the tray, leaving Edie to ponder the crime.

-

It had been a busy and tiring morning, helping Lili in the various rooms. The splendour of the bedrooms matched those of the areas downstairs, with their dark polished wood, luxurious upholstery and overstuffed cushions. Although some were still quite Victorian in style, they were nonetheless elegant with their bold greens and reds. Others had been updated, embracing the Arts and Crafts style she'd seen in more modern houses, with its angled and curved lines and Liberty fabrics.

The respect Edie already felt for the hard work achieved by the maids at Downland House deepened. Perhaps she'd made a mistake settling for this, as someone who had most recently sat tutoring all day. There was so much to do to keep the rooms looking clean and tidy. This morning Lili had shown her how to combine linseed oil, black treacle and a little gin to clean the dark wood. It was all fascinating, but back-breaking. And her poor hands!

They'd begun by opening the windows and removing the bedclothes, placing them across chairs to air.

'You need to turn the mattress across the foot of the bed to air it off,' Lili had told her. She hadn't understood what the maid meant until she'd demonstrated.

They'd carried this out in all their allotted bedrooms, before returning to the first. Then it was time to dust the rooms, brush the carpets and clean out the washstands. Some of the rooms were on the rota for a thorough clean, where they had to polish the furniture, wash the inside of the windows and wipe around the door frames, skirting and coving. After completing all that, it was time to return to the room they'd started on, to remake the now aired beds.

Edie was currently wiping the windowsill of the very last bedroom. Outside, the sun was shining. She stopped to admire the contrast between the deep green sea and the topaz sky. How she envied the walkers she could glimpse on the promenade! It certainly was busy for a Monday. She stretched her arms above her head and yawned. The lack of sleep was catching up with her. Was it only two nights ago that poor Mrs Hadley had met her end? With a deep shudder, she recalled her bloodied, limp body lying on the ground.

She twisted her waist and rubbed at the top of her corset, sitting just under her bust, wishing she could divest herself of the contraption. It would surely make cleaning easier without the bones confining her as they did. At least it wasn't as tight and all-encompassing as the old style corset her mother still wore. It wasn't like men had to put up with such discomfort.

'Are you all right?' asked Lili, leaning back from the other window. Her rosebud lips curved into a generous smile, though the slight crinkle to her brow betrayed some concern.

'I am, thank you.' She was surprised to find it was true. Despite her fatigue, she believed she'd achieved something today. 'Fanny and Gertie seem to have taken a dislike to me though.'

'I wouldn't worry about them. Like that with most people, they are, especially when they're new. They won't even talk to the two live-out chambermaids. I'd say that wasn't a bad thing, given the nonsense they often spout.' She chuckled. 'Right, you finished then?'

'Yes.' Edie placed the cloth in the bucket. 'I'm sorry if I'm holding you up.' She was aware she wasn't as nippy as her roommate.

Lili came to inspect the window, giving it another wipe over herself. 'Not a bad effort.'

'Oh dear, I'm sorry.'

'Don't worry, you'll get the hang of it. I did. Slow and sloppy I was when I started, and always getting into trouble with Mrs Leggett.'

'Is there a Mr Leggett?'

'No, and never has been. She's a spinster, but we've got to call the housekeeper Mrs, because it's respectful, like.'

'Oh, I see.'

'Now, we'll put the cleaning things away and get our dinner. Then there are other jobs to do.'

Other jobs? She only hoped they were a little less strenuous. Despite feeling she'd achieved something, she wondered how long it would be before the novelty wore off. Even though a governess was seen as an employee, they had a far easier time than a maid did. Life had seemed tedious for her at Downland House and at Lady Evelyn's. How much more so was it for the other staff?

'Do we have our... dinner the same time as the guests?'

'Only us staff what aren't involved in cooking or serving it. The others have theirs either before *luncheon*, as the guests call it, or after it's finished, see. And the porters take turns at being on duty. If you're lucky, it'll be Charlie's turn to have dinner early today.' Her eyes crinkled with mischief as she picked up her box and bucket.

'What *do* you mean?'

'Taken a shine to you, he has.'

'Nonsense. He's only being friendly.'

'Come on, let's get down. I'm starving.'

In the staff dining room Mrs Leggett and the other young women were already seated. There were two trays of sandwiches in the middle of the table today, tongue by the look of it, and a bowl of salad. Some had already helped themselves.

Charlie entered at this point, undoing his blue jacket with its three rows of metal studs to reveal a grey collarless shirt. He removed his cap and placed it on the table, exposing his thick, dark hair that was parted on one side.

'I'm ready for a sit-down,' he said. 'That Major Thomas had me running around looking for a watch he'd lost. Reckoned it was somewhere on the ground floor, but I couldn't find it anywhere. Turned out it was on his dresser, silly old fool.'

Mrs Leggett pursed her lips. 'Mr Cobbett, that is no way to talk about the guests.'

'I only mean it affectionately. I'm fond of the old codger.' Charlie seated himself in the chair next to Edie, grinning at her.

Gertie poured herself a cup of tea. 'What do you reckon about this archduke fella, killed a coupla days back?'

'And his wife,' Hetty, the stillroom maid, added.

'I don't think it's any of our business.' Mrs Leggett emphasised each word by tapping the table. 'We've got our own lives to get on with.'

Charlie, a sandwich half lifted to his mouth said, 'It's a serious business. That Princip bloke what killed them is Serbian. If war breaks out between Austria and Serbia, I reckon all hell'll be let loose and other countries'll get involved. You mark my words.'

'Been reading the papers again, Mr Cobbett?' Mrs Leggett eyed him with some chagrin.

'I like to keep abreast of what's happening in the world. Nothing wrong with that.'

The housekeeper pointed a finger at him. 'You should keep to your place. Leave the politics to the higher classes, to those in Parliament, who know better than you.'

'Reckon they could do with a few of the working class in there, so they know what life's really like.' Charlie bit into his sandwich and looked into the distance.

'And women,' said Nancy, the barmaid.

'Poppycock,' Mrs Leggett barked.

Edie, with her own opinion on this conversation, considered contributing, but what exactly to say without getting still more in the housekeeper's bad books? Any thoughts she might have expressed were cut short by Mrs Leggett's next sentence.

'Talking of class, Miss Moore, how do you find yourself in these reduced circumstances?'

'I beg your pardon?' Edie's heart started to race, and her face flushed.

'Governess, wasn't it? Plenty of those jobs around. And you with a grammar school education. You might have a glowing report from your last employer, or your only one, by the looks of it, but there's not much else.'

A murmur went round the table and Edie saw Charlie's eyebrows raised high as he considered her. Had the manager's wife disregarded her wishes? What could she say?

'As I explained to Mr and Mrs Bygrove—' Edie started. Ah, it was *Mr* Bygrove, not his wife, who had passed on the information. Of course. 'As I told them, I did not wish to become attached to another child, as it's distressing when they go on to boarding school and you have to move on. A little like losing contact with your own child, I would imagine.' This had only just occurred to her.

Mrs Leggett displayed a brief sneer. 'How would *you* know it's like that?'

Edie was tempted to retort, *how would you know it isn't?*

'Clearly you picked up too high an opinion of yourself while working for Lady Stansfield.'

There was yet more murmuring, before Fanny said, 'Just like I thought. I bet she's a spy who's come to report back on what we say and do to the nobs.'

Enough was enough. Edie stood in order to berate them all in her best 'Lady Moreland enunciation', as she always thought of it, but stopped herself just in time. 'Look, I tried to locate other jobs in the town, but this was the first one I was accepted for. I wanted to start anew, by the sea.'

'Sounds fair enough to me,' said Charlie. 'Since when have we poked our noses into each other's lives? Seems to me our pasts are our own business.'

Mrs Norris came lumbering through the door. 'Eat up quickly, Gertie. Annie is off sick, and Alice needs help in the scullery. She's getting behind on the pots.'

'That's not fair,' whined the chambermaid. 'I've got other duties.'

'Mr Bygrove said you're to do it.'

Gertie stuffed the rest of her sandwich into her mouth none too gracefully, chewing with cheeks bloated. Before she had time to finish, the manager's wife entered the dining room with her children, Dorothy and Arthur. The girl looked around six years old, her hair white-blonde, and the boy around four, with hazelnut-coloured hair and a cute grin. She was shy, half hiding behind her mother's skirts.

'Mrs Bygrove. And what brings you here to our 'umble dining room?' Mrs Norris's hectoring manner turned to jollity.

'Vera has taken to her bed with a fever, so I'm caring for the children today. We've come for the lunches.'

'Vera, too? It's the same with Annie. Come, I know young Jack was just serving up the food for the children. And I'm sure I've a little treat for them for pudding today.' The cook ruffled each of their heads and led them away out of the room.

Gertie left, still chewing her sandwich, mumbling under her breath. Mrs Leggett followed on soon after, having only eaten half a sandwich, leaving the staff to enjoy the remaining minutes of their dinner.

With the half hour up, amid the bustle of clearing away the plates and trays, Charlie indicated to Edie to wait.

After the others had left, he looked at her with a most serious expression. 'A governess, eh? I said you was middle class, and you denied it. You could have told me.'

'I couldn't have told you I was middle class, Charlie, because I'm not, I promise you.' With that, she took the three plates she was clutching tightly and made her way to the scullery, not looking behind for his reaction.

What had it got to do with anybody else, especially the porter, where she came from? Irritated, she used that reasoning to counteract the squirm of discomfort in the pit of her belly.

Chapter Five

A week later Edie was sitting in a pew near the front of St Mary's parish church, attending Mrs Hadley's funeral. Next to her was Julia Nye. Edie was wearing her maid's dress without an apron, it being the only black outfit she had access to. Over it she wore her one jacket, the long, dark blue one with purple piping and a raised waist.

'How sad that there isn't a better turnout,' said Julia, looking behind her at the sparse numbers.

'Yes, it is sad.' Edie shivered. The church was chilly, despite the warm July day. She peered up at the huge Gothic window with its stone mouldings and tracery and the leaded panes. In the sunbeams that filtered through, dust motes danced in the air. 'She may not have had any family, of course, but you'd think more of her neighbours would have attended.'

The vicar appeared at the front, robed, with book in hand. At the same time an old lady, clad in a shabby crinoline, took her place at the organ. The north door creaked open and shut. Edie peeped behind to find Inspector Davis walking down the aisle, divested of his coat today. He removed his homburg and took the pew behind them. She wondered briefly if he'd ever considered that either she or Julia, or both of them, might be responsible for the death, but dismissed it from her mind.

It wasn't long before the coffin was carried in by four men in tailed black suits and top hats, walking solemnly to Chopin's Funeral March. The tune had always depressed Edie at other funerals she'd attended, its sombre, minor tones a forewarning of hell rather than the doorway to any kind of heaven.

The service was impersonal and monotone, the minister clearly knowing little of Honor Ivy Hadley, as they'd discovered was her full name.

She was greatly relieved when they were able to rise and follow the coffin out into the churchyard. The blue sky and warmth helped her shrug off the gloom of a passing life. Around the grave the vicar said the few words he needed to. When no one came forward to throw in any earth, Edie felt compelled to do so. Julia followed her lead.

The small group quickly dispersed, leaving Edie with her friend and the detective.

'It was kind of you to come, Inspector,' said Julia, offering a timid grin.

'I thought you'd both like to know that the house has been left to her husband, Gordon Hadley.'

Edie shook her head. 'But how can that be? Unless she hadn't got round to changing her will.'

'Possibly. However, we can find no evidence of a death certificate for him. Had Mrs Hadley owned the place long, do you know?'

'I'd lived there eight months,' said Julia, 'and I think she'd been there for three or so years. Although I always believed she was simply the landlady, not the proprietress, as she called herself. I wonder where she got the money to buy such a property?'

'That's what we'd like to know. Do you have any idea from where she came, before Littlehampton?'

Julia pondered awhile. 'I believe she did mention Hampshire. Southsea, possibly?'

'And she definitely stated her husband was dead?'

Both women replied in the affirmative.

'I presume she'd also made some provision in her will for the funeral and grave plot,' said Julia.

Davis nodded. 'That is correct.'

'Do you still think that the murder was perpetrated by Jim or Pamela?' Edie enquired. 'Or that it was an opportunist break-in, to steal anything the thief could find?'

Davis considered her with a wrinkled brow. 'We have to consider all possibilities, though my money is still on Miss Brownlow and her so-called sweetheart.'

'You're a betting man then, Inspector Davis?' asked Julia.

A small grin lifted his face from the stern appearance. 'Merely an expression, Miss Nye. Now, unless you have any other information that would be useful, I'm afraid I shall have to take my leave of you. Miss Moore.' He lifted his hat. 'Miss Nye.' Another lift of the hat was followed by more than a glance in Julia's direction, though he soon moved away towards the path.

On an impulse Edie called, 'I think you're wrong about Miss Brownlow and Jim, Inspector.'

Davis simply raised an arm and carried on his way.

–

'There, I told you, didn't I?' Charlie held up a newspaper as he entered the staff dining room. He was on a late lunch today, and arrived as the room was being cleared after the middle lunch. Edie was sweeping the floor.

Mrs Leggett glared at him. 'What's all your noise about, Mr Cobbett?'

He stabbed his finger at the front page several times. 'Austria-Hungary, they've declared war on Serbia. And now Russia's mobilising her troops. Didn't I say?'

Joseph Norris came up behind Charlie, carrying a joint of salted pork over his shoulder. 'What's all that?'

Charlie showed him the headline, repeating what he'd just said.

'How long before Britain gets involved?' said the head chef.

'My thoughts exactly.'

'Then our army and navy will go and sort it out, won't they?' said Mrs Leggett. 'So I don't know what you're worried about.'

Joseph lowered the joint. 'What army? My understanding is there isn't much of one.'

'Stuff and nonsense. Now get back to the kitchen before your mother comes looking for you.'

'Nobody would think it's me what's the bloody head chef round here,' he said, lugging his tall frame through the door.

'And enough of that language... Right, the rest of you who've finished dinner, back to work. Except you, Miss Moore. I'd like a word.'

Oh dear, what had she done now? She still wasn't as quick as Lili, who'd been helping her out a little, but at least she was getting fitter and more able to carry out her duties. And for the first time today, she was ahead. 'What is it, Mrs Leggett?'

The housekeeper indicated they move into the corridor, giving Charlie a look that suggested she didn't want him listening in.

'It's come to my attention...'

Here it comes, thought Edie.

'...that you've worked very hard to learn the ropes since you arrived. This is what Lili tells me, and since she is one of my best workers, I can only take her word for it. I had my doubts about your abilities, with you only having done a dormant job before, for there's not much physical activity in teaching children.'

Edie was sure Julia would have had something to say about that.

'So, what I want to say is, well done, and keep it up.'

'Why, thank you, Mrs Leggett.' To say she was shocked at the compliment was an understatement. How kind of Lili to cover for her.

At that moment Fanny Bullen came out of the scullery.

The housekeeper lifted her arm to draw her attention. 'Fanny, a word.'

Edie took the opportunity to slip back into the dining room briefly to collect her cap.

Charlie gave her a wink. 'Well done. It isn't often the housekeeper showers anyone with praise.'

'You were listening.'

'Too right I was. Had my ear up to that door. Thought she might be about to give you a mouthful again.'

She pushed his shoulder playfully, immediately hoping she hadn't crossed a line. Stepping back, she said, 'I'd better get on, otherwise I will be given a mouthful again, as you put it.'

She left him to his sandwich.

Edie returned to her rota, now starting on rooms that weren't currently occupied but were awaiting clients the following day. The praise from Mrs Leggett put a spring in her step.

She had just finished the last room when Fanny knocked on the door and entered. 'Good, you're here. How long till you've finished the rooms ready for tomorrow?'

'I already have. I'm about to start on the rooms that are empty until the weekend.'

'Good. I'm not feeling well today. Could you give me a hand?'

'I don't want to fall behind and get into Mrs Leggett's bad books again.'

'But you're in her good books now, aren't you? I heard her saying in the corridor earlier. And you're ahead, by my reckoning. All I want is someone to finish a room I've started, so I can begin on another room, before old Leggett realises I'm behind. Got a telling-off from her today, I did, and I told her I wasn't feeling my best but it don't make no difference to her. Got a gripey gut, I have.' She bent over, gripping her stomach to illustrate.

This might be a way to make friends with Fanny, and also Gertie, who was her best chum. She didn't like the animosity between them.

'All right. Which room is it?'

'Room 202. Second floor. I'll show you. There's the wiping of the door frames and windows left, that's all. You are a dear. I won't forget this.' She grinned, though it didn't look completely sincere. It had almost certainly cost her a lot to lose face in this way, and Edie even felt a little sorry for her. Cleaning when you didn't feel well was rotten, but taking any time off would have meant losing money.

With her bucket and cleaning box, she followed the other maid through a door tucked away in a corner of the landing, up the back stairs to the floor above. Fanny pointed to the room in question.

'Thanks again, Edie.'

She breezed off, not looking at all ill now, but maybe the relief at not facing a scolding had perked her up.

The room was situated at the front of the hotel, overlooking the tennis courts across the road. Although they were not as expensive as those at the back, which had magnificent views of the coast, they were nonetheless smart. Heading straight to the windows, she pulled a cloth out of the bucket of water that was still clean enough to finish the job for Fanny.

Windows wiped, she crossed the room to wash around the door frame. It was only then that she noticed something on the floor: broken glass. Behind a curved carver chair sat a smashed picture, a small print of the sea from the promenade. She went to pick up the pieces, then changed her mind for fear of cutting herself.

Had the last guest staying in the room dislodged it from its pin on the wall? Surely, if Fanny had already cleaned the coving, she must have noticed it. Unless she hadn't done that either. There was nothing for it: she'd have to report it.

Having completed the task, she took herself down the back stairs to the ground floor. The housekeeper was in the kitchen, speaking with Mrs Norris when she found her.

The cook leant back to regard Edie. 'You need to refill your bucket in the scullery, not bring it in 'ere.'

'I'm sorry to disturb you, but I need to speak with Mrs Leggett.'

'What is it, girl?' The housekeeper's manner was curt once more.

'I was cleaning in Room 202 and found a picture on the floor. The glass has broken.'

The housekeeper lifted a piece of paper from the table, holding it close to her face as she examined it. 'But you're not supposed to be cleaning that room.'

How could she put this so that the other maid got into as little trouble as possible? 'I'd finished ahead of time so was helping Fanny out, finishing the room so she could start the next. To get everything done quickly.'

'Did Fanny break the picture?'

'I don't know. She didn't mention it to me. It was behind a chair, so she may have missed it.'

'Don't say much for her cleaning if that's the case,' Mrs Norris grumbled, stirring something on the range.

The housekeeper tutted. 'Quite so. You need to get some old newspaper from the scullery. Gather up the pieces in it, roll it up, then put them with the rubbish in the shed. You'll need to give the floor a thorough brush. Go on with you now. I'll come and take a look when I do my inspection of the rooms.'

Edie picked up the bucket and box and headed to the scullery as instructed.

Back in Room 202, she cleared up the glass first, before returning to wipe the door. She only hoped Fanny didn't get into too much trouble for not noticing it. It could be the end of any hope of a peaceful relationship with her.

–

At four o'clock Edie was on her way down for her break and a cup of tea. Lili, coming out onto the staircase just after, called her name before catching her up.

'All finished?' She walked just behind her.

'I am. Even did a bit of Fanny's room for her as she didn't feel well.'

'She looked fit enough at dinner time. I wouldn't start doing that. Lazy donkey she is, that one. You don't want to start feeling sorry for her.'

'Just this once won't hurt. I thought it might help smooth the animosity.'

'I'm gasping for that tea.' Lili went slightly ahead. 'Race you there!'

'With all this equipment?' Nevertheless, she tried to keep up.

The two of them clashed as they tried to get through the doorway, giggling at their effort to win.

The housekeeper came tearing out of the dining room. 'What is all this noise?'

The laughter ceased immediately. 'Sorry, Mrs Leggett,' they said in unison, looking suitably sheepish.

'Miss Moore, I wish you to come into the dining room.'

'I'll just take these back to the scullery—'

'Now!' She stormed off back to the room in question.

'Leave your things here,' said Lili. 'I'll put them away for you.'

She put down her equipment and went to join the housekeeper.

In the room the teapots, cups and saucers were laid up ready for the break. Fanny was standing at one end, Gertie at the other. Mrs Leggett was in front of the empty fireplace, arms crossed.

With no preamble, the housekeeper said, 'Fanny tells me that you went to the room where she was working and insisted on finishing it for her, and that the picture was not broken when she left it.'

'No, it wasn't, 'cos I remember looking at it as I left the room.'

Edie realised she'd been a fool. There was no doubt in her mind now that Fanny had dropped the picture and that she'd asked Edie to finish the room so she could get the blame. 'I'm sorry, but that simply isn't true. Fanny came to the room where I was working and pleaded with me to finish up Room 202 so she could start her next room. She said she was ill, and—'

'I'm not ill, you liar.'

'Yeah, she's a liar,' added Gertie, face screwed up.

Any last shred of compassion for Fanny vanished. Anger boiled within Edie such as she hadn't felt since the incident over the suffragist meetings.

This new life had been too good to be true. She thought she'd taken to it with such ease, despite the back-breaking work. It had all seemed so novel, but how long before it felt as dreary as her life back in Downland House? How long before people made it clear how lowly her position had become?

'Fanny told me she had a bad stomach and that she'd told you, Mrs Leggett, but that you were unsympathetic. I agreed to help because I felt sorry for her. It was when I went to clean round the door that I saw the broken glass there. Since Fanny claimed to have cleaned the rest of the room, I assumed she must have seen the glass. So, either she didn't clean the room, or she saw the glass and didn't want to get into trouble for it, or she broke the frame herself and wanted *me* to get into trouble.'

'Who are you, Sherlock Holmes, with your de… ductions?' Gertie struggled over the last word.

Fanny wagged her finger at Edie. 'You're a bloody liar. I didn't do no such thing.' She was almost shrieking by the time she'd finished.

Lili and Charlie came through the door, both speaking at the same time, interrupting Mrs Leggett. Charlie pointed to Lili, indicating she should go first.

'You're the liar, Fanny Bullen. You did this to me last year, when that teapot got broken. Told Mrs Norris it were me, you did. And I had to pay for it out of my wages.'

'Lili, this does not involve—' the housekeeper began.

Charlie stepped forward. 'And a coupla years ago you got that poor girl, Sarah Jones, in trouble by saying she'd swiped the biscuits Mrs Norris made for afternoon tea. She swore blind it wasn't 'er. I bet that was you, too.'

'You bloody sods.' Fanny burst into tears.

There were running footsteps in the corridor before Mrs Bygrove dashed into the dining room. 'What on earth is going on? The guests must be able to hear all this hullabaloo.'

Mrs Leggett explained the accusations and counter-accusations, having to shush the distraught maid several times. Edie thought it best to let the housekeeper get on with it.

'This is something we'll have to sort out in the evening,' said the manager's wife. 'We are very busy at the moment, and Anton has gone home feeling ill.'

'Another one?' said Charlie. 'That's three today.'

'Indeed. Günther can't cope on his own, so I need someone else to help serve afternoon tea in the conservatory.'

Charlie stepped back. 'Don't look at me. I'm clumsy as a bear when it comes to china.'

'I couldn't spare you from the foyer anyway. No, I was thinking of Edie, since she has close knowledge of the upper classes and knows how to act in their company.'

'That's not bloody fair,' Fanny sniffled.

The housekeeper took three long strides over to the maid, grabbing her arm and slamming her onto a seat. 'Miss Bullen, I would advise you to calm down. Are you surprised you're not chosen when you use such language? One more word and I will see to it you're dismissed, whether you're guilty of the broken picture or not.'

'Clearly a matter for later,' said Mrs Bygrove. 'But let us not be hasty in dismissing anyone.' She turned back to Edie. 'Would you change into a grey uniform with a serving apron and cap and come to the front desk, please, Miss Moore.'

Edie's hands were trembling, both with distress and anger. That wouldn't be conducive to serving tea. She had the chance to get away from this situation for a while. She needed to pull herself together.

'Of course, Mrs Bygrove.'

There might be war brewing in Europe, but there was trouble much closer to home now, here in the hotel. She only hoped she could find peace.

–

The first half hour serving had been busy as well as warm in the south- and west-facing conservatory. The windows and double doors had all been open; their tied-back net curtains fluttered in the breeze. Here there were ten tables, both square and rectangular. Almost all the seats were full, mainly with pairs or groups of ladies, though there was one family, a table of gentlemen, and one with Major Thomas and a male companion.

Edie placed a tray of tea things down in front of a trio of women in early middle age who were staying for a month at the hotel. They were the arty types she'd seen in the foyer when she'd come for the bookkeeper's job. She'd since discovered that they were all real artists. One had black hair and was called Ebony, another was a strawberry blonde named Marigold and the third, with the nut-brown hair, had the name Hazel. Edie wondered whether they were their real names, or whether they'd styled themselves as such to suit their hair colour. It did seem a bit too much of a coincidence, and they were artists, after all. Their dresses were loose and colourful. Each wore a turban with a jewelled brooch at the gathered front. How she longed to sit with them to discuss their painting, and maybe take a look at their work.

As she poured their tea, the major, at the next table, was holding forth about Austria-Hungary declaring war on Serbia, predicting doom and gloom. Günther, who she rarely saw as he took his meals at different times to her, came with a coffee pot for the major's table.

'What do you think of all this then, Günther? I'd value your opinion.' Major Thomas held up the front page of a newspaper.

'Your part of the world, isn't it? Do you think your lot will get involved with this?'

Mrs Rhys-Pennington, on the next table, who lived in one of the Georgian houses on South Terrace, leant over. 'Oh, Major, must you spoil the afternoon with such talk?'

'My dear lady, I fear we will not be able to ignore this for long. So, Günther, what are your thoughts?'

What Edie had gathered of Günther from the others was that he was a quiet man and rarely spoke. According to Charlie, he spent most of his spare time reading. Several other people had ceased their conversations to hear the waiter's reply.

'Sir, I leave the madness to the politicians.'

The major threw his head back and let out a hearty laugh. 'Well said, that man, well said.'

Günther bowed and left the table. Edie followed on half a minute later, taking the route diagonally across the dining room, which was now empty. Going straight ahead would bring one to the foyer. As she passed through, she heard an altercation from the desk. She knew she should ignore it and carry on to the kitchen, but she changed direction and peered round into the foyer, beyond the staircase.

One of the guests, Sir Reynard Strong, who she knew to be extremely rich, was at the desk shouting at Richard Watkins, the haughty receptionist she'd encountered on her first visit to the hotel. Mr Bygrove appeared at that moment and the guest started bawling at him, something about payment.

'I'm sorry, sir,' said Bygrove, 'but it is our policy for people to pay up until the time they have booked, otherwise we lose money on empty rooms. Especially as it's the bank holiday weekend.'

'Don't you realise there's been a major financial crisis due to the situation on the European mainland? The stock exchange has been closed and I need to go, now!'

Behind him was his wife with a nanny and a young child, who started to cry. The mother was also tearful, trying to cajole the little one.

'Well, if I must pay up, I will. I haven't got time to argue with you.'

Charlie came down the stairs; he and Edie spotted each other at the same time. He looked over the handrail before joining her in the dining room.

'Aren't you meant to be serving in the conservatory?' His mouth tipped up at one side and he widened his eyes.

'I heard this fuss, and wondered what it was.'

He tucked in next to her. 'I could hear it from the first floor.'

'You'd think he'd be able to afford to pay for the lost five days.'

Charlie tutted. 'The richer they are, the stingier. How'd ya think they got rich in the first place?'

They saw Mrs Bygrove appear at the desk. 'What is the problem?'

Her husband turned abruptly towards her. 'This is not your concern. Go and see to the staff.'

Even from their position they could see the hurt on her face. When they realised she was coming towards them, they shuffled backwards into the dining room. Edie headed back across the room to get to the kitchen. Charlie began walking forward once more as if he'd already been on his way somewhere.

'Afternoon, Mrs Bygrove.' Charlie lifted his cap.

'Good afternoon, Charlie. I believe Sir Reynard will shortly be wanting his luggage carried down from Room 106.'

'Very well, madam.' He set off at a brisk pace.

–

Before supper that evening, Fanny and Edie were summoned to the staff dining room by Mrs Leggett.

Edie had hoped that the conversation earlier would put an end to it, but she should have known better. Broken items at Downland House would always have to be paid for if dropped by a member of staff. Her stomach squirmed. Fanny would never own up, of that she was sure.

Mrs Bygrove, standing in front of the fireplace, asked them all to sit. 'I believe we have a problem from earlier to deal with.'

The housekeeper remained standing. 'Wouldn't it be better if the manager dealt with this?'

There was a fleeting expression of anxiety on Mrs Bygrove's face. 'My husband is at cricket practice, so I am in charge.'

'I see.' The housekeeper puckered her lips with disapproval.

'First, I should like to hear the story from each of the young women themselves. Fanny, you first, and please, no hysterics.'

'She volunteered, she did, to help me, just showing off, I reckon, 'cos she thinks she's better than us at everything.'

'Just the facts, please,' said Mrs Bygrove.

'It's like I said, she came to the room and said she'd heard I was ill so could she finish up for me and—'

Mrs Leggett stepped towards her. 'That is not what you said before. You accused her of being a liar for saying you were ill.'

'I-I meant, I wasn't ill, someone else was a liar for telling her that…' Fanny ran out of words and slumped back in her chair.

The manager's wife sat down next to the sulking girl. 'So, Fanny, would I be right in thinking you dropped the picture but were afraid of being chastised and fined?'

The maid's mouth turned down at the corners and her chin wobbled. 'I can't afford to lose money. I send it home to my mum, see, 'cos she's ill.' She pointed at Edie. 'I bet she's saved a pretty penny, being a governess, and don't need it.'

Edie was on the edge of feeling pity once more, wondering how desperate you had to be to make up such lies. She resisted the urge to reveal that governesses were not as handsomely paid as the young maid seemed to think.

'I see,' said Mrs Leggett. 'In that case… Wait a moment. You told me when you first arrived here that your mother had died and you had no home, which is why you wanted a live-in position.'

Fanny's chin dropped. She looked down at her lap.

'So, which is true?' asked Mrs Bygrove. 'For they can't both be.'

Fanny didn't reply.

'Well, I don't know who to believe,' said the housekeeper. 'They might both be liars for all we know.' She looked down at the two maids disapprovingly.

Mrs Bygrove stood. 'You can't possibly be suggesting that Edie is still responsible? Clearly Fanny dropped the picture.' She looked down at the girl. 'And needs to make amends, as well as promise she will not do anything like this again. Do you understand, Fanny?'

The maid nodded.

'And you will pay for the glass on the picture, that's only fair, but you can pay it off each week rather than all at once. And you will apologise to Edie.'

'Thank you, madam.' Fanny lifted her eyes from the table. 'Sorry, Edie.'

'That's all right.' Not that it was, but what else could she say? Deep inside she was still boiling with rage. She tried to content herself with the fact that at least they'd got to the truth.

The housekeeper did a sharp twist on her feet and left the room.

Mrs Bygrove stood. 'I don't want to hear of any more of these incidences. Now, the pair of you, please fetch the plates and cutlery for supper.'

Neither spoke as they went about their task. Slowly the rest of the off-duty staff filtered in, and the food arrived. Gertie sat with Fanny at one end of the table and looked to be questioning her, though she got little response. Edie gave Lili and Charlie, sitting either side of her, a brief rundown of the earlier conversation, still shaken from the episode.

After supper Fanny and Lili left promptly, on turndown duty. Charlie and Edie were the last two in the dining room.

'It's a lovely evening out there, after the cloudy day,' he said, straightening the chairs.

'I was thinking of taking a walk on the promenade, blow out some cobwebs, before the sun disappears completely. And to try to forget this awful business with Fanny.'

Charlie pushed in the last chair, biting his bottom lip. 'Um, don't suppose you fancy some company? I'm not on duty again tonight, and I could do with blowing a few cobwebs away meself.' He gave her a hopeful grin.

After an initial urge to say she wanted to be alone, she realised that wasn't the case. Charlie's offer of companionship was a surprisingly welcome gesture. A warmth settled inside her at the idea that he even wanted to spend time with her. It was good to make friends.

She wondered what her old friends were doing now. Those who were left. Most were inevitably married. The couple she had become pally with at the suffragist meetings had never seemed to want to get too close. Maybe they felt restricted by their status, being middle class, and were wary of becoming too friendly.

In a way, Charlie might prove a better friend, having no side to him. He accepted everybody.

'Yes, a bit of company would be good after this awful day. I'm just going to change first, though. I don't really want to go for a walk in an apron.'

'Ditto.' He pulled at his porter's uniform. 'I'll meet you by the side gate in five minutes.'

'Make it ten.'

–

Charlie was already at the gate when she got there, whistling to himself. He was wearing fawn trousers and a dark brown jacket, opened to reveal a cream waistcoat and uncollared shirt. On his head was a brown cap.

Before Charlie had asked to walk with her, she'd been planning on wearing the outfit Jenny had found for her at Downland House. Instead, she wore the blouse and skirt she'd bought on her first day in Littlehampton. What a shame she hadn't brought a change of hat with her from Downland House! She decided to buy a new ribbon for her current one on her next half-day off.

They chatted about their day as they crossed the common, Charlie regaling her with a couple of humorous tales involving new guests. He could spin a good story, able to extract the funny and absurd from a situation.

By the time they reached the bandstand and esplanade, Edie was feeling a lot better for having a good laugh.

Charlie pointed to the deckchairs in rows by the bandstand. 'Pity they've finished here for the evening. I like a nice musical interlude, me.'

'So do I. There are still a lot of people out with children, considering the time.'

'They call Littlehampton the Children's Paradise, did you know that?'

'I have heard that, yes. I can understand why. Did you like it as a child? Always assuming you were brought up here.'

He stopped to face her. 'Me? Oh yes, I'm a Hampton Shaker, born and bred.'

She laughed. 'A what?'

'It's what the Arundel lot used to call us, on account of the illness we endured living on the marshy plains of the river. Used to make people shake, see. We call them Arundel Mullets 'cos of all the fish what live in their bit of the river.'

'I've never heard that before.'

They headed up to the promenade, busy with walkers enjoying the orange and cornflower-blue sky. Over the river and the beach beyond it the sun had vanished, but still threw a golden light over the area.

'A walk towards the river, or Rustington?' Charlie pointed first one way then the other.

'The river.'

They strolled leisurely, not speaking at first. The fresh, salty air was such a change to the stench of the vinegar and carbolic she'd used to clean with earlier. The beach itself had few people on it now. The tide was far out, the lapping of the waves barely audible.

'Where are you from then?'

The question from Charlie was unexpected, throwing her brain off balance for a second. No harm in admitting that though, even if she was a bit vague.

'Hastings originally. And then we lived near Brighton.'

'I've been to Brighton a few times, on the train. It's good fun at the shooting galleries and circus acts on the Palace Pier. Went to that posher West Pier once, and saw some performing fleas. It's not like our bit of nothing here.' He indicated the short wooden pier at the end of the prom, bordering the river and the beach.

'I like it here. The coast is much more natural than Brighton. There's at least some sand here. And you've got the vast common and the river, not buildings and a road right by the beach.' Edie did a full circle, taking it all in.

She recalled their family trips to Brighton, where her mother had refused to go on the Palace Pier, declaring it 'down at heel' with its freak shows and circus acts. No, it was only the West Pier for them, with its concert hall. Her mother had not, however, been impressed with the performing fleas.

'I suppose it's more picture-skew here.'

Edie wrinkled her nose. 'Picture-skew?'

'It's how my old nan used to pronounce picturesque, bless her.'

'Ah.' She recalled her own paternal grandmother, 'Grandmama', who'd passed five years before. The threat of overwhelming sadness made her move on swiftly. 'Have you ever lived anywhere else?'

'Me?' He pointed to himself. 'I went away for a bit. But I came back.' He shrugged. 'It was better here.'

'Where did you go?' She was intrigued.

He stuck his hands in his trouser pockets and gave a brief chuckle. 'Portsmouth. Labouring. Didn't like it. Came back.

Eventually.' He started walking again so she followed. 'Before I went, I worked for my father. He's got a motor car repair garage on Western Road. I was a mechanic, but I didn't really like being bossed around by Dad so, yes. Went to Portsmouth, came back, but my old pap wouldn't have me back to work.'

'So, your family are just down the road and round the corner from the hotel?'

'Yep. But they don't talk to me since I went away. That's why I got a live-in job. Shame, really, 'cos I liked being a mechanic. Got persuaded to go by a mate, see, or not such a mate as it turned out.'

'I'm sorry to hear that, Charlie.' She and the porter were more alike than she'd first imagined. His situation made her feel even more depressed about her own. Were such fallings-out inevitable? 'Why not work for another motor car garage? The hotel has one, for a start.'

'No reference. And the hotel garage only houses the cars and does minimal work, like cleaning and changing tyres, not repairing engines like I used to do. Anyway, what about you, grammar school girl? Is governessing all you've done?'

'Yes.'

'And what about your dad? What's he do? Oh, presuming he's still alive. Sorry.'

'It's all right, he is alive. He sells timber. We don't exactly see eye to eye either.'

'Family, eh? Tell ya what, it's good to get away from talk of the trouble abroad. Sick of hearing it at meals and then in our bedroom at night. It's all Lorcan and Joseph can talk about. Günther keeps quiet, thankfully.'

'And now you've brought it up.' She tipped her head sideways to regard him with a grin.

He looked at her and laughed. 'You're right. End of subject. Would you like to hear the end of the Sir Strong episode?'

'Absolutely.'

'Good. Let's get a move on before it gets dark.'

Chapter Six

The hotel was extra busy today, being August Bank Holiday Monday, and it was likely to be so all week.

Edie considered this as she cleaned one of the smaller rooms overlooking the sea. The third of August, 1914. So far she'd been here one month and ten days. She'd now got into the routine. Lili had laughed when she'd told her she found the work testing but fulfilling. Despite the trouble with Fanny over the broken picture, the job was still a novelty that had not yet worn off. Come the winter, with cold winds, dull days and fewer guests, she might feel differently.

Old life, new life. Either way, her life ahead would be one of servitude in one way or another.

Out of the window she spied the throngs of holidaymakers on the common and the promenade. The seats round the bandstand were full as the brass band musicians gave it their all playing 'The Boy I Love Is Up In The Gallery'.

She'd never seen Littlehampton this busy, not on her visits nor since she'd moved here. Charlie and many of the others had said the same at morning break. It wasn't the warmest weather she'd experienced since being here, what with the sun constantly dipping behind the clouds. There was, however, an air of carelessness among the visitors. It was as if nothing else mattered, that they had to take full advantage of today because it might be all they had. She wasn't sure where that thought had come from, except that the papers were full of pessimism about the situation in mainland Europe. This was especially true now that Germany had declared war on Russia.

But most people reckoned it would come to nothing. That had certainly been the opinion of one of the town councillors who'd come in for luncheon the day before.

Edie was thinking about this again two mornings later, as she rushed down to breakfast at half past five. Even though she was on time, she hated being the last person there, knowing at the same time how idiotic that was. Lili patted the seat beside her, having saved it as she'd said she would.

'I reckon we're in for another hectic day,' said her friend, helping herself to two slices of bacon from the tray and placing it onto her buttered bread. 'I wonder if Mrs Bygrove will ask us to serve in the dining room again.'

'I wouldn't bank on that,' Mrs Leggett called from one end of the table. 'You were only required because Anton was still off sick. Two of you to replace one male waiter. What a waste. Mr Bygrove is making enquiries to bring in a retired waiter, John Smithson, to replace him temporarily.'

'Never have I seen anything like the crowds yesterday, on a Tuesday after a bank holiday.' Everyone looked up, surprised to hear the voice of Günther, who normally never volunteered an opinion on anything.

'I dare say it had a lot to do with Mr Asquith extending the bank holiday to Friday,' said Charlie, pouring himself a cup of tea. 'According to Major Thomas, it's because people took out large sums of money for the holiday, because they're afraid of what's coming.'

Miss Bolton, the in-house nurse and midwife, took the offered pot from Charlie, tutting several times. 'Scaremongering. I can't be doing with it. I was rushed off my feet yesterday, and what for? Nothing serious, I can assure you – just a lot of upper-class women having the vapours. It was all this talk of Germany declaring war on Russia and France. What with the banks, anyone would think we were in danger of imminent invasion and bankruptcy.'

Edie glanced at Günther, whose head was down as he munched on his bread.

Mrs Norris came in part way through the conversation with a bowl of boiled eggs. 'Funny lot, those Germans.'

Phoebe Sweeton, a stillroom maid, swivelled round on the bench. 'Mrs Norris, Günther is a kind and gentle man, and you should know better.'

'I'm sure there's exceptions, there always are to a rule.'

'I don't think—' the stillroom maid started again, only to be interrupted by the waiter.

'It is all right, Phoebe,' he said. 'I have done nothing wrong and need not to be defended.'

Lorcan, mouth half full of food, ploughed in next. 'I'm sure a lot of Germans are decent people. But if Austria-Hungary and that mad Kaiser keep declaring war on countries, he'll get to Britain in the end, so he will.'

'And him a cousin of our King, God bless 'im,' added Mrs Norris. 'And of that Tsar Nicholas, of course.'

There was a thud from the door to reception and clomping boots down the corridor as Mrs Norris said, 'Well, all this talk of war won't get my preparations done.' She heaved her tall, stout body away, only to be stalled by her son, Joseph, blocking the doorway, out of breath.

'The papers have come.' He lifted up the *Daily Express* for them to see, pointing to the headline on the second column. 'Look: "War Declared On Germany", it says. By us, yesterday.'

Günther leapt from his seat, exclaiming, '*Gott im Himmel!*' He pulled his fingers through his dark brown hair and puffed out a breath of frustration before rushing from the room.

-

Charlie was standing by the door that led from the foyer to the dining room, welcoming lunch guests and answering queries. Despite their being fully booked, he was thankful for the relative peace compared to the post-breakfast commotion.

It had taken an hour to extract Günther from their bedroom, convinced as he was that now nobody would want to be served by him. Mr Bygrove had ranted and raved, but it had been his wife in the end who'd persuaded the German to serve breakfast. Nobody had objected, as he'd feared, his dedication to duty when it came to his customers already having made him a favourite among the guests. At present he was serving lunch with three of the live-out waiters, including the older John Smithson.

Charlie had heard much discussion of the war among the guests that morning as he'd been working, carrying luggage for new arrivals, running messages for the major and returning laundry, washed at an outside business, to the guests. There'd been many opinions on the whys and wherefores of war, to which he'd simply listened without comment. But one thing they'd all agreed on: it would be over by Christmas.

He wished he shared their optimism.

As he was greeting a guest from outside, a deep, bellowing voice could be heard coming from the middle of the dining room. Charlie marched swiftly in to discover the problem, realising the trouble-free hours had been too good to be true.

On a smaller table a middle-aged man was ranting at Günther, who seemed rooted to the spot, holding two menus. Opposite the man was his wife, whose head was resting on her hand as she closed her eyes. Charlie had not long greeted this couple. Everyone else in the dining room had fallen silent.

'What's the problem?' said Charlie.

'I refuse to be served by a German. I know the accent when I hear it.'

The waiter beat a hasty retreat towards the kitchen.

'Günther is naturalised,' Charlie explained. 'So he's one of us.'

The man threw his napkin on the table. 'He will *never* be one of us. Do you know who I am?'

Ah, one of those, thought Charlie, who had no idea who he was, but he was sure he would soon tell him.

'I'm Sir Horace Stonely. I demand to speak to the manager.'

'I am the manageress.' Mrs Bygrove was already halfway across the room when she spoke.

Manageress. That was the first time he'd heard her refer to herself in that way. Where was Bygrove anyway – skiving off for some sporting activity again? He hadn't seen him all morning.

'Mr Cobbett, you may return to your post.'

The hell I am, thought Charlie, stepping back far enough to be out of view.

'And what business have you employing Germans? Answer me, woman!'

'If you'd like to step into the foyer, we will discuss the matter there.' Mrs Bygrove's arm pointed the way.

'No, I would not. I want luncheon and I want a British waiter to serve it.'

'Don't be ridiculous,' one of the lady artists from three tables away called.

'You're an embarrassment,' agreed one of her companions.

'Perhaps we could go elsewhere, dear,' his wife suggested. He ignored her.

'The rest of my waiters are fully busy with their tables, I'm afraid,' Mrs Bygrove explained, although they were all gawping at the spectacle presently unfolding. 'And Günther is the most experienced waiter we have. He's been with us for four years, and you're lucky to have sat at one of his tables.'

'Hear, hear,' called Major Thomas.

'I couldn't care less,' said Stonely. 'The Germans should be rounded up as spies, and believe me, they will be, naturalised or not.'

'And will that include our royal family, the Saxe-Coburg-Gothas?' asked Mrs Bygrove.

Charlie clamped his hand to his mouth to stop himself laughing, but when the rest of the restaurant erupted, he couldn't help but join in. So immersed was he in the humour, he didn't notice Mr Bygrove striding through the dining room.

'*I'll* take over now,' he told his wife.

'Reckon she's doing pretty well without you, old chap,' joked the major.

Even from where he was standing, Charlie could see the manager's jaw stiffen. 'Go back to reception, Helen. I will talk to you later.'

Mrs Bygrove walked away, her pursed lips showing she was angry. She indicated with her head that Charlie should follow her. 'I thought I told you to return to your post.'

'Sorry, but I'm glad I didn't miss that. Made my day, it has. You were magnificent. The royal family!' He laughed again.

'I fear I've made things worse.'

They'd barely reached the foyer when Lord Stonely marched past them, as if he were on parade, his wife running behind, struggling with her tight-hemmed hobble skirt.

Stonely stopped long enough to say, 'I'm only here a few days, but be sure I will be passing around how the Beach Hotel harbours enemies.' With that, he dashed out through the external door, not holding it open for his poor wife.

From the dining room a chant started up, more voices joining in, until Charlie could hear the words: 'We want Günther, we want Günther.'

Douglas Bygrove stomped out of the dining room, straight to his wife, standing by the reception desk.

'What on earth did you think you were doing? The customer is always right.'

'But they aren't always, are they, Douglas? And I'm certainly not going to kowtow to some ignorant man who's set on causing dissent where there is none.'

'I am the manager here, and you'd do well to remember it.'

'Then perhaps you should have been here to attend to the problem, instead of at the links playing golf. Now, I'm going to find Günther once more, and—'

A cheer went up in the dining room, causing the three of them to return there. Günther had arrived back, chaperoned by John Smithson.

Major Thomas stood up. 'Welcome back, Günther, old chap.'

There was a round of applause. Günther's face glowed red as he looked timidly around the room.

Charlie's first thought was how he couldn't wait to tell Edie at dinner time.

Edie? Why her and not the staff generally? Yes, he'd enjoy that, but it was entertaining Edie with the story he was looking forward to the most.

As he walked back to the foyer, two of the live-out porters came to take over from him and Lorcan, who'd been on the telephone booking theatre tickets and a motor taxi for two of the guests.

Lorcan put the receiver down as Charlie approached him. 'What in the name of Mary and Joseph was all that noise about?'

'Come on. I'll tell you at dinner.'

–

Edie lowered the sandwich she was about to eat. 'What on earth is going on now? It sounds like cheering.'

Lili cocked her ear to listen. 'I think it's coming from the dining room.'

'I hope they're not cheering about Britain going to war,' said Mrs Leggett, stiff-lipped. 'That is certainly not something to celebrate.'

There'd already been some commotion with slamming doors and Mrs Norris shouting something along the lines of, ''Ere, where are you going?'

The door was pushed open to reveal Charlie with a huge grin on his face, and Lorcan looking confused.

'What the devil is happening out there?' said the housekeeper. 'Sounds like the war's come to the Beach Hotel.'

Charlie blurted out in eager tones about the goings-on with Günther and Sir Horace, and the other guests' reactions.

Lorcan had already sat down and helped himself to a sandwich. 'You can't blame people for not wanting to be served by Germans. Did you read in the papers about them killing children? It's atrocious, so it is.'

'But Günther's not like that,' said Phoebe, the stillroom maid, her eyes creased with concern. 'You can't take it out on him.'

'I'm not saying I am. I'm just saying you can't blame people for feeling like that. What if it was your children?'

Phoebe put her sandwich down and placed her fingertips against her head.

Edie remembered something she'd read in the paper. 'Does anyone know if Günther has registered with the police yet? They have to, now, because of the Aliens Restriction Act the government's just passed.'

Phoebe looked up. 'He told me this morning he's going to do it on Monday, on his half-day off. I'll go with him to make sure he does.' She gave a weak smile.

'There are also appeals for men to enlist in the army.' Lili sighed. 'I hope those daft brothers of mine don't do anything so stupid.'

Mrs Leggett shook her head. 'And what would we do for waiters and porters, may I ask, if they all signed up?'

'Employ women, I guess,' said Edie.

Fanny and Gertie sniggered from their end of the table.

Edie frowned. 'What's so funny about that? We can do those jobs. We already have done some of them.'

'I'm not running around like a lackey,' said Gertie. 'It's not ladylike.'

Charlie helped himself to a cheese sandwich. 'Who are you calling a lackey?'

'Enough now,' said the housekeeper. 'I'm sure it won't come to that. Over by Christmas, it says. Now eat up, because time is short.'

Edie, lifting her skirt slightly as she ran along South Terrace in front of the Georgian houses, puffed at the effort. She'd been sent to the grocers on Norfolk Road for sugar. That's where she'd heard the alarming news. The quicker she relayed it to those at the hotel, the better. Changing her basket from one arm to the other, she swung round to cross the road. Almost stepping out without looking, she noticed the dairy's horse and cart just in time. She'd been so full of the shocking events at the Lifeboat Parade that she'd become oblivious to the world around her.

'Stop, calm down,' she whispered. She took a deep breath and swallowed with difficulty.

Mr Johnson from the dairy, from where the hotel got its milk, lifted his cap as the cart went by. She watched him, ready to cross when he'd passed, eager again to get back. She was foiled this time by a motor car, beeping its horn as the driver also recognised her. It was one of the live-out porters, bringing round a Rolls-Royce Silver Ghost for one of the guests, from the hotel's garage in Norfolk Place, at the end of South Terrace.

Finally, she escaped across the road, the short rest adding a spurt to her step. She hurried through the entrance to the kitchen, then placed the basket down on the table at the opposite end to where the kitchen maid was sniffing back tears as she chopped onions.

Mrs Norris turned her head from her position by the stove. 'Good Lord, you're all out of puff. We didn't need it that quickly.'

'I know, it's just—' She pursed her lips to blow out a breath. 'I heard some news. Disturbing news.'

'Well, come on, out with it.'

Mrs Bygrove strolled in. She had on a new dress, royal blue, with a bell-shaped skirt and wide overskirt. It clearly showed her ankles, which were not normally on display. No doubt it was to look her best for the guests arriving to the twenty-first birthday dinner of the young Isabella Raynolt this evening. Her parents, Lord and Lady Raynolt, had hired the whole of the dining room and the ballroom, where a quartet was due to play.

My goodness, thought Edie, *what if—*

'Edie here's got some news, though she hasn't managed to tell me yet, so puffed out is she.'

Mrs Bygrove came towards her, a worried frown appearing on her flawless forehead. 'What is it? You're red in the face.'

'A customer at the dairy, she told me a troupe of musicians has been arrested.'

'Musicians?' The manager's wife looked confused. 'Oh dear, they're not the ones performing this evening, are they?' She clasped her hands together.

'No, *German* musicians, performing at the Lifeboat Parade.' She plopped down on the bench seat on one side of the table.

Both the cook, the maid and Mrs Bygrove looked perplexed.

'What have they done?' asked Mrs Norris.

'They haven't done anything, except be German. Sorry, I'm not explaining it very well. They were arrested as aliens, under the new act. The customer reckoned a couple of foreign waiters have been arrested at a boarding house, too. None of them were registered.'

Mrs Bygrove's hands flew to her chin. 'The Aliens Restriction Act. I do hope Günther has registered.'

'Phoebe said he was going to go on Monday, his half-day.'

'Silly man! If he'd told me that, I would have sent him straight off. No time like the present. It's only afternoon tea. You could cope with that again, couldn't you, Edie, if you took his place?'

'Yes, of course.' She only hoped the other maids wouldn't complain too much of having to share out her load. Still, it should only take the waiter an hour or less to get to the police station and back. It was just behind the railway station.

'You know where the uniforms—'

The door to the kitchen was flung open. Mary Lovelock, the bookkeeper, clutched her chest. 'There's trouble in the dining room. The police have arrived to take Günther away, but he's refusing to go. The place is in uproar with customers shouting and Charlie trying to talk to the officer, who's ignoring him.'

'Where's my husband, do you know?'

'Um,' the bookkeeper looked sheepish. 'I believe he went to play tennis.'

There was a moment of wildness in Mrs Bygrove's eyes before she exited the kitchen in great haste. Edie followed on, ignoring the cook's barked enquiry as to where she thought she was going.

Out in the foyer the two of them heard a great deal of fuss. They rounded the desk to find Charlie and John Smithson standing in front of Günther defiantly. Major Thomas was wagging his finger and telling the police what he thought. Several of the lunch guests had vacated their seats to witness the proceedings.

Edie was relieved to see that it was Detective Inspector Davis, along with the rather genial sergeant. Mrs Bygrove opened her mouth to speak, but Edie got in first.

'Inspector Davis, what is the problem?'

His wide eyes told her he hadn't expected to see her there. 'We've had a report from a Sir Horace Stonely that a Günther Schultz working here is a spy.'

'That is nonsense,' said Mrs Bygrove. 'Sir Horace came for lunch three days ago and refused to be served by a German, even though he's been naturalised. The man swore to make trouble.'

'We've also discovered that Mr Schultz hasn't registered at the police station, as was ordered.'

'I have not had a chance, with work,' Günther said. 'I was going to do it on Monday.'

'An order's an order, I'm afraid.'

Sergeant Gardner tried to weave around Charlie and the older waiter to grab at the German, but they shifted so he couldn't reach him.

Inspector Davis stepped back. 'Gardner, go and get the two constables in, would you.'

'Yes, sir.'

When the sergeant had gone, the inspector took the two women to one side. 'It's not personal, you know. But I've got a job to do.'

'Look,' said the manager's wife, 'we have a large function on this evening, and as it is, we have all the waiters coming in to serve. We couldn't possibly do without Günther. He's the head waiter. I'll bring him down to the station now, and he can register. How does that sound?'

The inspector sighed. 'I'm sorry, but it's gone past that. Sir Horace has got someone in the House of Lords involved. Registered or not, Mr Schultz is a German and as such will be sent to an internment camp in Newbury.'

'An internment camp?' said Edie. 'What, like a prison camp?' Surely not.

Davis lifted his hat to rub his head. 'I'm afraid so. Look, if I don't take him in, they'll send someone else to. I don't like what's going on either, picking on people who've been here a long time and, as you said, naturalised in many cases. But I've got a job to do, whether I agree with it or not.'

Mrs Bygrove nodded. 'Of course, Inspector. What about his belongings?'

'You can take Mr Schultz to his room to pack, but only a small bag. The sergeant will go with you.'

'In case I let him escape?' She raised her eyebrows.

Davis narrowed his lips but didn't reply.

Mrs Bygrove shook her head. 'I have no choice then.'

Edie's soul sank. Poor Günther. It seemed so unfair. If she ever got hold of Sir Horace's scrawny neck… No, she mustn't think like that, though she was furious with the man. And Phoebe, where was she at this moment? She'd be so upset when she discovered what had happened. She suspected there was more than a friendship between the two.

Their group joined Charlie and John, still standing rebelliously in front of Günther.

'Smithson, Cobbett, stand down, gentlemen,' said Mrs Bygrove. 'I'm afraid we're going to have to comply with the officer.'

'Bad show, old boy,' the major told Inspector Davis. 'Günther here's the best waiter I've ever been served by. And I've come across a few in my time. Not a scrap of harm in the man.'

'It's not personal, sir. It's my job.'

'That's Major Thomas to you, young man.'

The porter and waiter looked at each other. Charlie flicked his eyes up briefly and tutted, before stepping away. Smithson did the same.

'I'm sorry, Günther,' said Charlie, looking disappointed in himself.

'It is not your fault,' said the head waiter. He stepped forward and put his clenched fists out.

Davis looked down at them, then up at the waiter, puzzled.

'Handcuffs, Inspector?'

'No need for that.' He explained about getting a bag of belongings.

Soon the waiter headed to the staff door with the sergeant and Charlie, who Mrs Bygrove had decided would accompany him. The standing guests returned to their seats and there was a rumble of conversation. The major followed on, grumbling to himself about overzealous reactions.

Helen turned to Edie. 'It looks like I'll need you to take over from Günther for a bit longer this afternoon.'

'Very well. I'll go and get changed.' About to make her way back to the servants' area, she noticed Mr Bygrove pushing open one of the large oak and glass doors.

He marched over to his wife and the inspector, face puffed up with irritation, arms swinging back and forth. Over one shoulder was a kitbag. 'What is that police van doing outside my hotel? If this gets around, I'll lose custom.'

'It's all right, dear,' said Mrs Bygrove. 'It's nothing to worry ab—'

'You can be quiet,' he barked, pointing at her.

The inspector looked at the manager curiously. 'There's no need to speak to your wife like that. She's been most helpful.'

'What are you doing here?'

The inspector related succinctly what had occurred and why. 'But Mrs Bygrove appeared and calmed things down.'

It was partly right, though Edie could tell the inspector was encouraging the manager to look favourably on his wife.

'I'm sure she did nothing of the sort,' said the manager. 'She's more likely to create a situation.'

Mrs Bygrove, far from being downhearted, pulled herself up straight, folding her arms across her chest. 'Actually, you are wrong, Douglas. And since you weren't here, yet again, to deal with a difficult situation, I'd say you are in no position to talk.'

The manager looked taken aback, flicking his gaze between her and Davis, maybe hoping he hadn't lost his veneer of authority. What a silly little man he was, thought Edie. Not little in terms of size, but in his lack of imagination or generosity. How had Helen Bygrove, so kind and perceptive, ended up with this cold fish? The inspector betrayed a faint smile, suggesting he approved of Mrs Bygrove's rebuke.

Edie decided it was time to change and get on with the task she'd been set. As she entered the servants' area, she saw Phoebe scurrying down the corridor.

'Where's Günther? Where is he? Mrs Norris said the police have come for him.'

Edie grabbed hold of the girl to keep her still. 'He's collecting his things. They're taking him to an internment camp as an alien.'

'No, they can't do that,' she yelled, breaking down into helpless tears.

Günther appeared at the bottom of the back stairs with Charlie and the sergeant. The distraught girl pulled away from Edie, but she caught hold of her once more.

'Best to forget me, *Liebling*. Goodbye, dear girl.' The German's shoulders drooped as he was led back to the foyer.

'Let me go, let – me – go!' After struggling in her embrace, Phoebe finally broke away from Edie, who tried to catch hold of the stillroom maid once more – but she was too quick. Edie trailed after her, back to the foyer, only to see her snatched up once more by one of the constables. He held onto the wailing woman until long after Günther had disappeared through the doors.

Mrs Bygrove spotted her and walked over. 'Oh dear, poor Günther. And we're going to be short of staff tonight for the dinner, too, for he's worth two of anybody. I'm going to have to get two women to serve. I could certainly be one of them.' She considered Edie for a moment. 'I know you will have a lot of shifts, but would you be the other, please?'

Edie was fit to drop, what with running back from the shop and wrangling Phoebe. And there was still the rest of lunch to serve, and afternoon tea. But she knew that the obliging staff were the ones that received the most appreciation. At least, from Helen Bygrove. And she had asked nicely.

'Yes, of course. We can't let Lord and Lady Raynolt's daughter down now, can we?'

The older woman grinned, patting Edie on the shoulder. 'Thank you, my dear. I'm sure you'll do a good job.'

Chapter Seven

'Where the devil is Lorcan?' Charlie considered his wristwatch. Seven thirty-five. And he was normally a couple of minutes early to catch up with anything he needed to know about the guests.

His fellow porter's half-day was over, and Charlie was starving. And he was looking forward to seeing Edie at supper. His heartbeat raced, leaving him a little breathless but also euphoric. Not one for any sentimentality, particularly not since he'd returned from Portsmouth, he'd have to knock that on the head. He had himself to look after and think about, and that was enough for now.

He checked the clock once more. Nearly twenty-to. The manager walked from the dining room, where he'd been mingling with the diners, ensuring they were happy with their experience. Charlie humphed. More like couldn't be bothered to do any proper work. Not like his missus, who was ready to get stuck in if they were short-handed.

'Cobbett, I thought you were off duty now. Wasn't Foley due to take over?'

'He hasn't made an appearance yet.'

'I'm afraid you'll have to remain in your post until he does. Where's Drew?'

'Running a message for Mrs Webb-Johnson—'

He didn't have time to add the 'sir' before Lorcan came rushing out through the staff door.

'Where on earth have you been?' Bygrove tapped his watch.

'Sorry, sir. Got carried away celebrating with some new pals.'

Charlie was keen to get to supper, but was also curious to hear what Lorcan had been up to.

Bygrove screwed his features in tightly. 'Celebrating? You're meant to be working, man.' He looked around, no doubt to make sure none of the guests were nearby. He came up close to Lorcan and sniffed. 'You've been drinking. Disgraceful! You will do a double shift tomorrow and have money taken from your wages.'

Lorcan flung back his head and laughed. 'You can do what the hell you like, so you can.'

As Bygrove's face went a deep red, he clenched his fists and pressed them against his legs. Charlie stepped backwards. His head, full of possible outcomes, tried to put in place several solutions. Should he get Mrs Bygrove? Where was she, even? Watkins on the desk was ignoring the whole charade so was unlikely to be of any use.

'Gonna hit me, are you?' Lorcan chuckled.

What on earth was wrong with him? He'd lose his job for sure.

'Well, go on then,' he continued. 'For I'm out of here tomorrow, to be part of Kitchener's New Army.'

'You're *what*?' Bygrove's voice reached a crescendo.

'I've enlisted, sir. Kitchener's 7th Service Battalion.'

Charlie hadn't seen that coming. He'd never have had Lorcan pinned as a particularly brave soul, though he was a foolhardy one, true enough.

'You bloody idiot,' said Bygrove. 'The war will be over before it's started, then what are you going to do for a job?'

Lorcan shrugged, his attention soon elsewhere as a group of four people entered the foyer. 'Excuse me, sir.' He headed over to greet the newcomers.

'Get to supper, Cobbett, before it's over.'

Charlie briefly saluted the manager before making a quick escape to the staff dining room, his stomach rumbling as he went.

Mrs Leggett already had a half-empty plate in front of her. 'Where have you been?'

'Lorcan was late for his shift. He's only gone and bleedin' enlisted.'

There were gasps and exclamations around the table, even from Fanny and Gertie, who normally only cared about themselves.

'Good Lord,' said Miss Bolton, the in-house nurse. 'It makes the conflict seem so real. It felt distant when they announced Britain had declared war.'

'I hope you're not thinking of signing up too.' The housekeeper wagged her finger at Charlie.

He took a fleeting look at Edie, who was staring at him. Would she have cared if he had? She hadn't spoken at all yet. 'Not thinking about it at present, Mrs Leggett. Storm in a teacup, if you ask me.' He wasn't sure it was, but he was always keen to look on the bright side.

'Well, what with Günther gone, and now Lorcan, I hope no more of you young men decide to enlist.' Mrs Leggett tutted three times. The concern on her face turned once more back to the usual expression of irritation she favoured. 'Now help yourself.'

He sat in the middle and did as he was told, his mouth watering as he ladled lamb stew onto his plate.

–

From her seat near the end of the table, Edie watched Charlie from the corner of her eye as he helped himself to the lamb casserole. She wondered how she might have felt had it been him who'd enlisted, not Lorcan. He and Lili were the two she felt closest to here, as close as she could feel after such a short acquaintance. She'd yearned for friends like these: ones you didn't have to be on your best behaviour with. After that first walk out, she and Charlie had taken a few evening strolls together, when he wasn't on a shift, sometimes joined by Lili.

Those walks had proved a soothing way to end some very busy days.

The subject of enlistment expanded in her mind to those she knew outside of the hotel. What if her brother joined up? He was so hot-headed he'd most likely get himself killed the first day. Her heart constricted at the thought.

What of the rest of her family, come wartime? Her mother, despite all outward appearances of being in control, had been known to crumble quite easily at times in private, with no one else to see her. And her father had never been quite sure what to do when she became so emotional. He was more likely to go to work than face any trouble at home. Her brother had never been able to handle their mother's melancholy at the best of times, and was inclined to run off with his friends to some entertainment or other.

Should she go home? War was surely a time to be with family. It was something she'd have to consider, and it was too big a decision to make quickly.

–

Edie was in the storeroom three days later, hunting for a new tin of beeswax polish, enjoying the coolness of the thick-walled room in comparison to the heat of the bedrooms. She hadn't been there long when Bridget Turnbull, the storekeeper, entered. A woman in her late forties, with greying brown curly hair, she'd lost her husband in the shipyards of Newcastle twenty years since.

'What are you lookin' for, lass?' she said in a winsome tone, her Tyneside inflection still strong.

'The beeswax polish. I thought it was on the lower shelf last time I came.'

'It was, but I had a clear-up and a move-around. It's on the top shelf now, in the blue box.'

'Ah yes, I see it. There are only six left.'

'Aye, somethin' else for my list, though goodness knows, it might not be long before the pantry and store cupboard are bare. And how will we run a hotel then, I should like to know.'

'It won't come to that, will it?'

Mrs Norris bustled in, the manager's wife coming up behind her. 'I should like to know how bad it's going to get, too. What with the government going on in the papers about how we should keep buying because everything's all right. Then they tell us that some tradesmen are charging too much, expecting shortages, and to report them. It makes you wonder whose got the measure of it.'

'And why can't we grow all our own wheat instead of importin' it?' Mrs Turnbull was clearly of the same frame of mind. 'Makes no sense. And now with Britain declarin' war on Austria-Hungary...'

Mrs Bygrove just managed to fit into the room with the other three women. 'How much flour do we have left, Bridget?'

Mrs Turnbull counted the sacks behind her. 'A dozen left here.'

'Pass me one over then,' said the cook.

'You should get one of the men to heave this back to the kitchen, pet.'

'Nonsense. Give it 'ere.'

Bridget dragged the sack, which reached to the tops of her legs, out from its place. Mrs Norris heaved it up onto her back with little trouble, soon tramping down the corridor to the kitchen.

Mrs Bygrove looked around the storeroom. 'We must make a list of what's needed, Bridget, and maybe get a little extra to tide us over in case of shortages.'

The storekeeper looked askance. 'We shouldn't be hoardin'. If everyone did that, we'd soon run out.'

'I know, I know, but what if we can't meet the requirements of the guests? In these times, it wouldn't take much to lose a lot of custom.'

Edie could see both points of view, but maybe came down slightly on Bridget's side. 'I think everyone, eventually, including the upper classes, will have to cut their cloth accordingly. There won't be anywhere for our guests to abscond to, because if we're short, they'll all be short, too.'

'What a sensible young woman you are,' said Mrs Bygrove. 'Let's just hope the government's telling the truth and everything will be fine. For if the German ships get into our waters, there'll be nothing imported.'

The door creaked open to reveal Mrs Leggett, her hair even more severely pulled back in its bun today. She seemed paler than normal. 'I've just heard that another one of the live-out porters, Jasper Jupp, has left to sign up.'

The manager's wife rubbed her forehead with her thumb and forefinger, her expression suggesting she was in pain. 'And it's not like we can even advertise for male staff aged between eighteen and sixty, with this Defence of the Realm Act. I suppose there might be some fit older gentlemen we could hire.'

Bridget shook her head. 'Well, lass, beggin' your pardon and all, but it might help if Mr Bygrove didn't go out such a lot.'

Edie's muscles stiffened. It was true that the manager was once again on the tennis courts opposite the hotel, but that was no way to talk to your employer's wife. She anticipated at least a retort, but none was forthcoming.

'I agree, it's not ideal.'

'Well, I'll make a start on that list. I'll go to the pantry first.' Bridget left the three of them.

Mrs Leggett came further into the room, pulling out crates and boxes on the shelves, looking for who knew what.

'I'd better go.' Edie held up the tin of polish.

Mrs Bygrove placed her hand on the maid's arm. 'Before you do, I've been looking for someone to attend a meeting for a charity with me, one that helps impoverished children in the area. I was wondering if you'd like to come along, especially with your experience of working with a child.'

'Oh.' Edie was astonished to be asked such a thing. It was on the tip of her tongue to decline the offer. She could just imagine what Fanny and Gertie would have to say about her being a favourite. And there was the housekeeper in the room, no doubt listening in even though she seemed to be focused on the boxes. But it did appeal to her, doing something worthwhile with children. 'Yes, I'd like that very much.'

Mrs Bygrove clapped her hands together twice. 'I'm so glad. I'll talk to you about it this evening, after supper.'

'Yes, all right.' She smiled, although she was disappointed she'd miss her walk with Charlie.

The manager's wife had been gone but a few seconds when Mrs Leggett stepped in front of her, blocking her route out of the room. 'Acting above your station again, are you, Moore?'

Of course she'd bear the brunt of it, because the housekeeper couldn't berate the manager's wife. 'I'm only doing what Mrs Bygrove asked.'

'And why has she favoured you? Clearly you've been toadying up to her.'

'I assure you I have not,' said Edie, in what she hoped was her best offended tone.

'*I assure you I have not*,' mimicked Mrs Leggett, making Edie realise too late that she'd overdone it.

There was a shuffling from the other side of the door indicating that somebody was there, listening. My, the day was full of eavesdroppers.

'Who's there?' called the housekeeper.

Bridget poked her head round the edge of the door before stepping in. 'Leave the poor lass alone, Imogen. Do you really want to go helpin' the bairns in her stead?'

Imogen? Edie had never met anyone who looked less like the Shakespearean heroine from *Cymbeline*, with her purity and virtue.

This was her opportunity to escape the storeroom and Mrs Leggett's ire. Two steps out of the room she heard the housekeeper say, 'No good will come of it, mark my words.'

The idea of going home came into her mind once more. It would be a way of escaping Mrs Leggett's dislike of her.

But what could she do at home? They'd never really needed her. Her mother certainly wouldn't appreciate her help. She'd always felt apart, not quite one of them. At the hotel, she could be so much more useful. And now she had an opportunity to help needy children as well, not just one rich one.

So that was that decision made. War or peace, she'd sit it out in Littlehampton.

–

Edie had not spoken to Mrs Bygrove that evening. Her husband had returned as the maids had been heading to supper, a little worse for wear. He'd announced quite cheerily to his wife in the corridor that he'd been taking a drink at a gentleman's club, with some very influential people. His wife, a phony smile upon her lips, had ushered him away upstairs to their rooms with bitter-edged honeyed tones.

Instead, the manager's wife had visited the dining room during the early staff lunch the following day. Here Edie had been given details of the event and her possible contribution. The whole affair had been organised, she was told, by a Miss Sophia Perryman.

Gertie and Fanny, as usual, had grumped and moaned about not being chosen. Now, to add insult to injury, as far as they were concerned, she'd also been asked to make up the shortfall once more in the conservatory, to serve coffee and tea.

Coming out of the laundry room, tying up the apron of the smarter grey uniform, she almost collided with Mrs Leggett.

'Do watch where you're going, girl. You'd better hurry along, for the conservatory is already filling up with patrons. I don't know, by rights it should be me deciding who goes where. I am the housekeeper, after all.'

In the conservatory, the bright sun streaming through the windows was softened by long net curtains. Edie had soon taken several orders and conveyed them first to the kitchen, then to the stillroom.

Edie picked up the first prepared tray with its silver teapot and the china set, with its green and gold gilt-edged cups and tiny, delicate pink roses. She shooed away the shadow marring her contentment, determined that Mrs Leggett wasn't going to spoil the day for her. Striding out of the stillroom with the tray held aloft, she looked forward now to the afternoon. Increasingly her life felt like it might have some purpose. And her parents weren't here to tell her otherwise.

As she left the kitchen and entered the corridor Charlie passed by, grinning. 'You look like the cat that got the cream.'

'Oh, better than the cream. A whole fish.' She giggled.

'Lucky you. Perhaps you can tell me about it later?' He raised his eyes hopefully.

'At supper time, if you wish. Though not in the housekeeper's hearing. She's already annoyed with me.'

'What's new? But I'm looking forward to hearing what it is even more now.'

In the conservatory, Edie soon spotted Lady Blackmore and her younger companion by the window overlooking the garden. They were another pair she'd seen the first day she'd stepped into the hotel for her interview. The older woman had a look of Queen Mary about her with her high, tight neckline, the large, over-feathered hat and full skirt with a slight train. There were two other tables occupied by the windows. Another, on the opposite side of the room, had a new patron, a young man by the looks of it, examining *The Windsor Magazine*.

She placed the teapot and accompaniments down carefully on the table, asking as she stood upright, 'Would you like me to pour, My Lady?'

Lady Blackmore lifted her head high enough to have to look down her nose, though she may have been short-sighted. 'No, thank you. I do find it tastes better when I serve it myself.'

'Very well, My Lady.' Edie dipped her knee and walked a few steps backwards.

After turning to continue, she heard the older woman say, 'And no sugar for you, Cecelia. You're plump enough as it is.'

Poor Cecelia. She was always being bossed around by Her Ladyship, who acted as if she owned the woman. In a way, Edie supposed, she did. She shivered. Being a companion must be worse than being a servant: at least one got a little time to oneself as the latter. She'd come across other eminent women with companions who seemed to rule every second of their day.

She noticed an empty tray on a round table near the door and changed direction. About to lean over to retrieve it, she heard a voice.

'Why, Edith, is that you?'

Her head shot up in shock at the sound of Daniel Duke's deep tones. He was a friend of her brother's. Sure enough, he was at the next table, his suit immaculate and his fair hair swept into a side parting. There was amusement in his eyes. A wave of queasiness assailed her, throwing her off balance momentarily. No, not here, not when she was getting on so well.

She took a quick glance at Lady Blackmore at the far window, but she was giving forth to her companion and taking no notice of them. She composed herself.

'Edith?' The look of confusion on Daniel's face was almost comical. He placed the magazine down.

'Dan, what on earth are you doing here?' She played at fiddling with the crockery as she hissed the question.

'I stopped off for refreshment on my way to visit my great-aunt Bertha on Empress Maud Road. More to the point, dear Edith, what are *you* doing here, dressed as a maid? Freddie and your parents have been frantic.'

Daniel began to laugh, drawing the beady eyes of Her Ladyship towards them.

'Please don't give me away,' Edith whispered, her breathing rapid. 'I've a new life. I'm content here.'

'You have to be joking. The *Honourable* Edith Moreland, serving tea in a hotel? And I thought Freddie was the bohemian!'

'I am not joking. Please, I'm begging you.'

'You there, girl,' called Lady Blackmore. 'Get on with your work, otherwise I shall inform Mr Bygrove that you are disturbing the guests.'

Edith lifted the tray. 'Leave me be,' she hissed, before exiting the room.

Her heart thumped uncomfortably in her throat as she hurried into the foyer to the servants' area, forgetting she should have gone across the dining room. This was a disaster. She had a picture playing in her head, like one of the overdramatic films at the picture house. In it her mother was dragging her from the hotel, with Mr and Mrs Bygrove standing incredulous on the porch. Meanwhile, Mrs Leggett was shaking her head and folding her skinny arms across her chest. Fanny and Gertie were of course laughing at her downfall.

So involved in the fantasy was she that she didn't notice the door to the servants' area begin to swing open a moment before she reached it.

Edie gasped as the door hit the tray, the same time that Nancy, the barmaid, gave a little shriek. The teapot, cups, saucers, milk jug, sugar bowl and spoons clattered and crashed to the floor. Edith stood helplessly looking on.

'What the blazes?' came a rasping voice behind Nancy. Mrs Leggett shoved her way past the barmaid, her mouth puckered as she spotted the broken crockery. 'Well, well, that'll cost you a pretty penny out of your wages, my girl. What a careless nincompoop you are. And why are you even coming this way?'

Worse than the lost wages, Edie feared Mrs Bygrove would never allow her to serve the customers again, once she heard of her clumsiness. The housekeeper would certainly not lose the opportunity to tell her.

'Get a dustpan and brush and the mop and clear this up immediately.' Mrs Leggett pointed towards the scullery. 'And *you* can stop gawping, Nancy Hubbard, and get back to the bar!'

Nancy scurried away. Edie rushed to the scullery to carry out the housekeeper's instructions, quickly returning with the necessary items. She hunkered down to gather up the smashed china, which crackled and crunched as she brushed it into the pan. The footsteps on the marble floor caused her to look up. Daniel stopped in the middle of the foyer, ramrod straight like a soldier. The look of amusement had now vanished. Instead, he considered her with a pained expression.

She shook her head, eager to communicate both a wish for him to keep his distance and a hope that he would not utter a word to anyone of what he'd seen. He twisted around abruptly and left.

Chapter Eight

For the last three days, Edie had been on tenterhooks, expecting someone to turn up from her past life and cause trouble. Perhaps even Freddie. Daniel surely wouldn't keep this to himself.

'What on earth is wrong with you, girl?' The barked voice behind her in the kitchen made her jump. She swung round to find herself eye to eye with Mrs Leggett, who was as tall as her. 'We're waiting for the potatoes for supper.'

Mrs Norris placed the large dish of boiled potatoes on the table. 'Give the poor girl a chance. Hannah's only just dished them up. She has been a bit distracted today though, haven't ya, duck? Not got a sweetheart, have you? You seemed very chirpy when you came back from your afternoon off, day before yesterday.'

Edie reddened. 'That was because I met up with my friend, Julia Nye, and we had an enjoyable time together. I don't have a sweetheart.'

The housekeeper snatched up the potatoes, declaring, 'I should jolly well hope not. There's far too much to do in this hotel for thoughts of sweethearts, especially when we've lost four men to the army. Now, you stay and collect the cabbage.'

As the housekeeper headed away, head held high, Edie pondered the older woman's words. It was certainly true that none of the live-in staff were married. Mrs Norris was a widow of many years, having brought up Joseph and his sister, Mary, by herself, as she was keen to tell people. So many unmarried women in one place, some of them in their late twenties and thirties. To her mother, that would constitute being 'on the shelf'. Mrs Leggett must be well into her forties. Why had she never married? Even as she considered this, the answer was obvious. The woman was objectionable and petty. Had she always been like that, or had years of service to others made her bitter?

And what of her own marriage prospects?

Mrs Norris hummed 'Burlington Bertie' to herself as she fried two portions of chicken in a frying pan, while watching several other pots. The savoury whiff of duck and the tang of asparagus made her stomach grumble. They never got either in the servants' dining room, and she was rather fond of both.

'Marriage.' Edie whispered the word to herself. No. She'd nearly got caught in a betrothal once, realising in time it was not what she'd desired.

'Here you are,' said Hannah, handing her the cabbage. She was a live-out under-cook who was married with four grown-up children and was always moaning about the lot of them.

No, single and free was the best prospect for women in this day and age, with no man to rule her or take possession of any money she had. Even if it did mean being poor for the foreseeable future.

-

After supper, Edie and Lili took a stroll along the promenade down towards the river. The fading day was pleasant, with a warm breeze from the west calming Edie's fears of being discovered by those from whom she'd run away.

Arriving at the pier, they headed north along the bank of the Arun, watching the Jumna steam tug chugging as it guided in a large sailing ship. Apart from this, the river was tranquil, its golden length curving upriver past the warehouses and timber mills. Somewhere unseen, someone, maybe a fisherman, must have lit a wood fire. The smoky fragrance took Edie back to her childhood.

The peaceful scene was interrupted by a flock of swans honking as they took flight.

As they passed the Kursaal and the windmill, Lili pointed to several recruitment posters attached to the walls, declaring, *A Call to Arms!! Kitchener's Army. Your King and Country Need You Urgently*.

'When my sister Dilys wrote to me she said my brother Wyn had been talking of enlisting. Our mam apparently gave him a right clip round the ear for suggesting it. My other brother, Morys, told her to leave the poor bugger alone, as she put it, but I fear he'll encourage him and...' She didn't have to finish the sentence for Edie to know what was on her mind.

They were passing the Oyster Pond, quiet now with no toy yachts sailing across it, when Edie looked over at Mrs Hadley's old house, just visible at the end of a row. She shuddered, remembering what had taken place there. It was still empty, and she wondered what would become of it with Mr Hadley being dead. They'd heard nothing further from Detective Inspector Davis, but she always felt slightly on edge, being out and about, in case she came across the attacker at the Kursaal, the man who she was still convinced had killed Mrs Hadley.

'What's the matter –' Lili started, then noticed where Edie was looking. 'Oh, I see.'

She got no further when they both noticed a figure rushing towards them, his step lively and his manner cheerful. His mischievous smile was endearing. Edie had trouble placing him at first, in his waistcoat and striped trousers. It was the lack of railway uniform that had confused her.

'Well I never did. I'm glad I've seen you.' It was the young railway porter who'd been so welcoming when she'd arrived at Littlehampton station.

'Mr Stubbs, isn't it?' Edie held out her hand to shake his.

'That's right. Fancy you remembering.' He shook her hand then raised his cap to Lili. 'I hope you found somewhere to work and stay and have settled in, miss.'

What a tale she could have told, but a simple answer would suffice. 'I'm working at the Beach Hotel which provides me with both, thank you for asking, Mr Stubbs.'

He took up the place beside her and they set off once more, even though he was now returning the way he'd been coming. 'Norman, please. And you've made a friend, I see.' He leant forward to look at Lili.

'I have. This is Miss Probert.'

'Lili, please,' said her friend, bestowing on Norman a brilliant smile. Her hand shot out, causing Edie to halt suddenly, so her friend could shake Norman's hand.

This was far more informal than Edie was used to, but so were her interactions with the staff at the hotel. She found she preferred it to the stuffy use of surnames and titles. 'In which case, I am Edie Moore.'

'Well, Edie, I must say I'm impressed you managed to land a job at the Beach. My cousin tried to get work there as a porter a couple of years back but was turned down. Reckons it's lovely inside, a real treat for the eyes.'

'It certainly is. A first-class hotel, no less.' Lili had never been this animated since Edie had known her. She was always a happy soul, but right now she had a particular sparkle in her eyes.

'Look at that.' Norman pointed to a stand filled with glass bottles of drink. 'Still out at this time. Guess he wants to get rid of the rest of his stock. Would you ladies like a ginger beer each? My treat.'

They'd barely agreed when he was off past the hut opposite the Nelson Hotel, talking to the vendor.

Lili stayed Edie by placing a hand on her arm. 'What a pleasant man. Are you involved with him?'

'Of course not. You heard what he said. We haven't met but once, when I first arrived.'

'But are you… interested in him?'

'Interested?' Edie's brow creased as she tried to work out in what way she might have an interest in Norman. Then she realised. 'Oh, you mean *interested*.'

Lili elbowed her arm gently, treating her to a cheeky grin. 'You know what I mean.'

'The answer is still no. He's all yours.'

The other woman's features widened in mock indignation. 'What makes you think *I'm* interested? I'm only asking because, well, there's Charlie, isn't there?'

'Charlie is a friend, like you.' Edie frowned at her.

'But you go on walks with him, without me.'

'And I go for walks with you, without him. It doesn't mean I'm romantically attached to you.'

Lili giggled, putting a hand to her mouth. 'Of course you're not. That would just be silly, wouldn't it?'

Edie laughed too, yet she knew such attractions happened between women, and between men.

Norman approached them, clutching three bottles with plain white paper straws. He handed one each to the women. 'What are you laughing at then?'

'Life,' said Edie when Lili glanced in appeal at her. 'It's good to be alive.'

'It certainly is,' Norman confirmed.

They turned back towards the pier and set off once more. Edie sucked at the straw. The pungent sting of ginger hit the back of her tongue and she was transported once again to past trips here. Too many memories. She pulled her mind to the present. It was all that mattered now.

–

As Edie came down the back stairs, she spotted Mrs Bygrove talking to Mrs Leggett.

The manager's wife looked up and smiled. The housekeeper, on the other hand, pursed her lips. 'Are you sure it's necessary to take Miss Moore?'

'We need more volunteers for the Arun Children's Aid Project fundraiser next week, so yes. It's such a worthy cause, raising money for the impoverished children of the area, don't you think, Mrs Leggett?'

'Well, yes, of course. Not sure why *she* has to go though, when we've staff who've been here a lot longer.'

'She's worked with a child, so she understands them better than some here would. And I know she'll be an asset.' The slight irritation in Mrs Bygrove's voice indicated she was getting tired of hearing Mrs Leggett's opinion.

'It's your decision, of course. If you'll excuse me, some of us have work to be getting on with.' The housekeeper headed for the kitchen.

About to ask a question on the day ahead, Edie was interrupted by Mr Bygrove, coming down the corridor from his office and calling his wife's name as if he were a headmaster and she a schoolgirl.

'Helen, are you off somewhere?'

'Douglas, I told you last night I was going to the Children's Aid meeting today.'

'Did you? I was probably concentrating on something more important. And it's Saturday. We might get busy. And you're surely not taking a chambermaid with you.'

'Yes, I am.'

'You shouldn't be joining the group of women running that charity. They're suffragettes, from what I've heard.'

'First of all, some of them are suffra*gists*, Douglas. There's a difference.'

Douglas looked heavenward. 'Anyway, they'll have you doing all sorts. It's hard work, helping a charity.'

'I'm not sure how you'd know that, dear, as I'm not aware that you've ever helped any, but may I remind you that you are always off on jaunts, playing your various sports. This is one of the few times I get out of the hotel. And for your information, though you should already be aware, I've been to several of their evening meetings over the last few months.'

'Have you?'

Edie, feeling like she was playing gooseberry to this, to her mind, ill-matched couple, stepped back a little. This contentious conversation was in danger of escalating into an argument.

Bygrove pulled himself upright, looking down his moustache at his wife. 'My *jaunts*, as you put it, do us very well, I'll have you know, and during these gatherings I act as an ambassador for the hotel, encouraging the members of my various clubs to use our facilities.' He pulled his lips into a tight circle and nodded his head once.

'And *I* have made a very good contact in Miss Sophia Perryman, who is the daughter of James Perryman, who owns Haydon's shipyard. They have a good deal of influential friends. And just to remind you, though once again I have already told you, I will be out most of next Saturday, when the Children's Aid Project is running.'

With that, she did an about-turn and headed for the staff exit in the scullery. Edie followed quickly, touching her hat to make sure it was still straight. She heard Bygrove grunt as she left the corridor.

When they'd exited through the staff gate, on one side of the hotel wall, Mrs Bygrove halted. 'I'm sorry you had to witness that to-do. I'm afraid my husband is not a patient man and, at times, rather inclined to self centredness.'

At times? thought Edie. Apart from accommodating the guests, the man only ever seemed to think of his own wants and needs.

'Well, I dare say he's feeling the pressure of the busy season.' She was being overgenerous, but he was the woman's husband, after all.

'It is kind of you to give him the benefit of the doubt. Come on, we don't want to be late, for there'll be much to organise and finalise with the event only a week away.' They'd gone a step or two out of the side gate when she halted once again. 'Edie, when we're out and about like this, please, do call me Helen. Not in the hotel though.'

'All right.' Edie was rather pleased to be allowed this familiarity.

They walked quickly to Norfolk Road, taking that route out of Beach Town to end up in East Street, into the 'Town' proper, and onto High Street. Almost at the other end of it, they stopped outside the Congregational church, on the corner of Arundel Road.

'Here we are,' said Helen. 'The meeting's in the hall around the back.'

Inside, the throng of women made Edie feel suddenly nervous. She'd been to so many such meetings in her time, but not in her current role. Yet, looking around, she saw women from different walks of life. It really was daft to get so het up about something so familiar. Yet the anxiety stayed with her.

'Are you sure they need an extra body to help? They seem to have sufficient numbers here.'

Helen considered her indulgently. 'Don't be nervous. Some here will be running other campaigns. They won't all be helping next Saturday.'

'I see.'

'Ah, there's Sophia.' Helen led Edie over, who used the few seconds it took to calm down and remind herself that she'd been a strong, self-reliant woman, and still was.

Miss Perryman spotted them before they reached her. 'Helen, I'm so glad you could make it. And you've brought a new recruit?'

'This is Edie Moore. Edie, this is Sophia Perryman. She was heavily involved in running the Worthing and Littlehampton Women's Franchise Society before the war. They're a member of the National Union of Women's Suffrage Societies.'

Sophia offered her hand. 'How do you do?'

'How do you do?' Edie took the woman's hand. 'I know, of course, of the work of the NUWSS, as I was involved with them in Brighton for a while.' She had a moment where she wondered at the wisdom of mentioning this, as a lowly chambermaid, or even a governess, but there'd been all manner of women there too. Or was it possible Miss Perryman would know someone who knew her? *Stop worrying!*

'How splendid. Then you'll know that now we're putting all our endeavours into the war effort. And Brighton, you say? You must have met Dame Millicent Fawcett. A splendid leader and orator.'

Edie had met her personally a couple of times but decided not to mention this. 'I've heard her speak on a number of occasions. She is a very good leader.'

'Tonight, of course, we'll mostly be discussing next week's Children's Aid event, though we're also going to go over a few of our other activities, including our campaign to collect money for smokes and other Christmas treats for our boys overseas.'

'So you think they'll still be there by then?' said Helen.

'I have no doubt. This war isn't going to end any time soon, I'm sure of it. Otherwise, why encourage men to enlist?'

'I fear you may be right,' said Edie. 'I'm happy to do whatever you need me to.'

'I'm glad to hear it. Come, take a seat, as we're about to start.' Sophia pointed to the chairs laid out in rows.

Edie and Helen picked seats in the second row, and Sophia carried on to the front.

Chapter Nine

The young lady entered the foyer mid-afternoon. Charlie had only that moment returned from running an errand for Major Thomas, taking a handwritten note to his chum, another ex-army officer, on South Terrace, in one of the lodging houses.

The woman looked to be in her mid-twenties, fashionable with her calf-length skirt. Charlie enjoyed peeking at her ankles, revealed as they were above beaded shoes. At the same time he felt ashamed, imagining what his mum would make of his shocking behaviour. Above the skirt she wore a velvet jacket, green, nipped in tightly at the waist. She carried a matching umbrella over one arm, necessary with the earlier morning showers, and a beaded handbag with a chain handle over the other. Very pretty she was, with her dark auburn hair and green eyes.

If truth be told, the young woman would probably only be interested in dresses, horses, balls and flirting. He'd seen and heard it all before, these vacant aristocrats and gentry.

This one's not as pretty as Edie, a small voice in his head told him. Enough of that. She might be his friend, but she'd never look twice at him for any other reason. Would she? Silly fool he was, of course she wouldn't, no more than this attractive woman of the upper classes would.

He stepped forward, bowing his head a little as he said, 'Can I help you, madam?'

Her laugh was hearty yet merry and the following smile playful. 'Miss, yet it will shortly be madam, that is true. Fancy.'

Her wide-eyed expression suggested she couldn't quite believe it herself. 'And yes, you can help me, young man.'

The last two words were said mockingly, probably because she couldn't have been any older than him. Her voice was one of the plummiest he'd ever heard.

'I wonder if you have a young woman working here named Edith.'

Did she mean Edie? She'd used the name Edith when she'd first introduced herself to him. The woman didn't seem angry or bothered, so it may not be anything bad. If it was their Edie she was looking for. 'We have an Edie Moore, a chambermaid, working in the hotel. Could it be her?'

'Moore.' She chuckled. 'Edie Moore. Of course. Yes, I believe it could be her. Would I be able to speak to her?'

'I'm not sure. Is she in trouble?'

'Good gracious, not at all, not with me anyway, though it's nice you seem concerned. I simply wish to, to return some money she lent me. I was… I was at the railway station, at the ticket office, and I found I had forgotten my purse. She was standing nearby and was kind enough to lend me the fare. She told me she worked here, so I promised to return the money. Yes.'

Charlie wondered why Edie had been at the railway station and where she'd gone. Still, what she did on her half-day off was none of his business. 'I'll have to speak to the manager to make sure it's all right.'

'Of course.'

'Who shall I say is asking, miss?' He was agog to know who this mysterious young woman was. He didn't remember her visiting the hotel before, and he had a good memory for faces and names.

'It's Lady Lucia Forsyth,' she pronounced with a flourish.

He bowed his head once more. 'Oh, I beg your pardon, m'lady. I won't keep you a moment.'

As he walked to the servants' corridor, towards the office, he looked back at her. She was doing a slow circle, taking in her surroundings.

At the manager's office he knocked, waiting for a reply. He wasn't surprised to hear a woman's voice bid him enter, as he now recalled seeing Mr Bygrove leave earlier with his golf clubs.

'There's a Lady Lucia Forsyth in the foyer, Mrs Bygrove, who wishes to speak with Edie.'

The manager's wife looked intrigued. Charlie told her the reason the young woman had given him.

'I will go to the foyer to speak to her. Meanwhile, would you fetch Edie, please? She's in the storeroom helping Mrs Turnbull sort through the latest delivery.'

'Yes, Mrs Bygrove.'

Charlie left as she rose from the desk. It had become a habit of the manager's wife to send Edie to do different tasks, not just cleaning and maintaining the guest rooms, for which she'd also brought in a part-time live-out maid. It had caused some contention with Gertie and Fanny, but then that wasn't hard. Still, the chambermaids normally stuck to one job.

He'd reached the storeroom by this time, poking his head round the door.

'Why Charlie,' Edie greeted him. 'To what do we owe this honour?'

She did a good imitation of one of the many Lady Someone-or-others who visited the hotel. Whether they were all titled as such he sometimes doubted. 'You're a great mimic.'

She went bright red, not being good with compliments, as he'd discovered, and he regretted embarrassing her.

'Mrs Bygrove wants you to go to the foyer. There's a Lady Lucia Forsyth here to see you.'

Mrs Turnbull stopped rummaging through a box and took an interest.

From bright red Edie went as pale as the bleached cotton sheets. 'D-did she say what she wanted?'

'Something about paying you back for the loan of a train fare.'

Edie looked confused. 'I-I suppose I had better speak with her. I'm sorry, Mrs Turnbull, may I leave for a while?'

'Of course, pet. I've other stuff to be gettin' on with, and we can continue with this when you return.'

'Thank you.'

-

Edie walked behind Charlie, who looked around at her every few moments. She was tempted to run away, feeling sick to her stomach with worry as she did, but what else could she do? Back in the foyer she approached Mrs Bygrove. She ignored Lucia but could see out of the corner of her eye that she was smiling. The porter returned to his place a couple of feet away from the desk.

'Ah, here you are, Edie,' said Mrs Bygrove. 'Lady Lucia here would like to speak to you, so I suggest you both go to the private dining room. I'll bring you both some tea and you can take your afternoon break now.'

'Are you sure that's all right?' Edie didn't want to take advantage of Mrs Bygrove's kindness.

'Absolutely. You were very kind to spare a train fare. Now, show Lady Lucia into the room.'

'Very well.' Edie led the way, her heart thumping uncomfortably against her ribs. This must be Daniel's work. At least, for the moment, it seemed he hadn't told anyone at Downland House. Unless this was a trap and they were waiting outside. She had trouble catching her breath. No, Lucia wouldn't do that to her, she was certain.

They were seated in the small dining room, at one end of the eight-place table, before Lucia laughed. 'My goodness, Freddie always said you were good at imitating people. You remind me of my governess. Now, perhaps you'd like to tell me what the dickens you're up to.'

'I suppose Daniel told you I was here.'

'Yes, but no one else knows, apart from Freddie, luckily for you. Everyone has gone spare with your disappearance, Freddie in particular. It's only because that maid, Jenny, told them she saw you go with a carpetbag that they haven't got the police involved. They didn't want a scandal. Though believe me, they've used their numerous contacts to try and ascertain your whereabouts.'

Edie leant her arms on the table, looking Lucia squarely in the eyes. 'I was sick and tired of being controlled. *Do this, Edith, do that, Edith, don't do that, you silly girl*, as if I have no mind of my own.' She lifted her fist, about to thump it on the dark wood, but thought better of it. 'I wanted to do what I liked for a change, to have a choice.'

Lucia tugged at the lace on Edie's apron. 'And *this* was your choice? Did you honestly think you'd get away with coming only twenty miles down the coast and not be recognised by someone? Especially in a prestigious hotel such as this. I mean, really, Edith?'

'Nobody has so far, apart from Daniel. People seem to come from the local area or from much further away.'

'Then you've been darned lucky, I'd say. Why on earth Littlehampton?'

'Happy memories of childhood holidays here, with Miss Langley and Nanny Street. It represented freedom to me from my parents' expectations. The governess and Nanny let us be children. And since it was freedom from my parents I wanted...' She shrugged.

Lucia also laid her arms on the table and leant forward. 'My dear, that is the curse, but it is outweighed by the privilege of being the daughter of Baron Moreland.'

'To you the privilege may outweigh the curse, but to me it's... well, the privilege itself has become a harness. If I cannot have one without the other, I'd rather have neither.'

'I'm sure in time you will change your mind, when you have wearied of this charade and want your comforts back. For being cooped up as a maid here, however luxurious the hotel,' she lifted her head and hand to indicate the building, 'must be unbearable.'

Edie thought about this. If she left now with Lucia, how would she feel? The truth was, there were things she'd miss. Or rather, people… 'We'll have to beg to differ.'

'You'll come round, in time. And maybe this will persuade you.' She took a deep breath which had Edie fearing some bad news, but the smile that formed suggested otherwise. 'Freddie and I, well, we got engaged the week after you left. Darling, you missed such a wonderful celebration.' Lucia's grin became wider, suggesting she was persuaded that already Edie would be changing her mind. She took her hands. 'We're going to be sisters-in-law.'

'Engaged?' A flash of surprise coursed through Edie. 'I thought, well, I believed…' But she could not bring herself to voice her reasoning. Instead, she went with the more ambiguous, 'I did not think my brother was the marrying kind. I thought him more a… a free spirit.'

'But he is the marrying kind. And there's no time to waste, what with the war.'

This panicked Edie. 'Is Freddie enlisting?'

'Good heavens, no. But who knows what will happen with Japan declaring war on Germany now? The trouble spreads further and further. But I'm straying from the point. You simply *can't* miss the wedding. And would you have your parents go mad with worry for evermore?'

'I'm sure they'll get over it. Mama will have the vapours for a while, then she'll be back organising events with her Right *Honourable* friends.'

'You are impossible, Edith. This is what you were born into, and you just have to accept it. What do you think you'll do in this world, especially as a woman?'

Edie rose and walked around the table. 'That, coming from someone who used to be active with the suffragists! What would my parents think if they knew, given I was virtually locked up when they found out I'd been involved? My mother even suggested I might end up in an asylum if I continued to act so *irrationally*, as she put it.'

Lucia gave a little laugh. 'Of course you wouldn't have. Your mother was just trying to scare you. And as much as I hate to say this, the fact that my father is an earl and probably several times as rich means they are likely to say very little about it. Freddie has done well, is your mother's opinion. Don't get me wrong, I don't feel I'm marrying down, no, not at all. Freddie and I are equals, in my eyes, and see eye to eye on so many important issues.' She sighed. 'Some of which I doubt we'll ever see validated in our lifetimes. If any of our parents really knew the full extent of it, well…'

Edie stopped her pacing. 'What do you mean?'

'It really doesn't matter now.' Lucia pushed her chair back and stood. 'Freddie and I have got a special licence, just in case the war *does* interfere. So we're busy getting it all organised for September the twelfth. If you don't come to the wedding, at least consider visiting Freddie and I in our new house. Papa has bought us a darling little place near Lewes. We're moving in a week after the wedding, after a short honeymoon.'

'That was nice of him.'

'Oh *please*, do think about attending the wedding. Here are the details.' She handed Edie an invitation which had her name at the top in Lucia's neat hand.

'September the twelfth is a little hasty, isn't it? That's less than three weeks away.' She lowered her voice. 'Are you… you know?'

'No, no, nothing like that.' She chuckled. 'But it will be a splendid wedding, despite the short notice.'

'I-I don't know.' Could she really miss her brother's wedding? He had let her down, it was true, but this would be an important day for him.

There was a knock on the door and Lucia replied, 'Enter.'

Gertie struggled in with a tray of tea things and biscuits. Edie hid the envelope in her dress pocket. She only hoped the maid had not been listening in on the conversation.

'Mrs Bygrove said I was to bring you this.' She put the tray down gently, taking the opportunity to scowl at Edie.

'Thank you,' said Lucia. When Gertie didn't budge, she added, 'That will be all.'

The maid moved off slowly, turning as she shut the door to treat Edie to a last glower.

'What have you done to her?' said Lucia.

'Long story.' Edie returned to her seat.

'We've got time while we drink this tea.' She picked up the teapot and started to pour.

Edie gave in to the request and described her run-ins with Gertie and Fanny in as succinct a manner as she could. Lucia found it all highly amusing.

'My dear, if you get nothing else out of this experience, then you will be able to write a book about it. How enlightening it would be. I believe Virginia has been working on a book she's hoping to get published.'

'Virginia?'

'Woolf. I spent some time with her and a group of others when I was in London a while back.'

Lucia filled her in on the meeting, though Edie was only vaguely aware of this woman. It wasn't long before she was back to the subject of the wedding, giving precise details of her dress, the venue and the guests. No doubt this was to tempt her to attend. Edie only half listened, racked with guilt at letting people down.

By the time Lucia came to a halt, she'd made up her mind. It was the only choice she felt she had.

'No, I'm sorry.'

'I beg your pardon, sorry for what?'

'However much you try to entice me, I will not attend your wedding. I am so sorry to be missing your special day, you and

Freddie. I wish things were different, I really do, but… there it is. I will not be coming back. I am enjoying my freedom. And if you tell my parents where I am, I will run away once more, to somewhere none of you will ever find me.'

Lucia nodded solemnly, as if accepting the inevitable. 'All right, I will have to respect your decision, but if you do change your mind, even at the last moment, please come. And Edie, do think at least of visiting us in our new home after we're married, on a weekend off.'

Edie shook her head. 'You really have no idea, do you? How often do you give your servants a whole weekend off?'

'Well…'

'Exactly. It's no different in a hotel.'

'I will send an invitation to you anyway. To "Edie Moore", of course. Then it's up to you if you accept it. Mrs Bygrove seems very understanding. Perhaps we could say your mother was poorly.'

'Yes, Mrs Bygrove is understanding, but her husband much less so, and I don't want to take advantage of Helen. Send the letter by all means, but I very much doubt I'll come.' She heard the clock in the foyer chime the half hour. 'Now, I believe I've overstayed my time here.' She stood up. 'Farewell, Lucia. I hope you and Freddie have a wonderful wedding day, and I wish you well for the future.'

With that, Edie left the room, her tea half drunk. Charlie was standing near the reception desk as she entered the foyer.

'All sorted out then?' he asked, coming forward. 'She repaid you?'

Edie realised she had no money on her with which to prove this. She patted her dress pocket, which was bulked out by the invitation, and hoped that would persuade him. 'Yes, thank you.'

'What a kind person you were, helping the woman out. I've been told by Mrs Bygrove that the Lady Lucia Forsyth is the daughter of an earl, and quite something in society circles. Not that I'd know anything about that,' he chuckled.

'I've got to get on, otherwise Mrs Leggett will be having words with me.'

He lifted his hand. 'See ya at supper.'

She simply nodded and hurried off, speeding up once more when Lucia left the function room. There was no desire in her to speak with her future sister-in-law again today.

–

Edie was alone in the servants' dining room that evening, until Gertie and Mrs Norris entered, both holding aloft a dish of vegetables.

'So, you been invited to Lady Lucia Forsyth's wedding,' said the cook, without any preamble.

Gertie had been listening at the door after all. Edie went cold. Pulling herself together, she said in an incredulous voice, 'And why on *earth* would I be invited to her wedding?'

'That's what I said, but Gertie 'ere insists she heard you being invited.'

Edie frowned as if to show the absurdity of the idea, while trying to think of a plausible excuse for what was overheard. 'Why would you – oh, of course. Lady Lucia was relating a story of a friend of hers, the one she was visiting when I offered her the train fare.'

Gertie thumped the potatoes on the table. 'Why would she tell *you* the story?'

'I think she likes to talk,' said Edie, amused. 'It's the way with many of these society ladies.'

'But I heard you reply in the same plummy voice.' Gertie was not going to let this go by. Others had entered the room by now, including Charlie and Mrs Leggett.

'Just putting on those hairs and graces,' said Mrs Norris. 'They don't fool no one, duck. I could tell you was nothing special, just mimicking the gentility, and not doing a good job, if you ask me.'

'Which no one did,' Charlie remarked, taking his place next to Edie.

'Mr Cobbett, keep your opinions to yourself and sit down,' said Mrs Leggett.

Mrs Norris humphed and left the room, Gertie flouncing out in her wake.

'Let that be a lesson to you, Miss Moore,' said the housekeeper as everyone took their seat. 'Even for a governess you've been acting way above your social class. You might fool Mrs Bygrove, but you're not fooling anyone here.'

'Leave her alone, Mrs L,' said Charlie. 'People can't help what they speak like. I guess that's what happens if you live with the nobs.'

Mrs Leggett carried on as if he hadn't spoken. 'A lot of the governesses who come to Littlehampton put it on, thinking they're a cut above the other servants, but you must remember, Miss Moore, that they *are* only servants.'

There was so much that Edie could have replied, but she kept her head down and started helping herself to vegetables.

'Yeah,' said Fanny, warming to the theme as Gertie returned with Mrs Norris and her son, with the last of the food. 'I reckon there was something dodgy about why you left your last place, nothing to do with that kiddie going to school.'

Edie felt sure the housekeeper would bring this line of enquiry to a close, but she was disappointed.

'Did you get into trouble?' said Gertie as she took her seat.

'No, I—'

'Why don't you shut up and stick a fork in ya mouth instead,' said Charlie, holding his own fork up, almost as a threat.

'Mr Cobbett,' Mrs Leggett warned, on a low note.

'I bet you 'ad an affair with the master of the house,' said Fanny.

Gertie and Mrs Norris laughed at this accusation, both insisting Edie should tell them more.

'I could do with a bit of excitement,' said the cook.

'Be quiet, Mother,' said Joseph. 'Leave the poor girl alone.'

'Fancy the men sticking up for her,' said Fanny. 'I wonder why. She offering something we ain't?'

Edie went a deep red at the implication. Did she really mean what it sounded like?

'That is *not* funny,' said Charlie.

'It's only a bit a' fun,' said Mrs Norris.

'What, bullying someone?' said Joseph. 'There's too much of that here, if you ask me.'

'Nobody did ask you,' said his mother. 'And where's your sense of humour? Like ya father, you are, a right old grouch.'

Joseph stood suddenly, almost knocking Hetty off the bench at the end. 'Can I remind you that *I* am the head chef here, not you, and you're supposed to do what I say? But it's always the bloody same, putting me down. I'm sick of it.' He lifted one long leg after the other over the bench, picked up his plate and cutlery and stormed off.

'Well, that told me,' said Mrs Norris.

All the while, Mrs Leggett stayed quiet, which was unusual for her, normally so quick to put any kind of argument down. Unless she was causing one. But then, this all added to her own discomfort, Edie realised, which Mrs Leggett was only too quick to encourage.

'Hetty, did you say you'd had a letter from Lorcan?' Charlie asked, leaning forward past Edie to ask the scullery maid.

'Your sweetheart, is he?' said Fanny, nudging Gertie.

'No, of course not.' Hetty sucked in her lips and looked embarrassed. 'He just wanted to keep in touch with someone, that's all.'

Charlie scowled at Fanny. 'I think it's nice someone's keeping in touch with him.'

'He doesn't say much, anyway, just talks about the training at Colchester.' Hetty shrugged.

'So he's all right, then?' Charlie asked.

'He seems to be enjoying it.'

There were nods and murmurs of 'good' and 'glad he's all right', which seemed to mark the end of the conversation. The staff now concentrated on eating, for which Edie was grateful.

After they'd finished, as Edie was left to clear up by Mrs Leggett, Charlie lingered.

'So, I'm guessing it ain't true that you had an affair with the master in your last job.'

Edie stopped gathering plates, looking up at him with wide eyes. 'Surely you don't believe that piffle Fanny and Gertie made up.'

'No. It was just, I wondered if there was some grain of truth, by your embarrassment. You know, maybe Lord Stansfield pursued you and you turned him down, and that's why you left, but his wife knew what he was like and that's why she still gave you the reference?' He shrugged.

Edie couldn't help but giggle. 'My, what an imagination you have, Charlie Cobbett. You should be a writer.' She was reminded of Lucia's similar statement earlier.

'Maybe I should, eh?' He threw back his head and laughed.

'I can assure you that Lord Stansfield was rarely in the house, let alone with any time for chasing servants. I barely even saw him.' The man had been heavily involved in the House of Lords and various committees, so this was true.

'Right, I'm on an evening shift tonight,' said Charlie, looking at his wristwatch. 'Better get going.'

When he left, she felt the most alone she had since she'd arrived. How she'd loved to have had someone to confess her problems to. But it wasn't to be. She continued with the clearing.

–

Charlie was relieved to get out of the hotel for his afternoon off the following Saturday. He'd been kept especially busy that morning, and all through lunch, what with people arriving to stay and other guests wanting him to run errands and telephone this place and that to order items and book tickets. And just as he was about to leave the foyer, the major had caught him.

Not wanting to waste any more time eating his dinner, he'd nabbed some brown paper from the kitchen and had grabbed a cheese sandwich from the staff table, to take up to his room to eat while he changed. Should he wear his new linen jacket? Yes, why not. He was going to see Edie, after all.

Out in the fresh air, he wound his way through the crowds on the common, some picnicking, some walking to or from the promenade. In the background, he could hear banjos playing and indistinct voices drifting over from the bandstand, where an audience was crowded in on deckchairs.

As he approached the prom, he could see a group of perambulators assembled there, and he gathered that's where the Children's Aid Project must be taking place. The beach here had a gap in bathing tents and was filled with children doing different activities. There seemed to be a sandcastle-building competition in full swing. On the flat, damp sand nearest a tide that was out, a group of boys were playing cricket.

Charlie smiled when he spotted Edie, on the damp sand closer by. She was attempting to skip, among a group of giggling girls all trying to do the same. Her long skirt wasn't helping, and the girls had the advantage of short dresses. He jumped down off the low wall onto the pebbles, then strode towards them.

'That looks like fun!'

Edie twisted around, beaming when she realised it was him. 'Charlie, I'm so glad you came.'

'I said I would. Was a bit late leaving me shift as the major wanted me to telephone and book a theatre ticket.'

'You are kind to him.'

'It's me job, isn't it?'

'Still.' She put the handles of her rope into one hand.

'Are you giving up, miss?' said a girl with white-blonde plaits down her back.

'No, but I wondered if Mr Cobbett here had any more skill than me.'

Charlie lifted the flats of his hands towards her. 'Ooh, I dunno about that.'

'We're all having a practice so that we can have a competition in a while, to see who can keep going the longest.'

'Not something I was in the habit of doing as a lad.' He laughed.

'Are you saying it's too girly for you? Or are you afraid of failing?' She looked at him askance, with mischief in her eyes. It gave his insides a little jolt of pleasure, which encouraged him to take the offered rope.

He removed his linen jacket and put it on a nearby deckchair, then took the handles in his hands, ready. 'It's gonna be harder on this surface than somewhere like the prom, but I like a challenge.'

He twirled the rope over his head and jumped as it reached his feet, taking his lead from the girls. He managed six skips before the rope got tangled with his legs.

'That's better than I managed,' said Edie. 'I used to be able to go for ages as a child.'

'Charlie, how lovely to see you here.' Mrs Bygrove strode over from a mixed group of younger children attempting to play quoits, a few yards away.

Charlie gripped the handles as if ready to go again. 'Good afternoon, Mrs Bygrove. Thought I'd pop over to see how it was going, and to lend a hand.'

'And I'm very glad to see you. The more the merrier. Showing the girls how to do it, are you?'

She grinned at him as he looked down at the rope self-consciously.

'Um, well, Edie set me a challenge and I could hardly turn it down.' He skipped some more, this time managing a dozen jumps.

'Well done, Mr Cobbett,' she said, clapping.

The girls cheered, causing several people in the crowd to look in their direction. Charlie felt a bit silly and handed the rope back to Edie. 'Think I've demonstrated how it should be done. Over to you, girls.'

Detective Inspector Davis loomed into view in rolled-up shirtsleeves and waistcoat, stopping beside Mrs Bygrove. He tossed a cricket ball up and down in his hand. What was he doing here?

'Cobbett, isn't it?'

'That's right, sir. From the Beach Hotel.'

'How fortunate. Do you play cricket, Cobbett?'

'I, er, played a bit on the common with friends as a boy.'

'Then you can come and join us and the young lads. We're short of a few players.' He pointed over to the group of boys of various ages.

Damn and blast it! The last thing he needed was to join an activity with a copper. And he'd come here to spend time with Edie. Still, nothing else for it.

'I, um, well, yes, of course.'

'Good man.'

Charlie looked back at Edie as Davis clapped him on the shoulder and steered him seawards. This felt familiar, and not in a good way.

'See you later, Charlie,' Edie called.

He lifted a hand limply to wave and raised a weak smile.

–

Seeing the last of the likely contributors to the Children's Aid Project fund trooping wearily up to the promenade, Charlie took his metal bucket to where Edie was talking to Mrs Bygrove.

'All done then, Charlie?' the manager's wife asked.

'Yep. Think that's as much as this bucket's collecting today.' He held it up to rattle it, but it was half full and making more of a clonking noise.

'Sounds like a nice collection of coins.' Mrs Bygrove took the offered bucket from him and looked inside. 'Oh yes! Well done,

Charlie. You've obviously charmed the visitors into making a nice contribution.'

'You know me, Mrs B, gift of the gab, I've got.'

'As usual, you do yourself down, Charlie. Now I'll finish up here. You two go and get a well-earned rest before your next shifts.'

Charlie grinned. 'Thanks, Mrs Bygrove.' He looked forward to having Edie to himself. But what if she wanted to get back to the hotel, or be alone?

'Shall we walk down the promenade and get a ginger beer from the stall?' said Edie. 'I'm parched after an afternoon in this heat.'

Or maybe not. He really should have more confidence in himself.

'Yes, me too.'

When he'd shrugged his jacket back on, she took his arm lightly and they made their way up to the promenade.

–

Entering the door into the scullery, Edie felt a lightness in her heart, giggling at a joke Charlie was telling her. The charity afternoon had been a success, but for her, having him there had made it special.

'I shall laugh for the rest of the day, every time I think of that,' she said, closing the door that he'd held open for her.

'Wish I could, but I don't think Mr Watkins would appreciate that in the foyer. Miserable old sod – I mean so-and-so – he is. Sorry.'

Gertie burst through the door from the staff dining room, almost knocking Charlie over. 'There you are,' said the maid. 'There's a letter come for you.'

Charlie pointed to himself. 'Who, me?'

'Why would a letter come for you? No, for Edie, with fancy writing. Reckon it's from that lord what she had the affair with, in her last job. It's in the kitchen.'

Edie rushed past them both, panicking in case some busybody had opened it and found something to incriminate her with. But then, surely Gertie would have had more to say for herself.

When she entered the kitchen, Mrs Leggett, who was talking to the cook, quickly spotted her. 'Ah, Miss Moore. You have a correspondence. Applying for another job, are you?'

Spotting it on the large table in the middle of the room, Edie scooped it up, sighing with relief when it was clear it had not been tampered with. It wasn't Lucia's handwriting, as she'd expected. Nor was it Freddie's. If her parents had discovered she was here, they'd have arrived in person, not written her a letter, of that she was certain. Then who on earth could it be from? The cook and housekeeper looked on, expectantly.

With a 'Thank you, Mrs Leggett,' Edie escaped the kitchen, almost colliding with Charlie as he waited in the corridor outside the dining room.

'Bad news? You look a bit flustered.'

'Um, I don't know. I'm going to my room to open it while I get changed for work. I'll tell you later.'

Why had she said that? Now she'd probably have to make something up. She rushed away and up the back stairs, hoping that Lili wasn't in the room for any reason.

To her relief, Lili must already have gone to start the turndown shift. With only minutes before she was due to begin, she had better be quick reading this. She tore the envelope open impatiently, going straight to the signature.

It was from Daniel, writing 'on behalf' of Freddie, he said. She scanned the lines of the two sheets quickly. It was a plea for her to come to her senses and attend the wedding in two weeks. And if she couldn't do that, at least go to visit them in Lewes later in September, for which, he understood, Lucia would send a letter with a ready-made excuse.

Having finished the missive, she folded it swiftly and replaced it in the envelope.

Why had Daniel sent this, and not Freddie himself? Oh dear, he really must have taken to heart her angry words to him, after he'd told her parents she'd been to the suffragist meetings. He must be afraid she was still really mad at him. And she was, in a way. On the other hand, he'd given her the courage to free herself from her parents' oppression, so maybe she should thank him. And he had been an ally for most of their lives, as they'd covered up for each other when intent on doing various things their parents wouldn't have approved of.

It was time to forgive him, and she hoped he'd forgive her for her harsh words. But she wouldn't attend the wedding.

Looking around for a place to keep it, she decided the best course of action was to conceal the letter under her clothes in the chest of drawers that she and Lili shared. She'd tell whoever asked about the letter that it was from a friend, which it was.

Having completed the task, she set about changing for work. She wouldn't reply to Daniel.

This was her life now.

Chapter Ten

Edie took a last look out of the guest bedroom window after she'd collected her cleaning materials. The sun was shining over the sea but was partly obscured by a cloud. Despite this, light shimmered on the water, making her wish she could be on the promenade, taking in the warm day.

The first day of autumn. She'd have been here three months tomorrow. My, how the summer weeks had flown. How many more warm days would there be? She tingled with excitement as she remembered it was her half-day – *their* half-day. She so hoped the weather would hold out for the trip into town.

When she got to the bottom of the back stairs, Charlie was in the corridor.

'Ah, there you are. I was wondering if you'd like to eat out. That way we'd get out quicker. My treat.'

'You don't have to keep doing that. I can pay my way.'

He pulled a face. 'What, and have people say I don't treat a lady properly?' He was half joking, she knew, but his expression was still serious enough for her to suspect he'd be a little affronted if she insisted.

'Well, all right. But let me put this stuff away and get changed.'

'Meet you at the gate in five minutes?'

'Make it ten.'

He laughed heartily and she couldn't help laughing too.

A little over ten minutes later, she caught up with him as he called, 'How about the Cypress at the end of High Street?'

'That would be nice. It was the first establishment I visited when I came to Littlehampton.'

They strolled along the coast road, deciding to go the long way, chatting about their morning. Charlie related a couple of funny stories about the guests. Edie was content, yet at the same time a little alarmed at the ease she felt in his company. She'd always been one for conversations with the servants, much to her mother's chagrin, but this was something else again. Charlie made her feel… important. Relevant. That was it. Turning onto Pier Road, they spotted a sailing ship, a rarer sight these days, gliding down the Arun towards the sea.

'Come on, let's get a move on, otherwise all the tables might be gone.'

Charlie put his arm out to indicate they should hurry, and she thought for a moment that he was going to take her hand. When he didn't, it was both a disappointment and a relief.

Pier Road became Surrey Street, with its shops. Charlie tutted as they spotted the bill poster, sticking up several of the same advertisement, featuring an imposing picture of Lord Kitchener.

'Not more of these,' he said, as they stopped in front of one displayed in a grocer's shop. He shook his head before moving off.

At the end of High Street, Charlie pointed across the road, towards the restaurant. 'Look, isn't that your friend coming out?'

'So it is.' She lifted her hand to wave at the same time Julia did. She hurried across the road towards her. It was only after they'd kissed each other's cheeks that she noticed Inspector Davis lurking behind.

'Hello, Inspector. What a coincidence, seeing you here,' said Edie.

'Not really,' Julia admitted, looking sheepish. 'We've just been having an early luncheon at the Cypress.'

'Oh, I see. That's where we're about to go. You've met Charlie Cobbett, haven't you, Inspector?' She turned to find him hanging back, looking a little glum. Was he afraid they'd have to socialise with other people, and he wanted her to himself? More wishful thinking!

'That's right. He was a welcome arrival to the cricket team at the Children's Aid day. Hello again, Mr Cobbett.'

Charlie stepped forward reluctantly and shook his hand. 'Inspector.'

Davis gave him a curious look.

'We must be on our way,' Julia pointed towards her companion, 'for Philip has to get back to work.'

Philip? They were on first-name terms now?

'Can I just ask, did you ever get any further with Mrs Hadley's case?' Edie asked.

'I'm afraid not, Miss Moore. Since nothing has been seen of Miss Brownlow, or this elusive Jim, for whom we don't even have a surname, the case has now been closed.'

'I see.'

'Good day to you both, Miss Moore… Mr Cobbett. Enjoy your luncheon.'

Julia clutched Edie's hands as they bade farewell to each other. 'Let's meet for tea again soon, on your day off.'

She agreed enthusiastically, being curious to hear more of her friend's latest development.

–

'You've gone very quiet, Charlie,' Edie remarked as they entered the restaurant.

'Have I? Just hungry, that's all. Ah, there's a free table.'

When they'd sat down and been given menus, Charlie gazed at her.

'Why are you looking at me like that?'

'Are you worried about Mrs Hadley's murder still?'

She placed her menu on the table. 'To be honest, yes. I feel ill at ease that the case has been closed. I keep remembering Pamela's words when I'm out and about. She said that since

I was able to describe the Kursaal thief, who I believe to be the murderer, so fully, he'd recognise me if he came across me again. I try not to think about it, but sometimes it makes me feel panicky.'

Charlie nodded and placed one hand on hers. 'Look, I understand why you'd be worried, but if that bloke had any sense, he'd be long gone to where the police can't find him.'

She gave Charlie a smile. 'But what if… No, you're right. I'm just worrying over nothing. I just wish they'd spent more time trying to solve the case.'

'Maybe they did and they didn't get anywhere.'

'Yes. You're probably right. I fancy the pork.'

'Me too.'

–

When Edie and Charlie returned to the hotel later, they could tell as soon as they entered the scullery that something was up.

'What on earth's that hullabaloo?' Charlie hurried through the stillroom to the corridor.

Edie followed on, in time to see Mrs Norris with a rolling pin, waving it towards Alan Drew, the head porter, calling him several choice names. He was moving slowly backwards, hands lifted against a possible attack. The cook railed on.

'You idiot! I'm blaming you for this, 'cos my Joseph wouldn'ta been such a twit to think of doing such a thing.'

'What on earth's going on, Mrs N?' said Charlie.

'This nincompoop has only gone and encouraged my Joseph and one of the waiters to sign up. Yes, that's right, you scurry away, you – you scallywag! I'll catch up with you later.' She lowered the rolling pin, her face crumpling. 'Oh Joseph, my poor Joseph. Can't even face his mother with his idiocy.'

'When did this happen?' said Edie.

'Late staff lunchtime. Missed their meal, they did. We wondered where they'd gone. It's a sad day when a son creeps behind his mother's back to do something he knows will break her heart.' She gave her head a good shake and stomped back to her domain, the kitchen.

The door at the other end of the corridor opened, and Mrs Bygrove entered. 'What on *earth* is going on? I've got Alan Drew raving that Mrs Norris has gone mad, and Mr Watkins arguing with Joseph and Peter Smith.'

'Ah, Peter must be the waiter who's enlisted,' said Charlie.

'Enlisted?'

Edie related what they'd gathered from the cook. The furrows on Mrs Bygrove's forehead became ever deeper as the story progressed. Finally, she slumped against the wall.

'I have no idea what Douglas is going to say. It's going to be hard to replace them, what with businesses not being allowed to employ men between eighteen and sixty. Oh, Lord.' She closed her eyes and put her head back. She was in that position for only two seconds before she rallied. 'But panicking about it is not going to solve the problem. Let me think. Mr Drew is head porter, so we'll need someone to take his place... Mr Cobbett, you could certainly do the job.'

'Me?' He pointed both his forefingers at his chest.

'You've been here the longest of the rest of the porters, so why not? And really, that is the least of my worries. Where are we going to get a new head chef from?'

Mrs Norris must have heard, as she came scampering back out of the kitchen, shouting, 'You think I'm not up to the job? Who'd ya think's been running this kitchen the last five years? I'm not working under some Johnny-come lately who won't know my kitchen.'

'Calm down, Mrs Norris.' Mrs Bygrove raised her hands horizontally and lowered them slowly. 'There are the more complicated, foreign dishes that Joseph excels at.'

'And who d'ya think taught him those, eh?'

At this moment, Douglas Bygrove appeared in the corridor from the hotel foyer, charging down towards them. 'Have you heard the latest madness? I suggest you go to the recruiting office, Helen, and get them un-enlisted.'

'Can you do that?' said Mrs Norris, her face brightening.

'Nah, I don't think you can,' said Charlie.

The cook slumped once more.

The manager glared at him. 'Who asked your opinion?'

'I do believe he's right though,' said Helen.

Douglas clenched his jaw and his face turned pink. 'Then who's going to do these jobs?'

Edie looked back and forth at each as they spoke, wondering how long it would be before Mr Bygrove completely lost his temper, as he was wont to do increasingly these days.

'We have some of that at least sorted out,' said Helen, offering a smile. 'Mrs Norris is more than capable of taking over from her son.'

'But—' Douglas started.

'And Mr Cobbett knows the job well enough to take over as head porter.'

'But that doesn't—'

'And since we're not able to employ new male staff aged between eighteen and sixty, we'll just have to shuffle the female staff around and get a few more in.' Helen looked pleased with her decision.

The manager's face turned a dark shade of puce. 'Women? Women, doing the jobs of porters and waiters? Nobody wants that! Serving tea in a pinny in the conservatory's one thing, but women serving *haute cuisine* in the restaurant is an aberration.'

'Douglas, dear, we've already had women doing the odd shift in the dining room.'

He pointed a finger close to her face and screwed up his eyes. 'And how would *women* manage to carry the cases as porter, hm? Really, Helen, you have the tiny brain typical of your gender.'

Edie felt deep indignation on Helen's part. Even Charlie looked shocked, while Mrs Norris had her mouth screwed into a tiny, shrivelled circle.

She was about to speak up when Helen said, 'Edie and I have occasionally served in the dining room to fill the shortfall, where we did a good job. And despite what you think, Douglas, I do possess more than my fair share of intelligence. If you are so much brighter than me, please, do tell what ideas you've come up with.'

'I, well, I-I'm not stupid enough to come up with hasty ideas. I need more time to think through the problem to a logical conclusion. In the meantime, keep your inane suggestions to yourself. *I* will take care of this.'

He did a 180-degree turn on the balls of his feet and headed back down the corridor. When he'd disappeared through the door, the cook turned to Mrs Bygrove.

'Well, my duck, I wouldn't take any notice of him. As broken-hearted as I am, I'll do you proud as head cook, don't you worry yourself about that. Now, until that son of mine finally turns up to do his shift for the dinners, maybe for the last time...' She took a small pause. 'I'd better get the rest of the staff started.'

As she headed off, Charlie said, 'Do you still want me to take over as head porter?'

'Yes, Charlie, I do. I have every confidence in you. And there'll be a little increase in wages to reflect this promotion.'

He lifted his cap and scratched his head. 'Thank you, madam.'

'Would you go and find the three new enlistees, please, and ask them to come and see me. We need to know when exactly they'll be off.'

Charlie nodded and took the same path as Mr Bygrove.

'Well, it looks like everyone in the kitchen will be moving up a notch,' said Helen. 'Perhaps Alex would like to take on the job of second cook. And you, Edie, could take on a couple of Peter Smith's dining room shifts permanently, for you know how to present yourself to the upper classes.'

'Oh, do you think so?' She tried to sound as sceptical as she could. 'Don't you think the maids who've been here longer than me will be a little put out?' She was thinking of Gertie and Fanny in particular.

'I'm sure some of them wouldn't even want the job, but it's not their decision anyway. You think far too little of yourself, Edie. I am confident you would be excellent.'

'Thank you, Mrs Bygrove.'

'And maybe we could train up a couple of the other maids. I'm sure Lili and Phoebe would be competent enough.'

The door from the back stairs opened, revealing Lili with a bucket full of cleaning items. 'There you are, Edie. What's happened? Mrs Turnbull reckoned there was a right barney going on down here.' She came to a sudden standstill. 'Oh, sorry, Mrs Bygrove, I didn't see you there.'

'That's all right, Lili. I'll leave Edie here to explain what's been happening. I had better find my husband.' It was said in a peeved manner.

When she'd left, Lili put the bucket down and pulled a letter from her apron. 'Rescued this before either Gertie, Fanny or Mrs Leggett got hold of it, I did. Another with fancy writing on, and I didn't want them getting wind of it. They might have opened it.' She handed it over.

This time it was Lucia's writing for certain. Edie sighed. 'Thank you, Lili.'

'So, what's been going on?'

'Let me get changed, then I'll come and tell you.'

'All right. Gives me the chance to get rid of this lot, it does.'

Edie sprinted up the back stairs, opening the envelope as she went. Why couldn't Lucia just leave her alone? She'd got to her bedroom before she was able to pull the sheets from the envelope.

Inside the letter was another envelope with her address and a stamp. Reading the first letter, she ascertained that Lucia had written a note as if it were from a cousin, to tell her that her mother was ill and to advise her to get the following weekend off to see her. As if she would even be able to do that now, with the uproar and the staff leaving.

This time she would write to Lucia and tell her to leave her alone, and hopefully that would be the end of it.

Chapter Eleven

Things had not turned out as Edie had hoped.

Despite Lili's efforts to keep the letter away from other people, the second envelope had fallen out of Edie's pocket onto the staff dining room floor and had been found by Fanny. She'd taken it to Mrs Bygrove, saying it wasn't fair that Edie was getting the weekend off when they were going to be short-staffed, not realising that the manager's wife knew nothing about it.

Edie hadn't been aware of any of this until Mrs Bygrove had found her later that day, to tell her that she must go, and that the men who'd enlisted were not leaving until the following Monday.

So here she was, on a train to Lewes on a Saturday morning, dreading what might occur when she reached her brother's house. She was almost certain that he and Lucia wouldn't trick her and invite her parents down too, but one could never be absolutely sure of other people's intentions. Look what Freddie had done, telling her parents she'd been going to suffragist meetings for ages, even if he'd done it with the intention of showing support and highlighting how out of date they were.

Daniel Duke met her at the station in a Rolls-Royce Silver Ghost, a motor car she had been driven in a couple of times in the past, when accompanying him and her brother somewhere. He was going to drive her the two miles to Iford village, where Freddie's house was located on the gentle slopes of the South Downs.

'My parents aren't going to jump out at me when we get there, are they?' she asked Daniel as he put her carpetbag in the back of the car.

'No, of course not, Edith. Freddie wouldn't do that to you. And if it was his intention, I would have told you.'

'You mention only Freddie. You think Lucia would then?'

He glanced at her with an impatient frown. 'Of course not. Do you really think that, Edith?'

'No. No, I don't.' If anything, Lucia was more trustworthy than Freddie. 'Please, would you call me Edie? Freddie and Lucia do. And I prefer it.'

'Very well.'

The conversation on the way to the house consisted of nothing more contentious than the beauty of the green and chalky countryside. He didn't comment on her new life, and she was relieved about that.

'How was the wedding, by the way?' she asked.

'Very nice, especially considering it was arranged at such short notice. I'm sure Lucia will tell you all about it.'

Edie was struck by the house as Daniel drew up on the gravel drive. It wasn't as grand as she'd expected, although it was a good size, belying its name, 'Bergenia Cottage'. It was charming, with its stuccoed walls in cream, its Wealden-style tiled roof and its Georgian windows and door. The two chimneys were tall. Despite looking eighteenth-century, she suspected the facade hid a much older house. There was a mass of Virginia creeper growing across it, the leaves of which had a hint of red in them. In the extensive front garden was a large pond, on which she could spy a punt in the distance, under a willow tree. To the side of the house was a long, flint wall, and she wondered what lay beyond.

The front door opened and Lucia ran out, Freddie walking at a more leisurely pace behind.

'Edie, darling!' Lucia's arms were spread wide and caught her up in a hug as she met her. 'We're so glad you came.'

Freddie also hugged her, though in a less effusive way.

'Come in, come inside, and meet Clotilde and Percy.' Lucia took her hand. She stopped to look down at Edie's garb. 'But first, you must go up to the bedroom and change. I was able to sneak some clothes out of your room at Downland House, while Freddie kept your mother occupied. When you're ready, come down to the drawing room.'

In the bedroom Lucia showed her to, Daniel put her bag down on the wooden chair next to a three-part screen painted with bold lilies and vases. When they left, she peeped behind the screen, and was surprised to see a bath. Beside it was a sink. The square mirror above had a frame painted in the same green, white and purple shades as the screen. There were several paintings on the wall of different people, including Lucia and Freddie.

On the single bed was laid her light blue crêpe de Chine blouse with white embroidery down the front and on the cuffs. Next to it was her navy-blue skirt, with an overskirt effect and a short row of buttons. It would make a change to wear a different outfit, instead of her limited wardrobe, she couldn't deny that.

Hanging up on the wardrobe was her white taffeta dress with a silk-embroidered net overlay and high beaded neck. It had been one of her favourites. She could just imagine what the staff at the hotel would make of her turning up there in this, especially Mrs Leggett. No doubt it was there for her to change into for dinner.

'How tiresome,' she whispered. There were so many things she did not miss about her old life.

Having changed and tidied her hair, she made her way downstairs, realising she had no idea where the drawing room was, but as she reached the last step, Daniel appeared.

'I thought I heard you coming down. We're in here.'

He led her down the hallway to a room with French doors that opened on to the garden that she'd wondered about beyond the wall. The room was unconventionally painted, with rough yellow walls and green splodges above the picture rail, from which hung several modern paintings. The three double sofas were arranged around a large, rectangular fireplace, decorated with painted swirls and zigzags in bright colours.

Lucia was out of her seat on the sofa as soon as she entered. 'Darling, come and meet our other guests.' She pointed to each in turn. 'This is Percival Challen.'

The young man sitting next to Freddie rose to kiss her hand, leaving her rather perplexed. He was good-looking with his curly, untamed dark hair and his deep brown eyes. His clothes were, to her mind, rather foppish, with his loose shirt and undone floral waistcoat. 'Everyone calls me Percy.'

When he sat down, Lucia moved to the black-haired woman on another sofa, in her long green silk housedress. She wore a purple scarf wrapped around her head, in the manner of the artists at the hotel. 'And this is Mademoiselle Clotilde Dubois,' she pronounced precisely.

The young woman giggled. 'Just Clotilde to my friends,' she said in a French accent.

Edie sat on the third sofa, next to Daniel, while Lucia took a seat next to Clotilde.

'I must say, I am greatly impressed and amused by your subterfuge,' said Percy. 'What a wonderful wheeze.'

Freddie pushed his hand through his now chin-length hair, the same brown as Edie's. 'Our parents would not be of the same opinion.'

'Sometimes one has to break out of convention,' said Percy, 'As we all know.'

'Speak for yourself,' said Daniel.

Percy waved his hand in a dismissive manner. 'Oh Dan, you could if you wanted to. You're just afraid of what your father would say, and that he'd cut you off from the business.'

'But that's the point: I *don't* want to. I'm happy with my life as it is. And to be entertained by my bohemian friends with their unconventional lifestyles, of course.' He grinned and raised his eyebrows.

'Daniel, *cher*, you are such a tease.' Clotilde treated him to a coy smile, leaving Edie wondering if she had designs on him.

'Unconventional?' Percy laughed. 'I think we'll leave that to members of our class who go off to be parlourmaids and waitresses in hotels.'

'Chambermaid,' Edie corrected. 'Although I'll be doing some waiting in the dining room now more men have enlisted.'

'Oh, a promotion!' Freddie mocked.

'Leave the poor girl alone,' said Daniel.

Freddie tutted. 'You approve of what she's done?'

'No, but I respect her right to do what she wants. She's an adult.'

Edie was tiring of this conversation already. 'Have you invited me here only to debate my, my… departure from my old life? If so, I might as well go back to the hotel.'

'No, no, of course not,' said Lucia. 'Come on now, let us speak of other things.'

'First of all, I ought to ask how my parents are, I suppose.'

Freddie frowned. 'Still worried about you, even though I've assured them you are fine. And furious with you. Mother reckons it proves that you're unstable.'

'Of course she does.' It was what she'd said before, with the hinted threat of having her carted off to the asylum. She doubted now that they would have done that. After all, how would they persuade these suitors they had lined up to marry someone deemed to be mad?

'Now, inevitably, they are annoyed with me for not telling them where you are.'

'I was talking about their health and well-being, Freddie. Not everything is about you.'

'Charming thing to say after I kept your secret!' He crossed his arms and looked away.

Lucia intervened. 'Come, come now. No sibling fighting here this weekend. And to answer your question, Edie, they are in good health.'

'You two always did fight, especially when you were younger.' Dan seemed amused.

Edie looked sidelong at him. 'Don't all siblings?'

'Not like you two. Do you remember that time you went out on the boat on the river and had an argument? Freddie and I had just come back from school for the summer. You two were each so intent on taking charge of the oars, and pushing each other, that the boat tipped up and you both fell in.'

Lucia clamped her hand to her mouth, exclaiming, 'Oh my!' while Clotilde threw her head back and laughed.

'It was lucky you were both good swimmers,' said Daniel.

'You always were bossy,' said Freddie.

Edie pointed to herself. '*Me*, bossy? Talk about the pot calling the kettle black!'

'Mind you,' said Daniel, 'you were a formidable force when you stuck up for each other against others.'

Freddie nodded. 'Yes, that's caused trouble with our parents on many occasions.'

'Let's move on from that,' said Edie. 'I want to hear all about the wedding.'

Lucia beamed and rubbed her fists together in delight, before giving Edie a rundown of the clothes, the ceremony and the reception, Freddie and Clotilde interrupting now and again with some detail she'd missed out.

Eventually, the conversation moved, unsurprisingly, to the war: how some of their friends and acquaintances had enlisted, while others had become conscientious objectors.

Edie mostly stayed quiet during the exchange, feeling surprisingly out of her depth, when once she'd have ploughed in with an opinion. Eventually, in a gap in the conversation, she offered, 'There is talk of conscription, maybe, in the future, if not enough men enlist.'

'Then I shall definitely be a conscientious objector,' Percy declared. 'I have no desire to kill anyone.'

'Nor I,' said Freddie.

Daniel considered them. 'It may be that, or be locked up if it becomes law.'

'Right, that's enough of the war now,' said Lucia. 'Mrs Riddles is preparing luncheon for twelve thirty. We have time to do some painting in the study. There are the door panels, a table and the hearth there.'

'Painting?' said Edie.

Percy nodded. 'Yes, we're all adding our contribution to the decoration in the house. You see the fireplace here? That was my design.'

That would explain its eccentricity.

'Edie was a reasonable artist in our youth,' said Freddie.

'Not on furniture.'

'Then now is the time to try something new, since you seem to be so keen on that,' said Lucia.

Not that again, thought Edie. She counted the hours until she was able to depart the next day. She might as well fill it with something. 'All right. I'll have a go.'

–

Before dinner that evening, Edie was first in the garden room for the pre-dinner drinks. Since she was early and no one else had arrived, she went into the walled garden for a walk.

There was a large lawn with a small, rectangular pond at the other end. This area was surrounded by apple trees and various flowers. Beyond, she discovered other fruit trees, a rose garden and a kitchen garden. Next to that was a piazza with a mosaic in the centre, surrounded by seats, and with a fountain on one side.

As she was examining the detail of the mosaic, Daniel wandered out, one hand in his trouser pocket, whistling 'The Floral Dance'.

'Edie, how nice to find you here alone.'

She frowned. 'Why alone?'

He reached her side. 'Only because I find you the most interesting to talk to. And the most charming.' He tipped his head to one side and treated her to a tentative smile.

She looked up at him a little disapprovingly. 'Really, Dan, you're such a flatterer. You mix with a group of bohemians and you find *me* interesting?'

'Absolutely. I've always found you delightful. Like I said earlier, I don't exactly approve of what you're doing, but I defend your right to do it. I want to protect you from their derision. And if I'm honest, I admire your quest to go out on your own, to lead your own life and earn your own way, not rely on your wealthy father. You're an inspiration, Edie, and rather a pretty one at that.'

'Dan! Now you're mocking me. I'm going for a look at the water.'

She walked to the gate in the wall and went through to the front of the house, before starting on a circuit of the large pond. He caught her up and was soon walking beside her.

'I'm not mocking you, Edie, honestly.'

'Then why are you telling me this?'

'Slow down, will you? It's not a race.' He took her arm briefly.

'Sorry, yes.' She'd meant this to be a leisurely stroll, but his words had irked her.

'I'm telling you this because, well… I'm not good with words in these situations.'

He slipped his arm through hers. She didn't object; she'd known him since she was ten.

'Well, what then? You're normally more erudite than this.'

'I know. It's a delicate matter.'

Now she was confused. Perhaps this conversation wasn't going the way she thought it would. Was something wrong, with Freddie maybe, that he wasn't telling her? But what did that have to do with her being charming?

'Now you're scaring me, Dan.'

'Scaring you? I'm sorry, I'm bungling this rather. But you see, before you ran off to start a new life, I'd been thinking, that is, that I'd wanted to, well, see you on a more official basis, not just as my friend's sister.'

She came to a standstill, not at all sure she'd heard right, yet knowing she had. 'If you're saying what I think you are, then that's not possible now.'

'Why not? You wanted to escape your parents and all the restrictions placed on you. You wanted to avoid being married off to a batty old earl, or a self-interested viscount. If you, well, if you married me, you wouldn't have to worry about them anymore.'

'*Marry* you?' The shock of the request and the force of her reply had her coughing. She turned away from Dan to be polite. She leant over a little and he rubbed her back. 'Sorry, I'm sorry,' she said, as she got her breath back.

'My goodness, is it that terrible an idea? Or do you also consider me an horrific prospect for a spouse?' He chuckled cautiously, yet looked worried. 'You would have freedom with me, to do what you want, even to go to suffragist meetings. You know I admire those women.'

'I didn't know that, but I'm not surprised you do.' She had always known him to be an enlightened soul. 'However, they are not campaigning for women's rights at the moment, what with the war.'

'I know. But they're still doing good works.'

She took both his hands in hers. 'Oh Dan, I appreciate your suggestion, even if it is rather sudden and probably in jest, and certainly crazy, to be honest.'

Whether it was in jest she didn't know, but maybe her saying so would dissuade him from pursuing it.

'I would have the utmost respect for you, Edie. We would have a partnership.'

What about love? she wanted to holler. She could tell him she already had a sweetheart and pretend it was Charlie. Opening her mouth to voice it, she decided she'd better consider it first. Charlie wasn't her sweetheart. Dan wouldn't know that. But what if it got back to her brother? He might think that was the last straw and tell their parents where she was. They might do something to make sure Charlie disappeared from the scene.

'We may rub along together nicely, Dan, but it would still be another version of a sham marriage.'

'No, Edie, because—'

'There you are, you two.' Freddie appeared through the garden gate. 'Come on now, we're serving champagne. You don't want to miss it.' He headed back without waiting for a reply.

Dan and Edie glanced at each other. She wondered if he'd finish his sentence, but he said, 'We'd better go.' He put his hand out towards the gate to indicate she should go first.

What a weekend this was turning out to be. She'd have a laugh about it with – oh, no she wouldn't. Charlie knew nothing of this life. How she wished more than ever that she had the courage to talk to him about it.

–

After breakfast the following day, Edie was in the study, counting down the hours until she could return to Littlehampton. Yes, it had made a change to be served by someone else, instead of being the one serving, but at the same time, it had made her feel decidedly uncomfortable. And she had missed Charlie.

Now she was on her own, having agreed to paint a seaside scene on the top panel of the door. She only hoped the ability to produce a reasonably decent portrayal was still in her. So far, so good. It would certainly brighten up the room, which was white all over. She did up the artist's smock that Lucia had lent her, hoping she didn't spill any paint on the bottom of her dress.

Daniel had not endeavoured to get her alone to further persuade her to abandon her present manner of life, and for that she was grateful. The relief was short-lived when the knock came on the other side of the door on which she was working.

'Only me.'

Freddie entered with a paint pot and brush.

'I thought I'd work on the dado rail while you're in here. It gives me a chance to talk to you.'

'Look, if you're going to go on about—'

'I'm not here to badger you about the hotel, if that's what you think. I want to apologise.'

'Oh.' Freddie rarely apologised about anything.

'Let me set up and start, then I'll explain.'

He stood on a chair and began painting the dado rail sea green as she continued with her beach scene of sand, sea and a bathing hut.

'Lucia wants yellow on the walls as she thinks it will go with the seaside theme she's planning, your painting being the start.'

'It sounds like it will be a nice bright room.'

She hadn't been at all sure about the distinctive decor of the house, filled with its artwork of varying proficiencies, but having been shown around the house and the completed rooms, she had to admit it was rather appealing. Certainly more so than the staid decor of her family home.

'About the business before you left Downland House,' said Freddie, continuing to paint. 'When I told our parents about you attending the suffragist meetings, I realise now it was ill-advised, but I did it with the best of intentions, I promise you.'

'And that's an apology?'

'I'm sorry, Edie. I really am. My purpose was to make our parents see how out of date they are, especially our mother. My goodness, you think she'd be proud of you. I was. I am. Well, apart from your latest— That is, not to wander off the point, I certainly didn't expect them to threaten to lock you in your room until you "came to your senses", as Mama put it.'

Edie relived the anger and indignation of that threat. 'To say that I was incandescent with rage, Freddie, would be rather understating it.'

'I know, Edie, I know. I honestly thought that I could sway them with my logic. I said to Mama that she was a Moreland, the wife of a baron, and that she belonged to a moneyed family that had great respect in and around Brighton and the area, yet she had absolutely no say in who made the laws. I thought, being someone who likes a say in everything, that she'd see the point I was making.'

'Well, she didn't. Never go into politics, Freddie, for you would be no good at it.'

'No,' he said, his voice croaking and his mouth turning down in misery.

'But I appreciate you were trying to do good, and I particularly appreciate your apology.' She looked at the clock on the mantelpiece. 'I'll need to get ready in an hour or so, to catch my train.'

'I wish you could stay longer.'

'You know I can't.'

'Couldn't you tell them your mother took a turn for the worse?'

'Of course I couldn't.'

'Sorry. Again. Let's spend the time you have left in harmony then. I don't want us to part on bad terms.'

'Nor I.' She smiled at him, her foolish, prone-to-mischief and ultimately endearing brother.

'And Dan is driving you to the station, by the way.'

'Oh, good,' she replied, with mixed feelings.

-

'Have you got everything?' Daniel asked as he took the carpetbag from Edie.

'That's it, I'm afraid. All my worldly goods.'

His brow creased as he held the bag in mid-air and considered it.

'Daniel, I'm joking! I do have a few more things at the hotel.' Though not many more, she had to admit to herself.

'I'm glad to hear it.' He placed the bag onto the back seat of the Rolls-Royce.

Freddie and Lucia came forward to kiss her cheek in turn. Clotilde and Percy stood just outside the front door to wave and call their farewell.

Lucia took her hands. 'Now, do write.'

'If I have time. And please, if you write to me, make it look like an ordinary letter. None of your fancy seals or the copperplate writing.'

'Did I do that before?' She looked put out.

'It wasn't quite as fancy as usual, but still a little so.'

'It wouldn't hurt for you to telephone occasionally,' said Freddie. 'You have our number.'

'I'm not sure where I'd do that from, as I don't want to be caught using the hotel telephone for my own purposes.'

She got into the passenger seat and leant her arm on the door. 'Thank you for a lovely stay.' She called over to the other two guests, 'Nice to meet you, Clotilde and Percy.'

They both waved once more and called, 'And you.'

Daniel pumped a lever up and down before fiddling with some dials on the dashboard. He started the engine and they rolled slowly away across the gravel and through the open gates to the road.

'This is a beautiful motor car, by the way,' she said.

'You could drive it any time you wanted if you… came back to civilisation.'

'Don't start that again, Dan.'

'Sorry. But you know where I am if you change your mind.'

'Yes, I know.'

At the station he parked the car on the road and removed her bag from the back seat.

'I'll take that.' She held out her hand.

'No, it's all right. I'll come to the platform with you and wait until your train arrives.'

She was about to argue but realised there was no point. He purchased a platform ticket and they walked to a bench to sit in silence.

Would she have been interested in Daniel if she'd still been living at home? She'd always been fond of her brother's friend, though not in any romantic way. Perhaps she could have learned to love him, especially if it had meant escaping home. It was hard to know now, when all her feelings were for Charlie.

Charlie. She'd see him soon. It made her want to smile, but she didn't in case Dan asked her the reason.

People on the platform moved forward, and she realised a train could be seen approaching in the distance. They both stood.

'Here it is. Thank you for the lift, Dan.'

'You're welcome.'

She hesitated before leaning up to kiss his cheek. 'Take care. I'll—'

'See you soon?' he suggested.

She laughed. 'Probably not.'

'No.' he looked forlorn. 'Take care, Edie, and remember what I said.'

The last words were shouted over the chugging and hissing of the train as it slowed to a halt.

She climbed on and he handed her the bag. Remaining in the corridor, she leant from the window to wish him goodbye once more. Soon the whistle was being blown, and the train continued on its way. When he disappeared from sight, she went to find a seat in a carriage, feeling strangely sad.

–

Charlie checked his wristwatch as he leant against the door of the brown Sunbeam Cabriolet. Mrs Bygrove had insisted he take it to pick Edie up from the station, with the black clouds overhead threatening rain. Just as well, he thought, as the first drops pattered onto his cap. The train was due in any moment, so he'd better get going. He pushed himself forward, shocked at the jolt of emotion that travelled through him. It was one of pleasure but was so fierce that it was almost painful. The disorientation it caused made him stand still for a moment.

What on earth? Was that to do with him thinking about Edie's return? He had missed her while she'd been gone, the way she appreciated his jokes and listened to him as if he had something interesting to say. But still…

'Right, get going, you idiot,' he mumbled, shaking his head at himself. There was no place for sentimentality in his life.

He reached the platform as the train puffed into the station, its brakes hissing and squealing as they came to a halt. He moved from side to side, trying to spot her as people alighted. Was that – yes, it was her, coming down the train steps, wearing the black and lavender velvet hat she'd bought on their last half-day off together. He went forward, waving his arm to attract her attention.

She'd started walking before she spotted him. The smile she gave him was so full of joy and relief that it happened again, the whoosh in his stomach.

'Now stop that, Charlie Cobbett,' he muttered, moving towards her. She was his friend, that was all. The smile was probably an indication that her mother was fine. And relief that she'd have someone to carry her bag?

'Charlie, what are you doing here?'

'Come to pick you up, haven't I?' He took her bag and they walked back towards the station building. 'Mrs Bygrove asked me to bring the motor car as the weather wasn't looking good.'

'Have you driven a motor car before?' She looked concerned.

''Course I have. I was a motor car mechanic, remember? My dad taught me so I could drive people's vehicles back to their homes.'

'How useful.'

'Be even better if I had one of my own.'

'They're quite expensive.'

'Yep. But maybe one day I can save up enough money for one.' It was one of the reasons he'd ended up in Portsmouth. 'Anyway, how is your mother?'

Edie raised her eyebrows. 'She's fine. A big fuss about nothing. My sister-in-law is a terrible fusspot.' She gave a wry smile.

'I thought you looked cheerful. Welcome back.'

'Thank you. It's good to be back.'

They exited the station building. Charlie led the way to the motor car, unable to prevent the smile that formed because of her statement. *But it won't be because of anything you've done, pal.* No, and he'd do well to remember that.

Chapter Twelve

'It's very mild for November,' said Edie, as she and Lili stood outside the perimeter wall of the hotel, looking out across the common during their afternoon break.

'Still doesn't mean we'll get a firework display tonight.'

Edie looked at her friend, who was crossing her arms in frustration. 'It's getting overcast now, anyway, so probably wouldn't have been a good evening for one.'

'It's not fair, the government banning them. We've had such lovely ones here at the hotel.'

It wasn't the first time she'd heard this grumble from staff members and was getting a little tired of it, even though it was Lili who was moaning. However, she kept her voice light as she said, 'I'm sure it would have been lovely, and we'll have them again after the war.' She looked up at the clock above the hotel's public house. 'Let's get in to have our tea before we run out of time. I've got to go for another shift on the desk soon.' She'd been given these extra shifts as Richard Watkins had wanted to visit his ailing mother in Lancing. Stuart Coulter, the other desk clerk, had not been well himself and had been off all week.

As they entered the scullery, it was clear there was a fuss going on somewhere in the kitchen quarters.

'Not again,' said Lili. 'Always some argument going on these days, there is.'

Phoebe burst into the stillroom as they were about to leave it, colliding with them. 'Oh, sorry. I just had to escape the tea break. Mr Bygrove's in there arguing with Alex from the kitchen 'cos he and James Wood, the porter, have only gone and signed up, along with two of the live-out waiters. Doing his nut, he is, the manager.'

'Come on,' said Lili, pulling Edie along. 'I'm not missing my cuppa tea for nothing, even if there is a row going on.'

Edie had no choice but to follow, though she'd rather have stayed put. She'd had enough of arguments.

When they entered the dining room, the table was full of gaping faces as Mr Bygrove ranted, his finger wagging. Only the two live-in members who'd signed up seemed unconcerned. Charlie indicated he'd saved seats for Edie and Lili and they slipped in and sat down. He'd already served them each a cup of tea.

'And I've only just managed to find a replacement waiter, and him seventy odd,' raved the manager. 'And the maids are constantly having to take over, and many of them are useless…'

There were several tuts from the younger women.

'…particularly those two.' He pointed at Gertie and Fanny.

Fanny pouted. 'That ain't fair. We haven't even been waitressing yet.'

'Keep quiet!'

'But it's our duty, sir, to sign up,' said Alex. 'That's what we're told by the government. And now we're at war with Turkey, too, they'll need even more soldiers.'

Mrs Norris entered at this point. 'And what am I supposed to do for an under-cook, eh? Already lost my Joseph to the army, and now you, a half-decent cook, decides to go off too.'

'Would you let me handle this,' said Bygrove, glaring at her. 'And with another porter going, Mr Cobbett here will have to be doing a lot more shifts, along with Stanley and Leslie Morris, the live-outs.'

'Reckon they should be signing up too,' grumbled Alex.

'Not bloomin' likely,' said Charlie. 'And the twins are only seventeen, so they're not even old enough.'

'That is not the point!' Bygrove shouted.

Fanny jumped and started crying.

'For goodness' sake!'

They heard someone running down the corridor, and soon Mrs Bygrove was standing in the doorway.

'Douglas, I came in to speak to the staff and I find you shouting your head off. Again. This isn't going to solve anything.'

Edie was steeling herself for the repercussions of Helen questioning her husband, when Alex piped up with, 'Just telling Mr Bygrove here it's our duty to sign up.'

'Well, I'm not working even more shifts just because you're running away to war,' said Charlie.

'And I'm not useless!' yelled Gertie, 'and nor is Fanny.'

Helen looked confused. 'Who said you were?'

'Never mind that. How am I supposed to keep up with cooking *hort cuzzin* meals with fewer and fewer staff members?' shouted Mrs Norris, wielding a wooden spoon.

Charlie looked at Edie, mouthing, '*Hort cuzzin?*'

Despite the rumpus, she wanted to laugh. She mouthed back, '*Haute cuisine*.'

She could tell Charlie wanted to laugh too, but they both managed to hold it in.

'Look,' Helen declared, bringing the uproar to an end. 'We're going to have to face the fact that there will be a decreasing number of younger men left to do what are considered non-essential jobs.'

'But cooking is essential to a hotel and—'

'Yes, Mrs Norris, essential to keeping a hotel running, but hotels are not considered essential in the grand scheme of things where this war is concerned. Therefore, we're going to have to accept that we will need to employ more women to do what we judge to be men's jobs.'

'Poppycock,' Bygrove bellowed, but didn't seem to have anything further to back up this assertion.

'The ever-decreasing male staff can't just do all-day shifts.'

'I'm not having women completely taking over the jobs.'

'Then perhaps, Douglas, you'd be happy to take on some of the shifts yourself.'

The exchange fascinated Edie, and clearly everyone else, and they looked from one to the other as they spoke. It was like watching a play on the stage.

'*I'm* the manager.'

'Then manage, rather than fighting the inevitable. As for the waiting staff, some of the women here have shown that they are more than up to the job.'

Bygrove's fists were clenched by his sides. 'I'll see you in the office, *now*.'

'I'm busy right now. I need to speak with Edie, Lili and Phoebe, though she doesn't seem to be here.'

'I'll fetch her,' said Lili, rising.

'Then return here. Break time will be over soon, so we'll have this room to ourselves.'

Bygrove said nothing as he turned and left the room. Not long after, they heard a door slam in the distance, presumably the one to his office.

'Excuse me,' said Edie, her hand raised a little, 'but I'm due on the desk about now.'

'Of course. Charlie, would you ask Mr Watkins if he could hold on for ten minutes?'

'Yes, Mrs Bygrove.' He rushed through the door just before Lili returned with Phoebe.

'And Gertie, could you find Mrs Leggett for me, please? I believe she'll be on her inspection of the bedrooms.'

The chambermaid scooted past Phoebe and went on her way.

'Fanny and Hetty, if you'd be good enough to clear the tea things and take them to the scullery, please.'

They replied politely, but Edie could tell Fanny was annoyed by the surreptitious scowl in her direction.

When all was cleared and the rest of the staff had left, Mrs Bygrove shut the door and the four women sat round the table together.

'You already know the situation with staff,' said Helen. 'Edie, you've done an excellent job on your few shifts in reception, so I'd like you to take on a permanent job as a desk clerk. There might still be the odd shift in the restaurant though, depending on how things go. Lili and Phoebe, you've been tremendous at serving in the restaurant, so I'd like you both to do that as your job from now on.'

The two women both gave a little gasp of surprise and looked pleased with themselves. Edie was happy for them, and even more relieved to be escaping the maid's job once and for all, even though she'd been doing it less and less the last couple of months.

'Does that mean you'll be taking on new maids?' Lili asked.

'Yes, we'll need another chambermaid and a stillroom maid, at the very least.'

The door opened with some determination, and in stormed the housekeeper. 'You wanted to see me, Mrs Bygrove.'

'Ah, Mrs Leggett. I'm sorry, we've started without you. Here's the situation.'

As she explained, the housekeeper's mouth shrank into an ever-thinner line, until it looked as if she had no lips at all.

'What does Mr Bygrove think about this?'

'Mr Bygrove can see that we have to adapt in these difficult times. What we need to worry about now is advertising for maids. I'm sure, with some families now only relying on the soldier's separation allowance, that many wives and daughters will be glad of the extra money.'

The housekeeper did not look convinced. However, she said, 'Very well, Mrs Bygrove. I will organise adverts for the local papers straight away. I will even interview the prospective candidates, if you wish me to.'

'I would certainly like you to arrange the adverts, Mrs Leggett. I will, however, conduct the interviews myself, though I appreciate your offer.'

'Very well, *madam*.' She bowed her head briefly. 'Now, if you will allow me, I will use the telephone in the office to contact the appropriate people.'

'I believe my husband is in there at the moment and does not wish to be disturbed. I will come and find you when it's convenient.'

The housekeeper left without a word, her eyes narrowed as if she'd been insulted.

'You had better all return to work too,' Helen said to the maids. 'I will arrange for you to have some more shifts over the next couple of days, while the enlisted waiters are still here. You'll be starting in your new posts on Monday. And of course, Mr Smithson will still be there. So much for him being retired and temporary, poor man.'

Lili and Phoebe stood, both saying, 'Very well, madam,' before heading off.

Edie lingered until they were out of earshot. She questioned the wisdom of making the query she had in mind, but voiced it anyway. 'If you don't mind me asking, why do you allow Mrs Leggett to be so rude? I know it's not my place to ask, but I do feel she's out of order.'

'Don't worry, you are quite right. Mrs Leggett, despite enjoying the power she has as housekeeper, does not seem to believe that women should have any authority. Or maybe it's just married women she believes that of. But I'm not about to create an awkward situation with her. If she realised it bothered me, it would give her the upper hand.'

'I suppose it would.'

Helen lowered her voice to say, 'My goodness, imagine if there were a Mr Leggett. I doubt he'd have a say in any matter.' She gave a little chuckle, and Edie joined in. 'But that opinion is just between the two of us.'

Edie nodded. 'I had better go and relieve Mr Watkins.'

'Gosh, yes, before he comes storming down here to find you! Just refer him to me if he gives you any trouble.'

As Edie made her way to the reception area, she smiled to herself. Mrs Bygrove was well acquainted with the dispositions and shortcomings of her staff, and how to handle them, much more so than her husband.

It was such a shame she wasn't the manager.

–

It had been a busy and seemingly endless day today, despite being a November weekend. Charlie lifted the candleholder before he entered the store cupboard in the scullery. It wasn't worth the trouble of lighting the gas lamp in there. In addition, he'd keep the door open and use the gaslight from the scullery to find the box of matches that Alex had asked him to fetch up to their bedroom before Charlie started his night shift in the foyer. He could have sworn that Alex had only brought a box up that morning, but perhaps he hadn't got round to it.

Charlie had borrowed the key from Mrs Turnbull, who'd insisted he take it straight back when he'd finished. She was fussy about who had the store keys and for how long.

About to stretch out to the appropriate shelf and pull out a packet, the door slammed shut behind him. His alarmed huff of breath blew out the candle, already on its last legs and sputtering. Now he was in the dark.

At first he panicked, immediately admonishing himself. All he had to do was open the door again. Someone must have opened an outside door and caused a breeze.

He felt his way to the door, then twisted the handle round and pushed it, opening it slightly, but it immediately pulled shut again. That was odd. He tried again, but it wouldn't budge now, however far round he turned the doorknob. It was as if something heavy was leaning against it. A bead of dread slithered through his gut. No; it must only be a bit sticky, or need some wood shaving off. He gave it one more shove, dislodging it a little more than before, raising his hopes.

It was the door pushing itself immediately back in place that made him realise something was wrong.

'Hello, is anyone there? Can you open the door and help me get out? I've got a shift to go to.'

But instead, he heard the key turn in the lock where he'd left it. He felt sick, placing his head against the door and holding his mouth to prevent it becoming a reality. When he'd recovered, he called, 'Who's that? What's happening?'

'It's us,' came Alex's voice. 'Me and Jim. We reckon cowards should be locked up – 'cos that's what you are, Charlie Cobbett.'

'Yeah, you're young and fit, like us,' said James Wood. 'And we're gonna teach you a lesson.'

These two were well known for liking a joke, so Charlie was hopeful that this was another of their japes. 'Come on, Jim, you and me's worked together for ages. Don't be an ass.'

There was no reply. 'Alex? Jim?' He put his ear to the door. After a few seconds, he heard the door to the back stairs slam.

They'd gone. And he was here, confined, in the dark, due out on a night shift in five or so minutes. Could he find the matches again and try to relight the candle? Maybe feel around for a fresh one. Alex saying the box of matches in their bedroom was nearly empty must have been a trick to get him in the storeroom. Feeling along the shelf for them, the panic mounted. How would he find the matches and a candle and manage to light one up?

This was ridiculous. There must be someone else around. He banged again. It was approaching ten o'clock, so the kitchen still had staff in, preparing for the next day, and the scullery maids would be doing the clearing and the washing-up. The clatter of pots, pans and utensils might be blocking out the sound of his banging, though.

There were no sounds from the other side.

His hand went out once again, searching more desperately for the candles now. Before he realised what was happening, his hand bumped into something, knocking it off the shelf to clatter and crash to the ground on the other side of the shelf.

Charlie's breaths became ever more rapid and he found it hard to swallow. His heart was thumping against his ribs, making his chest uncomfortable.

I'm going to die, I'm going to die, his brain told him.

'No, you're not, Charlie, mate. You've been down this road before.' *Breathe slowly*. But in his effort to follow his own instructions, he found his breath hitching each time, making him feel like he was choking.

In desperation, he launched himself towards the door, banging and hollering. The effort of it made his breathing shallower still, and he felt light-headed. He slipped down the door, moaning in anguish.

He was halfway down when the door was pulled open and he felt himself fall forward onto his chest.

'Charlie, Charlie! Oh no!'

He knew it was Edie's voice, but the shock and a vague awareness of shame prevented him from replying.

'Charlie, are you all right?' It was Mrs Bygrove's voice this time.

He tried to mumble something, though he wasn't sure what, when he was turned onto his back and felt an arm around his shoulders.

'What happened to you?'

He opened his eyes to see Edie on her knees, her face crumpled with concern. Mrs Bygrove was hunkered down.

'Got locked in,' he mumbled.

'Who on earth by?' said Mrs Bygrove. 'Did they attack you? You're in a terrible state.'

How could he explain the state, as she put it, was all his own doing?

'Alex and Jim. They said I-I deserved it 'cos I was a coward for not enlisting.'

'They did what?' Mrs Bygrove sounded livid. 'But why are you so distressed?'

As much as he hated to admit it, he'd have to tell them the reason, or at least, part of it. What Alex and Jim had done to him was wrong, but he wouldn't have them blamed for attacking him when they hadn't.

Charlie sat himself up slowly. Edie moved back a little. 'I'm, I'm, well, you see, I don't like confined places. Panics me, it does.'

Mrs Bygrove stood. 'You suffer from claustrophobia?'

'Yes, that's the word… Oh, I'm sorry.' He got up abruptly, swaying. He clutched the wall. 'I'm meant to be on duty now.'

'Don't worry. Leslie Morris is still there, and there is no one around. It's very quiet.'

Edie stood up. 'Shall I go and tell Leslie to go home now? I don't mind covering the porter's job.'

'No, you take Charlie to the bar. He needs something for the shock.'

'Wouldn't say no to that, Mrs B.' The light-headedness had passed, but his hands were still trembling. He held them against his legs, hoping neither of the women would notice.

Edie led Charlie into the foyer, with Mrs Bygrove just ahead, where she came to a halt. 'I'll ask Leslie to hold on a moment, then I'd better tell my husband what the noise was. Edie, you carry on with Charlie and get him that whisky. Tell Nancy I've said it's free.'

'Thanks, Mrs B.'

'And be sure, I will deal with Alex and James as soon as I've spoken to my husband. Or he will.' She didn't sound so sure about the last statement. 'When you've had your whisky, come and find me. And Edie, if you could take over from Leslie for a while afterwards and send him home, I'd appreciate it.'

Charlie noticed Leslie looking over curiously, before Edie took his arm to lead him to a door on the right that led into the bar. There were only a couple of patrons left in there, sitting on the opposite side, probably due to the fact that the public house was now only allowed to sell alcohol until nine o'clock.

Edie sat him down at a table and went to the bar. She whispered to Nancy a quick rundown of what had happened. The barmaid put a glass up to one of the optics and drew a shot of liquid into it. She looked over at Charlie. 'He looks quite shaken up. Think I'll add another shot.'

Edie brought the whisky over and sat down as she placed it next to him.

'Thanks. Not normally one for whisky, me, but I could certainly do with this.'

'That was awful of Alex and Jim to lock you in the store cupboard. Do they know you're claustrophobic?'

'Yes. I got shut in the luggage store a while back, so it became obvious then. But what difference is it going to make what Mrs Bygrove does? They're leaving tomorrow, for good. They're not going to care.'

'They might want a job when the war's over.'

'S'pose.' He looked away, ashamed anew that he'd been weak enough to scream like a baby.

Disposing of the whisky in two gulps made him feel marginally better. He heaved himself out of the seat. 'Right, I'd better find Mrs B and see what's happening.'

-

Edie stared past the empty foyer, through the door and into the black night. With Sunday-evening meals only being served until nine o'clock, the patrons had all left the dining room.

The distant sound of voices came from the direction of the kitchen corridor, causing Edie to strain her ears. It was maybe only Charlie and Mrs Bygrove returning. She couldn't imagine him wanting to share a room with Alex after what he'd done. There was Joseph's empty room, normally used only by the head chef, but they might make an exception.

She was considering all this when she realised the voices hadn't been as close as she'd initially thought, but instead were shouting. The volume increased further until the argument burst into the foyer. She soon saw both the Bygroves with Charlie, Alex and Jim, the latter two with rucksacks slung over their shoulders. It was Alex and the manager who were arguing.

'You know what you can do with your job,' said Alex. 'I don't wanna come back to a place full of cowards. You can't be that old either, Mr Bygrove. You could sign up. Your wife's a better manager anyway, so it'd be no loss.'

'Get out of my hotel and stay out,' Bygrove growled. 'You've been nothing but trouble since you got here.'

That wasn't true, even if they did like a joke that went too far sometimes. And they'd been good workers. Edie watched their progress towards the front doors.

'You can run away now, but if they start conscripting men, then you'll have no choice.'

Bygrove let out a sharp, 'Hah! Of course they won't conscript anyone. It will all be over by Christmas, you'll see. Then where will you get a job? Or a reference, for I won't be giving you one.'

'If it's gonna be over by Christmas, they 'aven't got long to sort it out,' said Jim, pulling his rucksack back up onto his shoulder from where it had slipped. 'So good luck.' With that, he slammed his body into the door to open it and left, followed closely by Alex.

Bygrove rubbed his hands. 'You'll be all right for starting your shift now, Mr Cobbett.'

'No, he won't,' Helen interrupted.

'I'm fine now, madam,' said Charlie.

'You may well feel fine, but I'm certainly not leaving you here on your own in case those two decide to come back and cause trouble.'

'I'll stay on the desk,' said Edie, realising Helen was right. If they came back in that mood, they could do Charlie a lot of damage.

'No, you've been on desk duty all evening, and you are doing a shift tomorrow morning. Douglas, you're not on duty tomorrow morning. It would be far more sensible for you to stay with Mr Cobbett.'

'But I've got a meeting with the golf committee at ten o'clock.'

'Exactly. You're not working in the morning, and the golf committee is not as important, or as demanding, as our business.'

'Why can't you stay?' he said, looking cross.

'Because I'm meeting with Mrs Cunningham-Jones at nine thirty tomorrow, about her daughter's wedding reception next spring, which *is* important for our business.'

Despite going puce in the face, his mouth continually pouting and pinching, Bygrove seemed to have run out of arguments.

'Good, that's settled. And if there's any trouble, call the police.' Helen pointed to the telephone on the reception desk.

'The least you could do is get me a cup of coffee before you go,' said her husband.

'Yes, of course. I will get one for Mr Cobbett, too.'

Charlie caught Edie's eye, raising his eyebrows twice. Porters weren't normally allowed to eat or drink on duty.

'Come along, Miss Moore, you need to get some sleep if you're going to greet the guests with a smile tomorrow.'

Edie followed Helen, taking a last look at Charlie before she entered the staff area. He was already standing to attention in the middle of the foyer, looking towards the door. She thought again about the state he was in when they found him in the storeroom. Poor Charlie. It was such an overreaction, and she wondered if he'd been locked in a room as a child for being naughty. Such things could have a lifetime's effect on one. Perhaps one day he would tell her, but for now she was desperate for her bed.

Chapter Thirteen

It was the second time in six weeks that Edie had gone out in the Bygroves' Sunbeam Cabriolet with Charlie. How odd that she should get so excited about something that used to be a fairly mundane feature of her life, as she had often been taken out with her father in his Ford Model T to attend functions. It was strange how much more she appreciated these small treats in her new life.

This morning, a letter had come from Lucia, inviting her to stay with her and Freddie over Christmas, and to meet up with her parents to make amends. Even if she'd wanted to spend the holiday with them, she'd wouldn't have been able to. For that she was grateful, for it gave her an excuse to put in her reply, rather than voicing the fact that she was not inclined to either stay with them, or see her parents. That would surely have ended only one way, and it wouldn't have been in her favour. But she didn't want to be thinking about that during her time off, for she'd been looking forward to it for the last few days.

'Are we picking up the holly, etcetera, first?' she said, as he drove up Surrey Street, past the motor garage and the Norfolk Hotel.

'Yes. If it's anything like last year, it'll take up a lot of the back seat. Mrs B's put a blanket down so it doesn't ruin the leather.'

'Look at the shops, Charlie. There are more with Christmas decorations than last week when we came.' She looked at the greenery gracing some shops, and felt like a child again.

'Better if I keep my eyes on the road for now,' he chuckled. 'Don't wanna be crashing into the cart ahead. We'll have plenty of time to admire the shops once we've picked up the bits for the hotel. Personally, I'm looking forward to the *luncheon* she's given us a bit of money for. Bet she didn't tell her husband about that. Never done it before, she hasn't.'

'Gertie and Fanny weren't pleased about us getting two hours longer on our day off, either.'

'I bet. It's nice of Mrs B to reward our efforts for helping out in our free time, though.' Halfway down High Street, he said, 'Here we are then,' and stopped the car outside a shop that was a fruiterers and florist.

The streets were filled with shoppers, mainly women, wrapped up against a fresh breeze in winter coats and felt or velvet hats, a few with fur collars. Some were lugging shopping baskets or sack bags; a few had umbrellas looped over their arms.

Charlie got out and rushed round the car to open Edie's door. She got out and stood on the pavement, staring at the shop's windows. There was such a wonderful display of holly and mistletoe and ivy, with baubles arranged among them.

'How imaginative,' she said, admiring the work that had gone into it.

'Come on, it's a bit parky here.' He did up his jacket, pulled his cap down and wound his woollen scarf one more time round his neck.

The shopkeeper was a middle-aged woman, dressed in the bohemian manner of the three artists who'd stayed at the hotel during the summer. 'Ah, you must have come to pick up the Beach Hotel's order,' she said to Charlie, who'd been here several times before.

'That's right. Got some help today.' He indicated Edie with his head.

The shopkeeper beamed at her. 'So I see. Well, there's plenty of mistletoe to keep you two busy.'

'Oh, no,' Edie started. 'It's, um, it's not like that, is it, Charlie?'

'Nope,' he said, emphasising the 'p'. 'Just friends.'

His curt answer disappointed Edie a little, as if the idea was ludicrous. Still, hadn't she been just as adamant?

'What a shame. Still, I hope someone gets the use of it at the hotel. Maybe Mr and Mrs Bygrove, eh?'

As she turned to pick up the first wooden crate of holly, Charlie raised his eyes at Edie and mouthed, 'Unlikely!'

With the order loaded, Charlie said, 'Let's get the other stuff quickly, then we can start our day off. Those clouds are looking a bit dark, so it'd be nice to get it done before we eat. I fancy a bite at the Terminus Hotel, if that suits you. At least I can have a beer there. Oh look, there's Lili, and she's with someone.'

Edie twisted round to see her friend linking arms with a young man and laughing as they strolled up High Street. She was with Norman Stubbs.

'Well, that's a surprise,' she said. 'No wonder she declined the free lunch to help with the orders.' They came close enough for her to call, 'Hello, Lili, Norman.'

Lili's head shot up in surprise and she looked sheepish. 'Oh, hello.'

Edie strolled over to the couple. 'Charlie Cobbett, this is Norman Stubbs, who was kind enough to give me directions at the station on my first day here. I didn't know you two were walking out.'

'Been walking out since September,' he said proudly, 'since I bumped into Lili by the Oyster Pond, not far from where we first met that day she was with you.'

Lili held his arm closer. 'That's right.'

'You kept that quiet,' said Edie, a little hurt that her friend hadn't confided in her.

'Well, it's not like you tell me about your courtship.' She glanced at Charlie.

'That's because there's nothing to tell.' How many more times was she going to have to say this today?

'We're just off for dinner at the dining rooms in Surrey Street,' said Lili. 'Then we're going to look at Christmas presents.'

That was something Edie wouldn't have to worry about for her family this year. It was always a nightmare picking the right things, especially for her mother.

'Well, have a nice time, and we'll see you later.'

After they'd walked away, Charlie said, 'Let's get going.' After a few steps, he added, 'Did you really not know?'

'No, I didn't. We saw him a couple of times, walking out by the river, but I didn't know they'd met up on their own. Fancy that.'

'You sound a bit sad about it.'

'I know it sounds selfish, but I'm afraid if Lili marries, she'll leave the hotel and I'll lose her as a friend.'

'You don't live in the same place as Miss Nye anymore, but you still see her. And I'll still be your friend.'

'Yes, of course. I'm just being silly.'

Yet she had a creeping sense of doom. The war was only four months old, and had so far only personally affected them because of decreasing staff numbers. Yet she couldn't help feeling that it was going to change everything.

–

Edie was tired this morning as she sat at breakfast and wished another half-day off was due, but she'd only had one three days ago. She'd so enjoyed her time off with Charlie. He'd gone a bit quiet at the beginning of the meal but had soon perked up. Today, not only did she have a shift on the desk this morning, she was also serving lunch in the busy restaurant.

Fanny and Gertie were twittering away at one end of the table, Mrs Leggett was looking solemn at the other. A couple more of the staff trooped in, Lili bearing two plates of bacon, fried eggs and mushrooms, one of which was put down in front of Edie as her friend sat down. She was digging her fork into a mushroom when Charlie came rushing in.

'Look at this!' He held up the newspaper. 'There's been an attack on Scarborough, Hartlepool and Whitby by the German navy. Says here there have been at least nine killed and a load injured.'

Gertie let out a shriek. 'But Scarborough's by the coast, and so are we, so what if the Germans work their way round and attack us? We could all be killed!'

Fanny and Hetty caught her mood and started to whine. This in turn made Gertie wail louder. When all three became hysterical, Charlie blocked his ears. Finally, Mrs Leggett stood.

'Enough of that caterwauling! Stop it, this instant, or you will have to leave the room and miss your breakfasts!'

It didn't have the desired effect but instead made the maids worse. With other staff moaning and Mrs Leggett repeating her threat several times, ever louder, complete chaos ruled.

Edie stood up, then stepped up onto the bench seat, wobbling a little. Thankfully it was balanced by the other people sitting on it. Charlie's eyes widened with surprise.

Clapping her hands, she called, 'Silence,' in a loud yet controlled voice, just the way Nanny Street used to when she and Freddie were younger.

The whole room became quiet, including Mrs Leggett, who looked horrified. Edie decided it was more likely down to surprise than any authority she might have, though some in the hotel, particularly the newer maids, paid attention to her.

Edie stepped back down to the floor. 'Now, let's think about this logically, shall we?' She searched her mind for all the British geographical knowledge she'd gleaned from her governess, Miss Langley.

'What *do* you think you're doing?' said the housekeeper.

'I want to reassure people who are worried,' she replied. 'Germany is on the North Sea, the same as those English towns they've attacked, so those places are more accessible and therefore more vulnerable. It would be harder for the German warships to come down past the narrow bit of the sea in the English Channel between Dover and Calais, where they're more likely to be faced by our navy.' She hadn't a clue how true this was, but it seemed a reasonable deduction.

'Those poor people,' sobbed Hetty, causing all three of the maids to whimper. But at least they'd simmered down. 'Has anyone told Mrs Turnbull about it? She has family up that way.'

'She's gone to the post office,' said Mrs Leggett. 'I will inform her when she returns.'

Lili stood up and led the maids out. 'Come on now, you three, let's wash your faces and get you looking decent before you start your breakfasts.'

The words *at least nine people killed* came back to Edie. Her chin wobbled and a tear ran down her cheek.

'Don't you start as well,' said the housekeeper. 'So much for you trying to reason with the maids.'

Edie took a handkerchief from her skirt pocket. 'It's not fear, but sorrow for all the people who've died. What have they done to anybody?'

Charlie put the paper down on the chest of drawers and sat next to her, placing an arm casually round her shoulders. 'I feel the same. They're not even fighting in the war.'

Edie liked the feel of Charlie's arm around her. It reminded her of how Nanny used to comfort her as a child.

'You'd better eat up,' said Mrs Leggett, sounding more sympathetic than Edie would have expected. 'You're starting your shift soon, and you don't want to be doing that on an empty stomach.'

Charlie leant back to remove his arm, pulling a confused face at Edie, who shrugged. 'She ill, or something?' he whispered. Louder, he announced, 'Better go and get my breakfast, or else I'll be doing a shift on an empty stomach too.'

Edie watched him go, hoping he never enlisted, for she'd miss him. It was no different to what she'd said about missing Lili if she left, she told herself, yet deep down she knew it would be very different.

-

'My goodness, it's so busy today,' said Edie at lunchtime, as she passed Lili in the corridor carrying three empty plates.

'It always is coming up to Christmas, but I think we're even busier because people want something to cheer themselves up, like, with all the gloom in the newspapers. That's what it sounded like from what I overheard.'

'Stop yapping in the corridor,' called Mrs Norris from the kitchen. 'You've both got meals to serve.'

'I'll just take these dirties to the scullery and I'll be back,' Lili called.

Edie quickly collected her order, two hors d'oeuvres of oysters wrapped in bacon, for a very distinguished couple called Mr and Mrs Perryman, who she realised must be the parents of Sophia Perryman, the leader of the Arun Children's Aid Project. Helen had been right when she'd said to her husband that the connection might be beneficial to them.

Like Sophia, the Perrymans were being very polite and pleasant to her, not haughty and rude like some of their customers, and she wanted to keep them happy.

'Two angels on horseback,' she announced as she put down their plates.

'Thank you,' said Mrs Perryman. 'They look delicious.' She did a double take when considering Edie, and looked as though she was about to make an enquiry.

A thought struck Edie. Did this woman know her from somewhere, from an event she'd attended with her mother, maybe? Or from the suffragist meetings in Brighton? She broke out in a cold sweat. Lucia had warned her she'd be caught out at some point. This could mean her time at the hotel was over.

If the woman was about to say something, it was cut short by her husband. 'They do look good. Would you be able to bring me another glass of the wine, please?'

'Of course, sir.'

She took her leave, removing a couple of empty plates from another table on her way. The rest of lunchtime was hectic.

Whichever table she passed, Edie heard earnest talk of the tragedy on the East Coast. It was like there was no escape from this sad state of affairs.

When she served the Perrymans with their main course – sauté of chicken lyonnaise for her and filet mignon for him, the wife once again studied her face. Edie's body went hot, then cold, considering what this might mean.

She tried hard to concentrate on the clientele, the sumptuous food and being as quick but as graceful as she could be. There was no point becoming anxious about something that may not be as it seemed. And if it were? She heard Nanny Street's voice telling her, *Whatever will be, will be*, as she often did.

Towards the end of the lunch period there were only three tables left, one for each of the waitresses. Edie served her remaining customers with coffee.

Mrs Perryman gave her a curious look once more. 'May I say what a good job you and the other young ladies serving have been doing. I know people were sceptical about women serving in a high-class restaurant, but here, certainly, it's been a great success.'

Ah, that was what the odd looks had been about! A huge wave of relief travelled from her head to her toes.

'Thank you, madam. I suppose many establishments will have to follow suit if the war goes on.' She immediately regretted her boldness, remembering too late the rule about not offering opinions or saying too much to guests.

'Indeed, they will.'

Edie was about to leave when Mrs Perryman added, 'Excuse me a moment, I just want to point something out to my husband.'

He looked up. 'What's that, dear?'

'It's been nagging at me for the whole meal, that this young woman reminds me of someone. I've just realised, it's Agnes Haydon. Do you remember her, James?'

'Well, of course I do. She sold the shipping yard here to us when she was widowed.'

Mrs Bygrove had mentioned Haydon's Yard.

'Yes, a tragedy that was, to be widowed so young.'

Mr Perryman surveyed her face. 'Well, it's been thirty-odd years since we saw her, but yes, there's a likeness there. I don't suppose there's any chance you're related?'

'I'm sure that would be highly unlikely, sir,' she said, as if her humble state would not allow it. Funny though, because her mother was called Agnes. It was a common enough name. 'I don't know of any Agnes Haydon.'

'Of course not,' said Mrs Perryman. 'There is a remarkable resemblance, though.'

At this juncture, the major came blustering into the restaurant. He waved a hello. 'Sorry, I know I'm late, but Mrs Bygrove says it's all right to be served.'

'Of course, Major. There's a nice table here by the window, just right for enjoying the winter sun.' Edie followed him as he made for the table and sat down.

He placed his newspaper on the cloth, next to him. 'Winter sun it might be, but there's a very chilly wind out there. Somewhat appropriate, with the latest news from Scarborough.' He jabbed a finger at the front page.

Without a lunch companion, no doubt he'd be offering his opinion to her over the two courses he normally enjoyed. So be it.

–

The following afternoon, Edie was serving tea in the conservatory. Even on cloudy days, it was one of the lighter rooms in the hotel, particularly welcome in the midwinter months. Today, however, despite it only being three o'clock, the low clouds made it seem almost dark already, causing the manager's wife to light the gas lamps in the room early.

Edie brought out a stand of dainties for Lady Blackmore and her companion, which included madeleines, coconut tartlets and hazelnut meringue Genoese cakes. As she reached them, the sight of a new guest at one of the tables almost made her drop the stand. She stopped abruptly to compose herself, nearly spilling the contents. Luckily, nobody noticed.

It was Miss Langley, who'd been her governess from the time she was eight until she was sixteen. She lived in Norfolk now, so why on earth would she be here?

Having deposited the stand on the ladies' table, she casually strolled over to the new guest, who was looking over the hotel's garden. She could hardly ignore her, but dreaded what was coming. The woman turned.

'Miss Langley? What on earth are you doing here?'

'Oh, Edie, I'm so glad you're working here this afternoon. I couldn't be sure you would be.'

'You've come to see me? Please, talk as if you're querying something on the menu, otherwise Lady Blackmore will tell me off for chatting.' She indicated the woman in question with a slight motion of her thumb.

'Oh dear, there is always someone who can't mind their own business.' Picking up the menu, she spoke louder now. 'So, which of these would you recommend?'

Edie spoke in an undertone, pointing to the menu to say, 'What exactly are you here for?' It seemed ironic that she was talking about other people minding their own business, but she wasn't displeased to see her all the same.

'Freddie tracked down my address and sent me a letter. I'm now in Clymping, with my husband.'

'You married?'

'Don't sound so surprised! I'm only thirty-eight. Look, it's rather a lot to explain here, with Lady What's-her-name leaning around to see what we're doing. Would it be possible to meet later, to talk properly?'

'I can meet you at five o'clock. I'll be in between shifts then.'

'Yes, that would be good.'

'Outside, there's a public house on one side. I'll meet you on the pavement there.'

‘Thank you, Edie.’ Louder now, she said, ‘In that case, I’ll have a pot of the Earl Grey, a smoked salmon sandwich and a scone with strawberry jam and clotted cream.’

‘Very well, madam.’

Edie performed a small curtsy which caused Miss Langley to smile, before she went away to fulfil the order.

–

Edie did up the four buttons of a grey, single-breasted coat she’d bought from a jumble sale, as she made for the staff door a minute after five.

‘Where are you off to on such a blowy night?’ It was Charlie, trooping down the corridor from the foyer door. He rubbed his hands together. ‘It’s bloomin’ cold.’

‘I need a short walk after being inside all day. I’ll be back shortly.’ For once she hoped he wouldn’t suggest joining her.

‘You’re joking. A hot cuppa tea’s the best thing for an evening like this.’

‘I’ll come in and have one after I’m done.’

‘I’ll save you a seat.’

Out in the dark, it was indeed blustery. She had to grab hold of her hat as a gust of wind attempted to relieve her of it. What on earth had urged Freddie to write to her former governess?

Miss Langley was standing at the corner of the wall by the pavement.

Spotting Edie, she came forward to meet her. ‘Good, it’s you,’ she called against the wind. ‘Let’s walk on the opposite pavement.’ She led the way back and they crossed to where there were lamps illuminating the area.

‘What are you doing out in this weather, Edie?’ said a voice that she soon realised was Gertie’s. Of all the luck, they had to bump into her. She gave Miss Langley the once-over.

‘Taking a breath of fresh air. What are you doing here?’ It was as valid a question.

Gertie held up a basket with several bottles. 'I was sent to the dairy for some milk as we're a bit short. Don't know why they couldn't have sent one of the kitchen staff.'

'There's tea on the go in the dining room, and some fresh biscuits. See you inside.' Hopefully that would speed Gertie away and she wouldn't pry anymore into her own actions.

Without a word, the other maid hurried across the road. Edie waited for her to disappear down the side of the hotel before she suggested they walk in the direction of the river.

'How come you live in Clymping?' Edie asked. 'I thought you'd moved to Norfolk, to live with your widowed sister.'

'I did. But she died a year later.'

'I'm sorry to hear that.'

'She had no children, so left me the house. I sold it and moved to Littlehampton, remembering our lovely holidays here with Nanny Street. That was before I met Gerald. He's a general practitioner in Clymping, so I moved again.'

'Dear Nanny Street. It's so sad she died two months after retiring, and never got to enjoy it. I wish you'd written, like you said you would.'

'I did write you a few letters, but when no replies came, I assumed you didn't want to communicate.'

Edie walked backwards to look at Miss Langley. 'How could you think that?' Then she had an epiphany. 'My mother! She must have got to the letters first, saw they were from you and decided not to pass them on.'

She'd always disapproved of servants keeping in touch, even with the other servants in the household.

Miss Langley looked down. 'I'm sad to hear that.'

After a pause, they walked on once more.

'You said you'd married, so presumably you're not Miss Langley now.'

'No, I'm Mrs Harrison.'

'Clymping is only up the road. How come I haven't seen you around the town?'

'We have a maid who does much of the shopping, so I only pop in now and again. And please, call me Victoria. You're not a child anymore.'

That would take some getting used to, but she'd try.

'So, what have you been doing since I left your service?' Victoria asked. 'Freddie only told me about you running away.'

Edie gave her a quick rundown of the missing years, including the trouble over her attending suffragist meetings and the consequent sending of her to Lady Evelyn's to be a governess to her son.

'I hear you're using the nickname Nanny and I gave you. Lady Moreland always hated us calling you Edie, instead of Edith.'

'Yes. And was even more annoyed when Freddie started using it too. You said he wrote to you? Did he know you were in Clymping?'

'No, he didn't. His letter was forwarded to me from my old address in Norfolk. He thought I might be able to write to you, and was thrilled when I wrote back to tell him I wasn't far away.'

Freddie must have been pretty desperate to get in touch with Miss Langley. All the same, she was annoyed with him for interfering, even though she was pleased to be able to see her again.

'What exactly does he think you'll be able to do?' Edie asked.

'He and Lucia are upset that you've declined their invitation to go to their home for Christmas and make amends with your parents. For some reason, Freddie feels I may be able to persuade you.'

'No, nothing you could say would encourage me to do that. I've come so far, moving here, and I feel part of a kind of family. And, apart from anything else, Christmases at home had become a reason to invite eligible bachelors with whom to pair me off. That's what happened in the last four years.'

Edie felt the indignity of the various occurrences all over again, and knew the ire had come out in her voice.

'Sorry, Victoria. It's just… It became too much.'

'So, there's no way to persuade you?'

'None whatsoever.'

'I didn't think there would be, since you'd taken such an unprecedented step, but hearing you were close by, I liked the idea of seeing you again.'

'I'm so glad you did. How dare my mother confiscate your letters. I was surprised when you didn't write. And sad. But then I thought, you had a new life.'

'At least we've found each other again, albeit eight years after we last saw each other.'

'Oh, do let's keep in touch.'

'I'd like that. And if you need anything…' Victoria stopped to open her handbag, then took out a notebook and pencil. She wrote on one of the pages and tore it out. 'Here's my address. And we have a telephone.' She pointed to the number. 'What with Gerald being a doctor.'

Edie took the paper and placed it in her coat pocket. 'Thank you.'

'Now I know you're here, I will call in from time to time for tea, if you don't mind. And maybe we could meet on the odd occasion?'

'I'd like that. I've really missed you and Nanny. You were more like a big sister and a mother to me.'

'And I've missed you and Freddie. He's done well though, marrying Lady Lucia Forsyth.'

'Yes, I suppose, if that's what he really wanted.'

'What do you mean?'

'I'm not sure myself. Ignore me. They do seem happy.'

They reached the corner of Fitzalan Road, opposite the path to the bandstand, as Victoria concluded, 'That's the main thing.' She stopped. 'I'll bid you good evening now, and let you get back to the warm hotel.'

'Will you be all right, on your own in the dark?'

'I'm going to my sister-in-law's just down this road. She has a telephone, so I'll ring Gerald and he can pick me up in the motor car. I'll be fine, thank you.'

Edie waited on the pavement until Miss Langley, as she still thought of her, disappeared into the night with a wave.

Freddie's meddling might have had a good outcome on this occasion, but if he kept writing to different people about her, in the hope they'd be able to persuade her to go home, it would only make it more likely that her parents would find out where she was. With any luck, Miss Langley was his last-ditch attempt.

–

The following day, Charlie entered the staff dining room just after five fifteen, a couple of minutes late for the meeting that the manager's wife had called. The room was already crowded, so he stood next to the door. Mrs Bygrove was standing in front of the dying embers in the fireplace. One of them had better fetch some coal to build it up soon, otherwise it would be a cold supper time this evening.

He spotted Edie, sitting to one side of the fireplace, and winked at her as she looked up. She gave a coy smile in return, causing him a tingle of pleasure. Silly fool. He thought about what Gertie had told him that morning, about seeing Edie talking to a 'posh lady', as she'd put it. Probably something and nothing. And was it his business anyway?

'I think most of you are here now,' Mrs Bygrove announced. 'It looks like it's going to be a quiet Christmas here this year, with only four rooms booked, including the major.'

'A nice little Christmas present for us,' Charlie quipped.

'Not if the hotel loses money and you're sacked, Mr Cobbett.' Mrs Leggett looked over at him with narrowed eyes.

'Will we get the sack if there's not enough business?' Fanny whined, her face creased as if she were about to cry.

'No, no, there's no need to worry,' Mrs Bygrove said quickly. 'I was going on to say that we are almost fully booked for

Christmas lunches and dinners over the week, and we have five more rooms booked for the New Year.'

The housekeeper was not inclined to let this go. 'It's still a big loss, not having as many rooms booked for the actual Christmas period.'

Mrs Bygrove sighed. 'I fear the recent coastal bombings by the Germans has put people off booking time away at the seaside. We may have to rely on more local sources of custom.'

'But Edie said the Germans wouldn't come to our part of the coast,' Fanny wailed.

Mrs Bygrove looked stumped for a while. 'It's certainly less likely than the East Coast.'

The door was shoved open, causing Charlie to scoot along the wall swiftly. He raised his eyes when he saw it was the manager. What doom and gloom was he going to add to the proceedings? He stood ramrod straight, a pompous sneer on his face.

'Ah, good, you're already gathered. No doubt my wife has been informing you of the fewer room bookings and warning you of redundancies.'

'Um, no, Douglas, I don't think redun—'

'*I* am here to tell you that *I* have just secured several prestigious bookings for the Christmas period and beyond.' He pushed his lips out and surveyed the room with a manner that suggested he'd pulled off a considerable achievement.

'That is good news,' his wife said with a smile.

'Was it through one of your many contacts, Mr Bygrove?' Mrs Leggett added.

The manager waved his hand in the air as if swatting a fly. 'Oh, I dare say it was. The Earl and Countess of Middlesbrough, Lord and Lady Armstrong, shall be arriving from the north-east of England on the twenty-first of December, so in two days' time. With them will be his cousins, Viscount and Viscountess Stockton, Lord and Lady Elliot. Both couples will be travelling with family and their retinue. They will occupy *twelve* rooms in all.' He paused to display the smug smile once more. 'They are concerned about their safety, with the recent bombardment of that part of the coast, so will be staying for at least two months. I expect you all to give your very best service and attentions to them.'

Mrs Bygrove stepped forward. 'Of course they will, dear. We're lucky to have a very dedicated and capable workforce here.'

'They had better be, for if there are any complaints, the members of staff concerned will be looking for a new post.' He wagged a forefinger, moving it in a semicircle to include everyone in the room.

Charlie resisted the wry laugh he was tempted to give. Good luck with that, when they were already short-staffed.

'Right, chop-chop, back to work.' Bygrove clapped his hands together twice.

'But I haven't yet finished the meeting I was having with them,' said his wife.

'They've heard all they need to hear. Now off you go.' He flicked his hands towards them several times to hurry them along.

As those sitting down rose, he left the room promptly.

Mrs Leggett clapped her hands in the same manner. 'Come on now, you heard Mr Bygrove. Off you go.'

'But it's early supper for some of us,' Fanny moaned.

'Then get on with fetching it in,' said the housekeeper.

When Mrs Bygrove looked from one to another as if not knowing what to do, Charlie said, extra loudly, 'Was there anything else you wanted to tell us, Mrs B?'

'Um, I'd like a word with Mrs Norris and the kitchen staff. We'll do that in the kitchen.'

'Right you are,' said the cook.

'You hear that, you lot?' Charlie called to a couple of the kitchen maids chatting with young Jack, who'd recently been promoted to second chef. 'Mrs Bygrove wants to talk to you in the kitchen, now.'

The requested staff soon disappeared, along with the manager's wife.

'And who put you in charge, Mr Cobbett?' the housekeeper grumbled as the rest of the staff either walked off or got the table ready for supper.

'Mrs Bygrove said she hadn't finished, so I was helpin' 'er out, since others had been so rude interrupting her.'

'Huh! First you want time off in the Christmas period, now you're trying to take over.'

'I can't deny it'd be nice sometimes, to get bank holidays off.'

'If you want that, Mr Cobbett, you'd better find yourself a different line of business to work in.'

As she flounced off, he murmured, 'Maybe one day I'll do just that.'

'In a motor car garage?'

He jumped at the voice at his ear and the hand on his shoulder. It was Edie.

'Are you on early supper?' he said.

'Yes, thank goodness. It's been hectic in the restaurant today, and I'm back on at six thirty.'

'Good – to your break, not the hectic day!'

'I knew what you meant. I'm looking forward to our half-day off on Tuesday.'

'Me too. As long as his nibs don't cancel it so we can be in constant attendance on the earl and viscount's lot.' He rolled his hand and gave a bow.

Edie emitted an awkward giggle. 'I'm sure they won't be that bad. And you never know, they may be good tippers.' She nudged Charlie with her elbow.

He beamed. 'Yes, there is that. Come on, let's get some supper. I'm starving.'

–

Edie pushed open the door into the staff corridor and yawned. It was only just after eleven in the morning, and she was already fed up. The Earl of Middlesbrough and Viscount Stockton, along with their families and retinue, had arrived the day before and had demanded attention ever since. Even the nanny and nursemaid, who were served separately in the small dining room along with the four children, clearly thought themselves above the hotel serving staff with their requirements.

'How's it going, Edie?'

She looked up to see the welcome sight of Charlie's face beaming at her as he strolled down the corridor.

'They are shocking guests, our new arrivals, that is. They make Lady Blackmore look amiable and polite. Thank goodness some of our nice regular customers are here for coffee this morning, for I couldn't stand a whole two hours of the demands and total lack of "pleases" and "thank yous" from that lot.' She leant against the wall, exhausted by her outburst.

'Been much the same for me and Stanley, with their constant demands that we book this and get hold of that for them. No sign of any tips yet for our pains, neither.'

The small handbell was heard to ring twice in the kitchen. Edie stood upright once more. 'That will be the cakes for the three artists. I'm so glad they've come to stay for Christmas. They'll bring some civility to proceedings.'

'And they're good tippers, too.' Charlie winked. 'Still, I'm looking forward to our afternoon out.'

'Me too.' The jolt in her tummy confirmed this, though she was sure the fact that it had more to do with Charlie's company than the time off brought a blush to her cheeks. She hurried off, calling, 'I'll see you later.'

Edie turned to see him lift his porter's hat in farewell as she entered the kitchen, almost bumping into the live-out cook, Hannah.

'Watch it!' she said, stepping sidewards.

'Oh, I'm so sorry, Hannah.'

'The cake stand of pastries is ready for you.'

'Thank you, they look delicious.'

'Made the petits fours meself. Hope they're appreciated. I've heard the new families are moany devils.'

'Don't worry, these are for the artists, so they will be very much appreciated.'

'When you've delivered those,' Mrs Norris called, 'come straight back for the new stand of pastries for their nibses. Huh! How dare they complain about them being too plain.'

Edie carried the artists' stand towards the door, hearing Mrs Norris continue with, 'If these shortages carry on, they'll be lucky if I have enough sugar for any such fancies.'

In the conservatory, Edie was passing the tables in the middle of the room that accommodated the newer arrivals, when the earl's voice barked at her. 'You, girl! Is that cake stand not for us?'

'I'm afraid not, Lord Armstrong. These are for another table.'

'Then go and find out *what* has happened to *ours*.'

'Of course, sir, as soon as I've delivered these.'

'Mind that you do!' he called after her.

She reached the artists' table and placed the cake stand down. 'Here you are, ladies.'

'Thank you very much,' said the darkest of the three, Ebony, her black hair in a loose plait down her back, a scarf of turquoise and orange wound around the top of her head. She leant towards Edie to say in an undertone, 'We appreciate your service and your food, even if certain other people in this room do not.'

'They really are the giddy limit,' said Marigold, the auburn-haired one of the group.

Edie simply smiled in reply, giving a small curtsy before walking swiftly away to fetch the next cake stand.

Back in the staff corridor once more, she was approaching the door to the staff stairs when Gertie emerged from them, struggling with a cleaning box and bucket. She was grumbling to herself.

Seeing Edie, she said, 'I've never known such messy guests!'

'That doesn't surprise me.'

'Mrs Leggett would have our guts for garters if we left our rooms like they do.'

'And now I've got them complaining to me about their pastries, so I'd better fetch them.'

'Poor you, having to serve that ungrateful lot.'

Sympathy from Gertie? There was a first for everything.

–

'Are you sure you won't have some food before you go out, lass?' Standing by the staff dining room table, Mrs Turnbull linked her hands together, her head tipped slightly to one side. She considered Edie with the gaze of a mother hen.

'I won't, thank you, Mrs Turnbull. Charlie and I are going to have some lunch at the White Hart, in Surrey Street. I might have half a cup of tea though, since he's not here yet, as I am a little dry.'

Before Edie could help herself, the storekeeper was bending over the table to do the job. They were the only ones in the room so far, it being ten minutes before the early staff lunch began.

'So, you and Charlie are walkin' out, are you?'

'Oh, no. We're just good friends.' Even as she said it, she felt the regret of the situation.

She pushed the cup towards Edie. 'Here you are, hinny. Sit yoursel' down.'

Mrs Leggett marched in carrying a bundle of letters as Edie took a seat.

'One for you, Miss Moore, bearing a Lewes postmark again, I see.' She placed it on the table.

If the housekeeper thought Edie would divulge the sender's identity, she was going to be disappointed, yet again.

'Thank you, Mrs Leggett.' She placed the letter she knew to be from Lucia into her handbag.

'And one for you, Bridget, from Newcastle. Not bad news, I hope, given the recent bombardment up that way.'

Mrs Turnbull's smile disappeared, replaced by a deep frown on her forehead. 'I hope not, too.'

The housekeeper left promptly. Mrs Turnbull sat down, staring at the letter as if it were a bomb about to explode. 'It's from my sister in Hartlepool, I can tell that much. First letter I've had from there since the attack.'

The papers were now reporting that over a hundred people had been killed and over three hundred injured, but it still made it unlikely any of Mrs Turnbull's family had been affected.

'She's probably reassuring you she's all right.'

Mrs Turnbull opened the letter slowly as Edie sipped at her tea. Her eyes darted back and forth quickly as she read. When her hand went to her mouth and a small, choked sound left her lips, Edie knew it was not all right.

'Mrs Turnbull?'

'Oh no, oh no.' Tears spilled from her eyes and her head went down on the table.

'What, what's happened?'

'I thought before that no news was good news. My, my—' Without lifting her head, she slid the letter across to Edie and started sobbing.

Edie scanned the letter far enough to gather that her sister's husband and son had been killed on their way to the shipyard in Hartlepool.

'I'm so, *so* sorry, Mrs Turnbull.' She rose. 'I'm going to fetch Mrs Bygrove.'

As she ran out, Charlie appeared. 'You ready? Whassup?'

'I've got to fetch Mrs Bygrove from the dining room. Mrs Turnbull's had bad news.'

'I'll get her.' He rushed off immediately.

Edie went back to the staff dining room, hunkering down next to the storekeeper. 'Can I get you anything, Mrs Turnbull?'

She lifted her head a little and sniffed. 'No, lass, thank you. It's just such a shock. My brother-in-law, but even more so, my nephew. Only nineteen, he were. It's no age.'

'No, it isn't. I'm so sorry.' She meant the words sincerely, but what good did they do? They wouldn't bring the pair of them back, nor any of the people who'd been killed.

The door was pushed open and Helen ran in, followed by Mrs Leggett, and then Charlie.

Helen went to the storekeeper's other side. 'Oh Bridget, what's happened?'

Edie rose and stepped back, convinced the manager's wife would handle the situation far better than her. As Mrs Turnbull explained, and showed her the letter, Mrs Leggett took the seat on the other side and grasped her hand.

This surprised Edie, but she didn't have time to consider it before Helen looked up to say, 'You and Charlie get off now. We'll look after her.'

'Are you sure?' said Charlie.

'Yes, absolutely. This doesn't need all of us, and it's the last chance you'll get before Christmas.'

'Yes, you go,' said Mrs Turnbull. 'It's not like anythin' can be done now.'

She and Charlie vacated the room, both with heads down, to fetch their coats from the small staff cloakroom. Charlie had found a long duster coat recently from the same charity jumble sale that Edie had got hers.

'What a day,' he said, as he pushed an arm in. 'Still, I'd rather put up with a whole year of moaning from entitled guests than have poor Mrs T upset like that.'

'Sadly, we won't get the choice.' Edie slipped her arm through his. 'You're a good sort, do you know that, Charlie Cobbett?'

He looked down at her arm, though he was clearly not displeased. 'It's nice of you to say so. Come on, let's get some dinner, lunch, whatever you want to call it.'

She nodded and they left the building, still arm in arm.

Edie put her knife and fork down on her plate side by side, and sat back. The Christmas supper, their main meal today, had been delicious. She was used to turkey and sometimes goose at Christmas dinner, but the beef had been so tender that she'd enjoyed it all the same. The Christmas pudding had been the best she'd ever tasted, even better than their cook at Downland House had produced for the staff. Cook had always kept some for her, knowing how much she enjoyed it. The dessert of choice (or rather, her mother's choice) at Christmas had been a tall and elaborate charlotte russe.

'You've outdone yourself there, Mrs Norris,' Charlie called down the table, smart in his Sunday suit, with its waistcoat.

The cook looked pleased with the compliment. 'I dare say some credit should go to my staff.' She looked around at Jack, the only member of the kitchen staff left who was a live-in, and raised her glass of beer to him.

'The meal you did for the earl and his lot must have been good as well, as they barely complained at all,' quipped Phoebe.

'Just as well, as I'd have been tempted to take me rolling pin out to them if they had. I've had it up to here with their *opinions*.' Mrs Norris placed the inside edge of her hand to her forehead.

Mrs Leggett tutted. 'I don't think violence will solve anything.'

Charlie grunted. 'Tell that to Kaiser Wilhelm.'

'I would if I had the opportunity.'

Mrs Norris drained her glass of beer. 'It's a shame Bridget didn't feel up to joining us.'

'I took a plate of food up to her,' said Mrs Leggett. 'You can't blame her for not wanting to join in the festivities with her brother-in-law and nephew barely cold.'

'What a way to put it, Imogen. Now, since we all seem to have finished, all hands would be appreciated in clearing up.

Then Hetty and Phoebe can fetch the coffee and tea.' Mrs Norris clapped her hands to gee them up.

'Righty-ho.' Charlie stood to gather his and Edie's bowls together.

'Not you, Mr Cobbett.' The housekeeper raised her eyes. 'Mrs Norris was referring to the women around the table.'

'Not necessarily,' said the cook.

Charlie continued to gather up the nearby bowls. 'And it's not right, it ain't. They've worked as hard as us men. Harder in some cases.'

He headed off to the scullery with his haul. Edie rose to pick up some empty serving dishes from the centre of the table.

When all was clear, Phoebe and Hetty brought in pots of tea and coffee and placed them in the centre of the table. Charlie poked his head around the door and summoned Edie out into the corridor. In his hand he had a carefully wrapped parcel, with deer and fir trees on the paper and a ribbon carefully tied around it.

'Oh Charlie, you shouldn't have.'

'Of course I should. You've been a good friend to me since you arrived. Only six months ago, that was. It seems longer.'

She took the offered present. 'You've been a good friend to me too, Charlie. And I do have a little something for you. Hold on.' She passed the present back to him and went into the dining room to fetch her handbag, dangling it over her wrist. She returned to the corridor and pulled out a small square present.

She offered it to Charlie.

'And you told me I shouldn't have!'

'It's only something small, but hopefully useful.'

'You first,' he said.

Undoing the ribbon and pulling the paper off, Edie revealed a pair of gloves. 'Oh Charlie, they're the ones I admired in Hussey's! They're lovely, thank you.'

'I went and bought them when you were browsing in the bookshop.'

'You said you were going to look in the cycle shop!'

His nose crinkled. 'Yes, a little fib, just so I could get your present.'

She laughed. 'You now.'

He unwrapped the gift to find a set of four handkerchiefs, each with a 'C' embroidered in one corner. 'They're smart, thank you. Very posh.' He fingered the fabric. 'Lovely soft cotton, too. Can't have enough handkerchiefs, neither.'

'I also bought them while you were at the cycle shop, so I was glad of your little subterfuge.'

Before she had time to talk herself out of it, she lifted herself up onto her tiptoes to give him a peck on the cheek. 'Thank you again.'

The colour rose in his face, but he smiled all the same.

Edie placed the gloves into her handbag as Charlie split the handkerchiefs and placed two each in his Sunday jacket pockets.

Such a simple gift, gloves, but she liked that about them. Not like some of the gifts her parents had bestowed on her as she'd got older: more perfume than she could hope to wear in ten years, most with scents she wasn't fond of; endless decorative hats for all seasons and occasions; an elaborate new dressing table when there was nothing wrong with the old one. And so it went on. There was nothing entertaining, nothing enjoyable, like gramophone records or books. Nothing simple and useful, like gloves.

'Let's get that cuppa tea now.' Charlie opened the dining room door for her and followed her in.

'There you are,' said Fanny, sitting in a centre seat in front of the fire. 'Thought you two might have gone out for a cuddle.'

Gertie tapped her friend's arm with her hand. 'Fanny!'

'That's enough of that talk,' said Mrs Leggett.

'Well, we weren't,' said Charlie, following Edie to the seats they'd been sitting in at the far end of the table. 'We was exchanging gifts, that's all.'

Fanny crossed her arms and turned away. 'Hm!'

Edie poured two cups of tea, then pushed one towards Charlie, who helped himself to three spoonfuls of sugar. Several conversations were going on around the table.

'I wonder how Lili's getting on at Norman's house this evening,' said Edie. 'She was nervous about meeting his parents and sister.'

'He seems a decent sort. Wonder if they will tie the knot?'

'I know I mentioned it before, but isn't it a little soon for that?' Edie laughed.

'My parents had only been walking out two months when they decided to get wed, my mum told me.' He took several gulps of his tea and finished with a satisfied, 'Ahhh. That's better.'

'Two months? My goodness.'

'What about your parents?'

'I really have no idea.' She'd never thought about it before, how they'd met, how they'd got together, and she'd probably never have the opportunity to ask them now. Her mother was never that forthcoming about her life before she became Baroness Moreland.

She wondered what they'd be doing now. Her parents had never been much for games, leaving Freddie and her to play them in the garden room with Grandmama, who enjoyed such entertainment. The men – her father, a paternal great-uncle and two cousins – would retire to the drawing room for wine and conversation. The women – her mother and the great-aunt – were left to their tea in the garden room.

That was when they were young, before games were banned and she and Freddie were required to join the 'grown-ups'. From the time she was eighteen, one or two eligible bachelors would be invited for the evening, along with other influential people, and she'd be expected to scintillate and sparkle. She'd never taken to any of them, apart from one. And she'd very nearly got involved with him. Until she found out that he was romancing two other ladies at the same time. She'd promised herself then that she would never give her life to any man. But that was when she still only had the rich, pompous ones to choose from. Now… What?

All in all, Christmases at Downland House had become pretty lonely, even when there were plenty of people there. Here, in this lowly hotel kitchen, she felt much more at home.

She was grateful that Freddie had sent no more letters appealing to her to join the family for Christmas.

'You look miles away,' said Charlie.

'Just remembering Christmases past.'

'Nice memories?'

'Not bad, just a little boring. I'm looking forward to playing some games later.'

'Me, too. That's what I liked best about Christmas as a lad.'

'Same here.' Something else they had in common.

He picked up the pot to offer Edie another cup.

'I've hardly started this one yet.'

He refilled his own and she watched him smile to himself. The firelight danced in his now dark blue eyes. An image formed in her head, of him and her, sitting by a fire of their own, sometime off in the future.

Moving closer to him and lowering her voice, she said, 'Charlie, what you said the other day, about getting your own motor car repair business. Did you really mean that, or was it something you thought of after your comment to Mrs Leggett?'

'I told you before, I liked working in my dad's garage. And I was good at it.'

'That's not the same as running your own business.'

'No, but if I could choose to do anything, that's what it'd be. I'm saving up what I can, but… who knows?' He shrugged. 'It took my dad a long time to build up his business.'

'Maybe he'll forgive you in time and ask you to work for him again.'

'I doubt it. What about you? What would you like to do in the future?'

'Me? Oh, I've not really thought about it.'

'Go back to being a governess, maybe? Or you could become a teacher, like your friend Miss Nye.'

'Definitely not. No.'

Phoebe attracted Charlie's attention with a question at this point, leaving Edie to ponder her future. What were her plans long-term? She couldn't be an employee in the hotel forever, surely. She was getting fond of Charlie. But what kind of future could they have together, her the wife of a porter, or a motor car mechanic? Yet what did she want? Not to be the wife of an earl, a viscount or a lord, nor any of the self-interested, self-important men in her old life who her parents saw as a good match. Daniel was a little different to that breed, but he was simply the exception that proved the rule.

How could it work out with Charlie when she had such a huge secret? Maybe, just maybe, she could get away with never mentioning her past?

Even as she thought it, she knew that was wrong. She would have to confess eventually, and the sooner the better. Or maybe after she'd got to know Charlie more. Or was that wrong too, not letting him in on it? What did she want from him? More to the point, what did he want from her? She had no experience in actual romance.

She huffed out a silent sigh. The whole problem was going round and round in circles in her brain, making her anxious. It was Christmas, for goodness' sake. She just wanted to enjoy it. All this could be considered in the new year.

Mrs Norris stood, raising her cup aloft. 'It may only be a hot drink, but let's raise a toast to our boys overseas. I hope they've had as good a Christmas as they possibly can have.'

Everyone raised their cups, announcing 'Our boys overseas!' out of time with each other.

'And let's hope we'll have an 'appy new year that brings peace,' the cook added. This was echoed by the rest of the staff. 'And when these pots of coffee and tea are drained, we'll get in some more of those bottles of beer from the stillroom that Mrs Bygrove was good enough to treat us to, and raise a glass.'

'I'll drink to that,' Charlie announced, as they all raised their cups once more.

Chapter Fourteen

It was a particularly cold day today, and Edie was glad for the heat of the staff dining room fire to warm up next to as she held her teacup with both hands during the afternoon break.

It was past the beginning of February already. It seemed no time since they'd been celebrating Christmas. Still, she couldn't wait for the gloomy month to be over so they'd be slightly closer to the longer, sunnier days.

Gertie and Fanny sat at the end of the table nearest the door, whispering; no one else had come in for their break yet.

She was wondering how Lili was getting on during her half-day off with Norman, when she heard a shrill voice in the corridor asking where she was. Was that Lili? As if to answer her question, her friend came running in, her face wet with tears.

'Lili! Whatever—?'

'Oh, Edie! I-I—' she sobbed. Noticing the other two maids in the room, she said, 'Oh, you two are here.' She turned back to Edie. 'Can we go upstairs?'

Lili was several steps ahead by the time Edie reached the stairs. She didn't catch her up until she got to their bedroom.

'Whatever is the matter, Lili? Has something happened to Norman?'

'N-no. Oh Edie!' She ran to her friend and held onto her. 'N-Norman said he had something to speak to me about, and I thought he was going to propose.'

'Did he break things off with you?' Edie would be surprised if this were the case, given how taken Norman seemed with Lili when she saw them together.

'N-no.' She pulled back, her face a picture of misery. 'He's only gone and enlisted!'

'I'm so sorry, Lili. How worrying that must be.' She took her friend's arm and led her to one of the beds to sit down. 'But you know, they train for several months before they go abroad, so the war might even be finished by the time he gets to it.'

Lili clutched her hands together in her lap. 'I doubt it. After those airship raids on London a few days ago, I think the Kaiser means business. He's not going to give up any time soon.'

Edie had to concede that she was probably right. The war hadn't been over by Christmas, and more and more countries had got involved. It could go on a while. But she wasn't about to discourage Lili with this.

'We'll see. Meanwhile, he'll still be in the country for the next few months.' She placed an arm around her.

'But he won't be close by, where I can see him regularly.' Her head drooped forward and she sobbed some more.

Edie's heart went out to her. She felt grateful that Charlie was still around. Not that he was her sweetheart, but still... She knew she'd be upset if he enlisted. It was unlikely, him being against the war as he was. But with the whispers of the government conscripting men if they couldn't get enough to volunteer...

Now she was feeling downhearted too.

'Shall I bring you up a cup of tea?' Edie offered.

Lili pulled a handkerchief from her apron pocket to wipe her tears and blow her nose. 'No, it's all right. I'll come down and explain what's happened. Right fool of myself I've made.'

'Which is quite understandable. Come on then, before all the tea's gone.'

-

'The fifteenth of February already. The year has gone so quickly so far,' said Edie, as she and Charlie strolled in the direction of the train station in Littlehampton, appreciating a rare warm, sunny day.

'Not quickly enough for me. I can't wait for spring and longer days. Then we could get a train to some other place.' He pointed to the station as the brick building loomed into view. 'It'd be dark too early if we went now. And it might be sunny, but it's still chilly.'

'You're not going to moan the whole afternoon, are you?' she asked with a chuckle.

'Nah, that's it. I'm glad to be out, away from the Middlesbrough nobs. They've been even worse this week, if that's possible. They've whined about every little thing. I wish they'd go and stay somewhere else. Isn't two months in one hotel enough? Or better still, they could get home and give the hotel trade a break.'

'They do seem to have settled in rather. Mrs Bygrove told me she's afraid they'll put other guests off coming again, but that her husband believes they lift the tone of the place.'

'Huh! He doesn't know what they refer to him as, behind his back.'

'What's that then?'

He blew out a noisy breath. 'I'm not repeating it, for it's not for a lady's ears.'

'At least that couple from King's Lynn have been pleasant.'

'And they've been through the same, what with having bombs dropped on their area, but they don't whinge about it the whole time, like the earl and viscount's lot. I wouldn't be surprised if we don't get more guests from bombed coastal areas if this goes on.'

'Unless they start bombing us on the South Coast, of course.'

'How is Lili now, by the way? I haven't seen her much at mealtimes the last week. I gather Norman left for training a few days back.'

'That's right, though she did receive a letter from him yesterday. She's still crying at night, poor thing. I want to tell her she'll get used to him being away, but I know it won't help.'

'Nah, probably not. I still say he's a fool for enlisting.'

'I don't disagree, but it doesn't help to say it in front of Lili.'

'I know. Sorry, I should've kept me trap shut when she first told us. Don't think she's forgiven me yet. Anyway, what did he have to say for himself, do you know?'

'He's in the Pioneer Battalion of the 18th Eastern Division, apparently and he's enjoying the training in Colchester.'

'Colchester? I'm sure he is. Playing soldiers with a pretend gun must be a great game, like the sort we played as children, but— Oh, you know by now what I'm gonna say… I hope somebody misses me that much if I end up being enlisted.'

Edie wanted to tell him how much she'd miss him, but, still unsure if that was appropriate, went on, 'Of course people will miss you. You're very popular in the hotel.'

He laughed. 'Not with everyone.'

'And I'm sure Fanny would miss you.'

He looked at her and frowned. 'Is that supposed to cheer me up?'

They both chuckled as they reached the long, cream building of the Electric Palace, causing Charlie to stop and examine a poster there. 'I had thought about us seeing a film, but I don't fancy this meself.' He pointed to the title, *Tommy Atkins*. 'Get enough talk about the war in the papers and in the hotel, without being entertained with it.'

'No, it's nice to escape it sometimes.' Not that the soldiers abroad could do that, but she couldn't say that to Charlie, who might take it the wrong way. She walked away from the poster and he followed.

They chatted as they passed the houses and warehouses, stopping awhile to watch a steam engine chug into the station. As they reached River Road, Edie spotted the swing bridge with its dark green metal girders and small toll hut. Beyond it was Railway Wharf, where goods were exchanged from ships to the trains.

'You've really never been over the other side of the river and walked up to West Beach?' said Charlie.

'No. Lili told me it was pretty over there, but I haven't had the opportunity. And I didn't really want to do it on my own.'

Halfway over the bridge they stopped, looking downriver towards the harbour. A cargo steamer was travelling up towards the sea.

Edie lifted her hand to shade her eyes from the sun. 'It's quite a view, isn't it?'

'It is, despite all the warehouses. I remember when the Duke of Norfolk opened the bridge. It was only seven years back. I came with my mum. A right fuss, there was.'

She spotted a large building on the opposite bank, sporting a sign that read A. S. HAYDON. She pointed towards it. 'I presume that's something to do with the Perrymans, who dine at the hotel?'

'Yep, that's theirs.'

She recalled Mrs Perryman telling her how much she reminded her of an old friend, Agnes Haydon.

'Used to be owned by some fellow called Arnold Haydon. Come on then.' Charlie took her hand and linked it through his arm. They'd walked to places several times in this manner, but that's all it had come to so far.

Did Charlie really like her, in *that* way? Or did he just like having her on his arm for display? Yet he wasn't like that, her Charlie.

Her Charlie. She shook her head.

'What's up?' he asked, as a motor van passed them on the bridge.

'Nothing. I just can't believe it's so sunny today.'

'Enjoy it while it lasts. Mrs Norris reckons it's going to get wintry again, and she's rarely wrong.'

Reaching the end of the bridge, they turned left onto a road on which there were several warehouses and workshops. Eventually they reached a smaller path, where the river became visible on their left.

'Is that Pier Road over there?' She pointed across the water.

'That's right. And there's the ferryboat to cross the river. We can take it on the way back, if you like, to be quicker.'

'Maybe.'

A little further along, Charlie pointed to a large building, just off the path. 'That's the golf club Bygrove is always disappearing off to.'

'Lili pointed it out to me across the river once. Is he here today?'

'He went out, and it's not the season for tennis or cricket, so he could be. But who knows? Wouldn't surprise me if his trips out were sometimes to see another woman.'

Edie stopped abruptly. 'Charlie! Mrs Bygrove doesn't deserve that.'

'Nor does she deserve a miserable old blighter like Bygrove for an 'usband.'

'I can't argue with that.' They carried on walking. When she thought about it, she wouldn't have been at all surprised to find this was the case, but she didn't know what to think.

As they passed the golf course, there were several men there taking advantage of the sunny day, but they didn't spot the manager. Finally, they reached West Beach, with its wide, pale yellow expanse of sand and its long line of dunes. The tide was about halfway out, but, with the breeze blowing their way, she could hear the waves being tossed onto the sand.

'That is pretty,' Edie enthused.

'Told you it would be.' He looked down at her feet. 'Good, you've got sensible boots on. Let's walk a little further down the shore.'

They got halfway down the beach, between the dunes and the water. The sand here was damp and easier to walk on than the dry sand further up. There was no one else on the beach at all. Edie felt very small there, with the beach stretching away on one side, the river on the other and the English Channel lying ahead of them.

'You're quiet,' said Charlie.

'It's hard to believe that there's a war going on, the other side of the Channel.'

'Yep. Seems so peaceful here, on this beach, just the two of us.'

'It's so seldom we are completely alone like this, what with the hubbub of the hotel.'

'You're right. Seems an opportunity too good to miss.'

'In what way?'

Charlie removed her hand from his arm, turned to face her, then positioned his hand around the waist of her coat. Placing his other hand on her other side, he drew her closer. He didn't look at all sure about what he was doing, the frown showing his lack of confidence.

Oh my, he wasn't going to… was he?

He halted for a while, maybe expecting her to object. Her heart was thumping, but she was afraid he'd lose his nerve and move away. He was a nice-looking chap, so must have kissed a girl, probably several. He'd know what he was doing. She'd never been kissed before, never really wanted to be, until now. But what if she got it all wrong and put him off?

She wasn't sure what to do to encourage him when he finally bent his face towards hers, being careful to avoid her hat, and found her lips with his. The warmth and softness of them sent little tremors of delight through Edie. She lifted herself onto her tiptoes, placed her hands around his shoulders and moved in closer still. Charlie started to move his lips in a slight circular movement, making Edie quite flustered, though it wasn't at all unpleasant. Quite the opposite. He was clearly enjoying it, which helped her relax a little.

She gave a little moan of pleasure and Charlie broke off.

'Have I done something wrong?'

'No, not at all.'

'I thought you were complaining.'

She laughed. 'Oh Charlie, I wasn't complaining. It was appreciation.'

'Oh. Oh!' He grinned sheepishly. 'Good. That's good.' He bent to kiss her once more, and she sighed with delight.

-

Edie and Charlie were back at the hotel just after five forty, having sat on the pier for a while to admire the soft golden glow of the sunset over the river and far shore. They'd put their coats away in the cloakroom and were in the corridor, chatting about their day, when Fanny appeared from the staff dining room and glared at them.

'There you are, then. We could have done with you here this afternoon, dealing with the demands of the Middlesbrough lot. "Get this, get that. Order this, go out and buy that." They should have brought some more of their own servants with them if they wanted so much bleedin' attention. And you two've been out, gadding about in fancy tea rooms and shops, no doubt.' The complaint was aimed at Edie, at whom Fanny was scowling.

'No, we went for a walk over to West Beach, if you must know,' said Charlie. 'And we're entitled to our day off, as you will be on Wednesday, with Gertie.'

'Huh. Hardly the same, is it?'

'The same as what?' Charlie didn't wait for an answer. 'I'm gonna get a cuppa tea. You want one, Edie?'

'Yes please.'

As he walked away, Fanny barred Edie's way as she endeavoured to follow him.

'You're a mean one, you are, leading Charlie on like that.'

'I can assure you I'm doing no such thing.' How tiresome that she should be starting on her again. She clearly hadn't learned her lesson from last time.

'*I can assure you I'm doing no such thing*,' Fanny imitated, in her version of a 'posh' accent. 'You might think you're better than us, but you're not. And if you hurt Charlie, you'll have me to answer to, for he's a decent soul and not to be mucked around with by your wiles.'

'Well, now we've got that straight, if you'll excuse me, I'd like a cup of tea.'

When Fanny didn't budge, Edie went around her. Charlie would laugh when she told him how Fanny was trying to defend him against her 'wiles', as she'd put it. She'd been right about her attraction to Charlie. But maybe she wouldn't tell him about this, in case he got annoyed with Fanny and it started another argument. No, she'd keep what the chambermaid had said to herself. For now.

Chapter Fifteen

It was Easter Monday, and despite the overcast sky and coolish weather, the crowds were out and about the common and beach. Coffee morning at the hotel was particularly busy today. Edie laid down the silver tray for the three artists, listening as they talked of drawings they'd made of people on the promenade yesterday.

'I must say, the atmosphere in here today is so much more relaxing,' said the brown-haired one, Hazel. 'I should imagine you're relieved to be rid of the earl and his party for a while.'

'It's certainly quieter,' said Edie, not wanting to get into trouble for speaking out of turn. In truth, it was as if the whole hotel had breathed a sigh of relief, and the mood in the conservatory among the regulars was much lighter today.

'I don't suppose they've gone for good, by any chance,' said Ebony.

'No. They've hired an omnibus and taken their families to Brighton for the day.'

'I'm sure they must bring much money into this establishment, but I really hope they find a hotel in Brighton and decide to abscond there instead.'

This time Edie smiled, while raising her eyebrows. Ebony emitted a chuckle in reply, acknowledging Edie's silent agreement.

'Will there be anything else, ladies?'

'No, that's it for now, thank you,' said Hazel.

Edie went to clear the crockery from the next table, listening as the three women chatted about a trip out the next day by the river, to paint. The disappointment of not getting the Monday afternoon off with Charlie swamped her once more. But it was Easter Monday, so nobody got the day off. They had been promised an extra half-day off in the future by Helen, though, so she'd have to content herself with looking forward to that instead. It was hard to get close to Charlie here, in the hotel, with everyone else around all the time. At least the days were getting lighter in the evening, and the possibility of late walks by the beach came closer. She and Charlie would have to be satisfied with stolen kisses, hidden behind the perimeter wall in the dark, for now.

She carried the empty dishes to the scullery, where she met Mrs Bygrove.

'Ah, Edie. After luncheon, could you do a couple of hours on the desk? Mr Watkins would like to go out for a short time to visit his sick mother at the hospital.'

'Of course, Mrs Bygrove.'

Gertie, standing by the butler's sink, where she was wringing out some cloths, turned and treated her to her usual sour frown. When Mrs Bygrove left, she mumbled, 'That's not fair. Why can't I go on the desk? It's much easier than cleaning up people's mess.'

Edie knew that no reply she could give would satisfy Gertie, but she tried to be friendly. 'At least we don't have to put up with the earl's lot today.'

'Huh! Speak for yourself. You weren't cleaning their rooms this morning. Mucky lot. I swear they throw the bed linen around and make the bathroom as wet as possible just so we have to clear it up. And all the crumbs from the biscuits they order on room service. And their clothes strewn everywhere.'

Annie Twine, one of the scullery maids, had come into the room with pans from the kitchen. 'Oh do pipe down, Gertie. Always complaining, you are.' She went to the larger sink and placed the pans on one of the wooden draining boards. 'And hurry up rinsing them cloths. There'll be loads of dishes coming in from morning coffee soon, so we'll need both sinks. Here, Edie, put those down there.'

She did as directed, then turned to go back to the conservatory, to see if anyone needed her attention, but also to avoid any further gripes from Gertie.

–

An hour later, Edie was sitting down for the early staff lunch. She'd helped herself to a beef sandwich and some salad from the dishes on the table, as had the stillroom maids and scullery staff, and was about to start eating when Mrs Leggett stormed into the room, her face like a wet weekend, as Charlie would say.

Gertie and Fanny were lurking behind the housekeeper as she placed a long silk-covered box on the table. It was open to reveal a pearl necklace. Edie recognised it immediately as her own.

'Where on earth—?' she began.

'So you do recognise it.' Mrs Leggett crossed one wrist over the other.

'Yes, because it belongs to me. How did you—?'

'Now why on earth would the likes of you have a necklace like this, hmm? It clearly belongs to one of the guests, and *you* have stolen it.'

'I can assure you, Mrs—'

'Yes, she did. We saw her,' said Fanny, folding her arms tightly under her bust.

'Gertie and Fanny witnessed you sneaking it out of one of the rooms.'

'I don't even clean the rooms anymore. And which room? Have you asked the guests there if it's theirs?'

'I'd advise you to keep your tone civil, Miss Moore.'

'I would if I wasn't being accused of something I haven't done. That box was in my room, in my top drawer, so I can only imagine that someone has been snooping through my things, hoping to find something with which to accuse me.'

She looked around Mrs Leggett at the two chambermaids.

'They went to your room to find it as they knew you'd stolen it,' said the housekeeper.

The staff at the table said nothing, only looking from one to the other as they spoke.

'We didn't want to make an accusation and be left looking like fools when it wasn't found.' Fanny nodded her head once, satisfied with her answer. As an afterthought, she added, 'For you might have already sold it.'

'Yes, that Charlie probably knows some dodgy people he could sell it to,' Gertie added.

Fanny nudged her sharply with her elbow. 'Don't bring Charlie into it. He wouldn't do nothing dodgy.'

Ah. Was this Fanny's way of getting her into trouble to show Charlie what a bad person she was, so she could have him to herself? It fitted her theory that she had a fancy for Charlie.

'The fact is, Miss Moore,' the housekeeper continued, 'that whether you've been cleaning the rooms or not, you have access to the keys. Where else would you obtain an expensive piece of jewellery?'

'From Lady Evelyn Stansfield.'

'You mean, you stole it from Lady Stansfield.'

'No, she gave it to me.'

'Why would she?'

'As a present. She was generous like that.' She couldn't explain the real reason without having to reveal a whole lot more.

'Until you can prove it, this item will be locked away, and we will be contacting the guest who was in the room to find out if it belongs to them.' She shut the box with a snap and marched out of the room.

Gertie left too, but Fanny lingered to grin triumphantly at her before following on.

'She's a troublemaker, she is,' said Annie from the scullery. 'I'd believe you over her any day.'

Edie only hoped the guest in the room mentioned was honest and wouldn't say it was theirs, because no one could confirm or deny it. How on earth was she going to prove it was hers?

She considered what small white lie she could engage in to help the matter. Her stomach squirmed. That wasn't her way, and yet she was already deep into a deception about who she was. It wasn't really a lie; more a case of not revealing the whole picture. But if someone had done that to her, she'd consider it a lie.

Oh, what to do?

–

Later that day, when Mrs Bygrove had got wind of the trouble, round two of the dispute ensued.

They were back in the staff dining room, Edie sitting meekly at one end as Helen and Mrs Leggett stood to do battle at the other.

'It's clear to me that this necklace must belong to a guest, and that Miss Moore must be lying about Lady Stansfield giving it to her. Why on earth would she?' The housekeeper held her hands aloft in question. 'No, she's not to be trusted and should be dismissed.'

'I have found her completely trustworthy in the time she's been here,' Helen countered. 'If she says the necklace is hers, then I believe her. And you know, Mrs Leggett, even a thief arrested by the police would get a fair hearing.'

'We should contact whoever was in that room when Gertie and Fanny saw her leave it with the box.'

'When they *claim* to have seen her. I've checked the register – the room was empty, and had been for two days by that time.'

Edie sighed with relief. That should show the maids up for the liars they were.

'Then it was probably left behind by mistake by whoever had been in there last.'

'Then why didn't the chambermaid who cleaned the room when they left not find it beforehand?'

Mrs Leggett pinched her lips in, obviously unimpressed with Helen's defence.

'Now,' Helen continued, 'Edie is already late taking over from Mr Watkins, so we will continue this later. And *that* will be to deal with Fanny and Gertie, who seem determined to get Edie into trouble. Fanny clearly learned nothing from that incident with the broken picture.' She picked up the box that contained the necklace. 'In the meantime, I will look after this.'

'Very well, *madam*.' Mrs Leggett turned stiffly and marched off.

Edie rose and made for the door, whispering, 'Thank you, Helen,' as she went through and on to her desk duty.

The foyer was empty except for Richard Watkins, examining his watch. Seeing her, he jabbed at its face several times.

'Five minutes late, Miss Moore.'

'Apologies, Mr Watkins. I was delayed by Mrs Leggett.'

'Hm! Well, you're here now, so I must get going. My mother is waiting for me.'

'I hope you find her better today.'

She gave him a smile, causing his stiff countenance to soften into confusion.

'Oh. Oh, yes. Thank you.'

As he left the foyer, Charlie came into view, stepping off the last of the stairs that curved around the desk.

'Good, it's you on duty now,' he said.

'I'm a little late, due to Mrs Leggett and Mrs Bygrove discussing whether I'm guilty or not.'

His forehead puckered. 'Guilty of what?'

'I'm surprised you haven't already heard.'

'Been on a double shift, ain't I?'

She explained the situation as succinctly as she could. All the while, his expression became crosser and crosser.

'That's not on!' he declared, once she'd finished. 'I'll be having words with them two maids.'

'No, Charlie, don't get involved. Mrs Bygrove believes me, so nothing will come of it.'

'It better not. The nerve of those two.'

The outside door opened and a woman walked in. She was a welcome sight to Edie, even though it would be awkward to talk to her with Charlie there.

'Edie!' Victoria Harrison declared on spotting her.

'Miss Langley, sorry, Mrs Harrison, good afternoon. How lovely to see you. Are you here for our Easter afternoon tea?'

Victoria glanced at Charlie before saying, 'That's right. I imagine you're not serving today, since you're on the desk.'

'I'm afraid not, but Lili and Phoebe will be on hand to take your order.'

'Shall I show you through?' Charlie offered.

'No thank you, that's fine. I know the way.'

When she walked on into the conservatory, Charlie said, 'She seems nice. You've obviously served her a few times.'

What could she say to him? She didn't want to keep lying to Charlie, and now she thought about it, she could admit a little of the truth.

'Don't tell the other staff, especially Gertie and Fanny, but I know Mrs Harrison from before I was here. Miss Langley, she was then, which is why I keep calling her that by mistake. She was the governess at one time, at my old house.'

This was certainly true, as she'd been Edie's governess at Downland House.

'I thought *you* were the governess.'

Good point. 'She was the main governess, until she left.'

Oh no, another fib. Sort of. She'd been the *only* governess.

'Two governesses for one child! This Lady Evelyn Stansfield must be well off.' He tutted and lifted his eyes heavenward.

What could she say without creating more deceit? It hurt her to lie to Charlie, but she had never found the right time to tell him the truth. She thought it would become easier as they got to know each other better, but instead it had become harder.

She became aware of the staff door closing and was pleased for the distraction, even if it was Mr Bygrove. But the look of rage on his face soon made her think otherwise.

'Uh-uh, looks like he's on the warpath for some poor devil,' Charlie whispered. He stepped back to the side of the desk, hands linked behind his back.

It wasn't long before Helen was hurrying out after her husband. 'Douglas, wait!'

'Miss Moore!' he bawled. 'I have just heard that you've stolen a guest's property.'

'Douglas, I've already told you that is not the case.'

Charlie left his place to stand next to Edie, behind the desk.

'That's not what Mrs Leggett says, and she has witnesses.'

Mrs Leggett. Of course she'd have gone running to Bygrove with the tale as soon as he'd returned from his jaunt out.

Both the manager and his wife reached the desk in time for him to say, 'Mr Cobbett, get back to your post.'

'Not if you're going to accuse Edie of something she didn't do. Sir.'

'Douglas, please. It's afternoon tea and the guests might walk through here.'

'Then you will take over on the desk and I will deal with this in the staff area.'

'But she hasn't done anything,' said Charlie.

'It's all right, Mr Cobbett,' said Helen. 'We'll sort it out.' She indicated with her head that he should return to his place. In a lowered tone, she added, 'You have not been here to witness what's already been said, Douglas, but have only heard Mrs Leggett's biased opinion.'

'Which is why I'm taking Miss Moore now to sort it out,' he growled. 'Miss Moore, to the dining room!'

Edie left her place behind the desk to follow him.

Charlie started with, 'You can't—' but Edie saw Helen hush him once more.

In the staff dining room, Mrs Leggett, Fanny and Gertie were already assembled, the maids looking smug, the housekeeper triumphant.

Fanny stepped forward with, 'We saw her, we did, with the box that has the pearl necklace.'

'Enough,' said Bygrove. 'Mrs Leggett has already related this to me. I will ask if I want any more information.'

Fanny stepped back, pouting.

If only she'd been on afternoon tea, thought Edie. Bygrove would have been more reluctant to haul her away in front of guests.

Afternoon tea! Miss Langley! Of course. Why had she not thought of this before?

'Do you have anything to say for yourself, Miss Moore?' Bygrove asked.

'She doesn't, 'cos she's a liar,' said Fanny.

Mrs Leggett put a hand up in front of the maid. 'That's enough, Miss Bullen.'

Edie cleared her throat. 'Actually, I do have something to say. There is a lady who has come for afternoon tea called Miss L— Mrs Harrison. She was also a governess in my old place. She knows about Lady Stansfield's gift of the necklace. She can vouch for me.'

She should have thought this through first. Victoria would now be put in an awkward spot, being used as a witness like this. She only hoped it didn't cause them to fall out.

'I am not going to disturb a guest,' said Bygrove. 'And how would it look if she couldn't vouch for you, and it was obvious you were lying? She might spread it around that we have staff who steal from guests.'

There was some shuffling by the door. Edie looked over to see Mrs Turnbull and Mrs Norris standing there.

'Come on, Mr Bygrove, give the lass a chance,' said the storekeeper. 'I'm sure she wouldn't mention this lady if she couldn't vouch for her.'

'I agree,' said the cook, ladle in hand. It looked a little intimidating, though it was more likely she'd forgotten to put it down.

'And those maids have no business riflin' through a fellow employee's possessions. If they were concerned, they should have told management first,' said Mrs Turnbull.

'I am *not* going to disturb a guest, and *that* is *that*!' yelled the manager.

–

Mrs Bygrove was rattled, Charlie could tell that much, even from his position by the end of the desk. She'd been pleasant enough to the various guests who'd entered the foyer, mostly for afternoon tea. But in between she'd had a face on her, as his old nan would have said. Currently she was flicking none too delicately through the guestbook pages.

If only there was some way to help Edie. If he'd known more about her, he might have had some clue, but he was aware there were things she hadn't told him. It irked him, but he wasn't in a position to judge, since he was in the same circumstances. Well, similar, sort of – hopefully not the same.

Take that Mrs Harrison who'd come in earlier. Been in before, she had, but Edie hadn't mentioned their connection.

Mrs Harrison! Of course.

Charlie moved to the front of the reception desk. 'Mrs Bygrove, I think I might know how to prove Edie's innocence.'

'I'm all ears, Charlie.'

'There's a guest in the conservatory called Mrs Harrison. She was the governess with Lady Stansfield when Edie was first there as under-governess.'

'I wasn't aware she was ever under-governess.'

He shrugged. 'She was, apparently. But Mrs Harrison might know about the necklace.'

'Unless she'd left Lady Stansfield's service by then.'

'I hadn't thought of that.' Charlie slumped. 'But it might be worth a try.' He adopted the kind of hopeful expression he used to put on for his mum when trying to appeal to her better nature.

'Yes, it's worth a try.' She slammed the guestbook shut. 'Show me who she is, then you take over here, Charlie.'

'On reception? I've never done it before.'

'You've been in the foyer often enough with someone else on, though. You'll be fine.'

It was for Edie's benefit, after all. 'Righty-ho.'

'And well done for coming up with the suggestion.'

If it works out, thought Charlie, striding ahead towards the conservatory.

–

Mrs Turnbull and Mrs Norris were still arguing with Mr Bygrove. Edie wondered if the pair of them were emboldened by the shortage of staff and the unlikelihood of their being dismissed. It was then she heard voices in the corridor.

'Excuse me,' came Helen's voice, as she squeezed past the cook and the storekeeper.

'Who is that?' Bygrove pointed past Helen, and Edie was surprised to see Victoria.

But how would Helen have known?

'This is Mrs Harrison. She—'

'I'd already told Miss Moore that I would not summon a guest. How dare you go behind my back.'

'I could not go behind your back, Douglas, since I had no idea you'd already refused to see her—'

'Yes, but—'

'Mrs Harrison has some important information and I suggest we hear her out. *In private.*' Helen glanced at the other staff members.

Bygrove seemed a little flustered at first. 'Um, yes, I suppose that would be best. The rest of you, back to work.'

A slither of dread ran down Edie's spine. What had Victoria revealed exactly, in order to acquit her of the crime? That she was the Honourable Edith Moreland? She wouldn't be aware of the small deceit she'd just woven, for Victoria had never been a governess for Lady Evelyn. Not that she'd said she was, but she had implied it.

When the housekeeper showed no signs of moving, Helen said, 'You too, Mrs Leggett.'

'But I should stay, as I'm in charge of staff.' She looked towards the manager.

'Very well, you can stay,' he said. 'Close the door.'

Mrs Leggett smiled as she followed the instruction.

Without any preamble, Victoria said, 'I can confirm that Lady Evelyn Stansfield did indeed give Edie the pearl necklace.'

'But why would she give a lowly governess such a gift?' The housekeeper asked.

Edie panicked. Is this where Victoria would tell them all that Lady Evelyn was her godmother, and the necklace had been a gift for her sixteenth birthday?

'She was generous like that, Lady Evelyn,' said Victoria. 'She valued her staff greatly. In particular she valued Edie, who was a hard worker when it came to education.'

All of this was true, except her former governess probably meant she'd been a hard worker as a pupil, as she couldn't have known what she was like as a governess. She'd gone to teach young Maurice under sufferance, and much more recently than when the necklace had been given to her.

'Are you yourself still a governess?' Mrs Leggett asked, looking down her nose at her as if the opinion of such a person would count for nothing.

'No, I gave up working as I inherited a house and then married a doctor.' That wasn't quite how it happened either, but no doubt she'd said it to give herself some status and shut Mrs Leggett up.

'Thank you so much for clearing that up, Mrs Harrison,' said Helen. 'I'm sorry to have disturbed your afternoon tea.'

'Not at all,' said Victoria. 'I could not let Edie be accused of a crime she did not commit.'

'Miss Moore will escort you back to your table, and I will arrange for you to have a fresh pot of tea and a new stand of treats, since you had barely started the first one.'

Bygrove opened his mouth to speak, but Helen pre-empted him by adding, '*And* it will be on the house.'

The manager's mouth closed again in shock, but he said nothing.

'Thank you, Mrs Harrison,' said Edie, swallowing the urge to cry with relief.

'I will go and deal with those lying maids now!' Mrs Leggett left the room, her hardened expression making Edie almost sorry for what Gertie and Fanny were about to endure.

'I will return the necklace to you after your shift at the desk, Edie,' said Helen. 'Mr Cobbett is in your stead at the moment, so you can relieve him after you've escorted Mrs Harrison back to her table.'

Edie thanked Helen and led Victoria back to the conservatory. She heard the door to the staff dining room close and wondered what would occur between the manager and his wife.

'Thank you again, Victoria. I was a little worried, as you weren't to know just what I'd said about the necklace.'

'Mrs Bygrove told me your side of the story, so all I had to do was confirm it.'

'That was lucky. I'm so sorry about dragging you into all this. It is getting a little out of hand. When we meet again, would you take the necklace and look after it, please? I don't trust those maids not to steal it. And the letters from Lucia and

Freddie. It's fortunate they didn't find them when they looked in the drawers.'

'What awful women they are. Of course I'll look after them for you.' She stopped short of the conservatory door. 'Be careful, Edie. I'm not sure all this deception will end well. Freddie wrote to me yesterday to say he and your mother have fallen out because she's had enough of him not telling her where you are. What do you plan to do, ultimately?'

'Oh, Victoria, I really don't know.'

'Then you need to decide. Now, I can make my own way back to my table. You get back to reception.'

Edie nodded and stepped back into the empty dining room.

Poor Freddie. She hadn't meant to cause trouble between him and their mother. Then there was Charlie. He was an easy-going soul, but was unlikely to take her deception well. Then there was Lili, and Mrs Bygrove, not to mention the other members of staff with whom she got along. What would they think of her? She could lose them all if she weren't careful. And her job.

When she left Downland House, she'd only been thinking of a new life. She'd thought the complications would come from adjusting. Why hadn't she realised that it's not that simple to disappear and leave an old life behind? For someone reasonably intelligent, she had been dim in her belief that it could be that easy.

Her flight and the consequent duplicities were piling up. Each untruth added another problem. She really did need to decide what to do. She felt queasy at the thought. How to unravel it all?

But for now, she needed to get back to the reception desk.

Chapter Sixteen

'I can't believe we've not only *not* got rid of the Middlesbrough nobs, but got another one of them,' Charlie moaned as he lifted his cup in the early lunch break.

It was the second time Edie had heard this complaint from Charlie today, but she could understand his irritation. The 'Middlesbrough nobs', as they'd become among the staff, had not let up on their demands and untidiness.

Edie rested her arms on the table. 'The children are the best behaved among them. And that's only because the nanny is always telling them off, poor lambs.'

'As for that Lord Fernsby who's just arrived…' He tutted. 'He's someone or other's brother, I gather.'

'The viscountess, Lady Elliot's,' said Lili. 'And the son of the Earl of Scunthorpe, apparently.'

Edie humphed. 'He has a bit of an eye for the ladies, from what I could see when he was hanging around in the foyer.'

'A bit too forward, he was.' Gertie mumbled from the end of the table, next to the housekeeper. 'When he came into the bedroom yesterday, when I was still cleaning.'

Mrs Leggett put her cutlery down. 'Was he indeed? In what way?'

Gertie fiddled with her hands, looking uncomfortable. 'You know, making a comment about my *comely figure*, as he put it. He said it was probably all the exercise I got cleaning that kept me trim, and that the housemaids at his home were the same.'

'The cheeky devil! Who does he think he is? I'll not have my staff spoken to in that disrespectful manner.'

'That's not on,' said Lili. 'Short shrift I'd have given him, if I'd been there.'

'What are you gonna do though?' said Charlie. 'You know Mr Bygrove won't do a thing if you tell him. His missus would, but then she'd get an earful from her husband.' He put a forkful of food in his mouth.

Mrs Leggett looked set to argue but sat back and sighed. She probably knew he was right. Still, it wasn't like her.

'He's probably all talk anyway,' said Gertie.

Edie wondered whether any of the staff at her own house had suffered such harassment. They certainly hadn't from Freddie; and her father, whatever his other shortcomings, was a moral man who'd been known to upbraid the stable lad for pestering a maid. But she knew it wasn't always the case. One in particular came to mind: Sir Roger, a past associate of her father's. She shuddered, wanting to forget the whole unseemly affair.

Through the door came Fanny, who promptly plonked herself next to Gertie, but didn't reply to her greeting.

'Hello, Charlie,' she said. 'You 'ad a good morning?'

He finished chewing before he said, 'No. Not with their nibses insisting on this and that.'

'You should come for a walk with me this evening, if you're off. I'll cheer you up.'

He glanced at Edie before looking sidelong at Fanny. 'I'm busy,' he said, in a short manner.

'Another time then,' Fanny said cheerily.

'Not unless it's a thick ear you want,' said Lili. 'You know Charlie's walking out with Edie.'

'Lili!' Edie nudged her and noticed Charlie raise his eyes at her, too.

Fanny huffed out a brief laugh. 'So? I weren't planning nothing *naughty*.'

'I suggest you help yourself to a sandwich, Miss Bullen, and keep quiet,' said Mrs Leggett. 'You're not exactly in anyone's good books. You're lucky you still have a job here.'

Charlie pulled a face at Edie that turned into a smile. Edie smiled back, which was not missed by Fanny, who narrowed her eyes, before flicking Gertie's arm. 'Pass over them egg sandwiches, would ya?'

Gertie lifted the plate for her, and she helped herself to three halves.

'Put one of those back,' Mrs Leggett barked. 'You know it's two you're allowed. Only the men get three. And with the increasing food shortages, we'll be lucky to have that much soon.'

'That ain't fair.' Fanny plonked one of her sandwiches onto Gertie's plate, who only had one cheese sandwich.

'I don't like egg,' said Gertie, putting it back.

'What do you make of this bombing on the Kent coast?' said Edie, to change the subject. 'I heard the major discussing it with his chum as they walked in for morning coffee.'

'First raid by an aeroplane, too,' said Charlie. 'Hey, being up the coast, maybe it'll encourage the Middlesbrough nobs to bug— I mean, go elsewhere.'

'We don't want to lose trade, Mr Cobbett,' said the housekeeper.

'Nah, Charlie's right,' said Fanny.

'No one asked your opinion, Miss Bullen.'

Gertie nudged her friend's arm, as if to tell her to shut up. Fanny pulled her mouth into a snarl and pushed her face towards Gertie's. With that attitude, she'd get herself sacked at this rate, staff shortage or not.

–

It had been relatively quiet on desk duty for Edie that afternoon. Nearly everyone from the Middlesbrough group had gone out, giving the staff on afternoon tea, the porters, and her too, a break from their demands.

Edie was just enjoying a sit-down on the stool when she heard a voice on the stairs behind, singing. She recognised it as a piece from *Rigoletto*, called 'La Donna È Mobile'. She also knew it was Lord Fernsby, his booming rendition making it clear that he thought his voice equal to Enrico Caruso's and that all should hear it.

Edie lifted her eyes heavenward and slipped off the stool. No doubt he'd come to the desk with some demand or other. He was the only one of his group who hadn't gone to Brighton.

Sure enough, he appeared in front of the desk shortly afterwards, stretching himself to his full height, looking down his nose at her with his piercing green eyes. His dark brown hair was oiled and parted on one side. He twitched his small moustache as he considered her. He would have been handsome in his smart suit, if he hadn't been so pompous.

'I require afternoon tea in my room,' he said with no greeting. 'And I expect the kitchen to prioritise it.' He stretched out each hand in turn to tug down jacket sleeves that were already in place. 'Chop-chop.'

She wasn't supposed to leave the desk if she could help it, but there was nothing else for it. Unless—

'Would sir not enjoy the conservatory on such a sunny day?'

'No, sir would not! There's a better view from my bedroom window. And I'd appreciate it if you didn't try to emulate an upper-class accent, you impertinent little minx.'

She'd done it again. Trying to sound like a staff member being polite had just brought out her normal voice. About to apologise and leave to order the tea, she spotted Charlie arriving back at his position by the desk, after an errand.

'Excuse me, Lord Fernsby.' Edie went to the end of the desk. 'Mr Cobbett, would you take an order to the kitchen, please?' She tried to sound like Phoebe or Hettie, but she wasn't at all sure she'd managed it.

'Of course.' Charlie came to the front of the desk, touching the peak of his cap with respect as he passed the guest. 'Sir.'

'An afternoon tea to be delivered to Lord Fernsby's room, as soon as possible,' she said.

'No, not as soon as possible,' said Fernsby, 'Now. Before anyone else is served.'

'Sir.' Charlie bowed and headed off.

Edie hoped the man would head back up to await his food, but he continued to stand at the desk, appraising her.

'I bet you're a feisty one,' he said, assessing her as if she were a horse.

He leant towards her, his breath reeking of whisky. She resisted leaning away, in case he got cross.

'What do you do when you get off your shift?'

What a strange question. 'I have my supper, sir, and chat with my friends here.'

'Live-in, are you?'

'I am, sir.'

'Then I suggest you sneak up to my room tonight. What's your name?'

The very thought of being alone with him in such a situation made her stomach turn. Despite his good looks, he was utterly... she searched for the word. *Vile*. That was it.

'My name is Edie, sir. And I'm afraid I'm already spoken for.' There was no point saying what she really felt and offending him.

He threw back his head and gave an over-loud laugh. 'As if that makes any difference. I am a lord. Your... sweetheart, or whatever he is, is nothing compared to me. You should be flattered.'

It was oh so tempting to retort with, *and I am the Honourable Edith Moreland, and you sir, are a cad*, but of course she couldn't. She continued to look ahead, avoiding eye contact with him.

'Oh, I see your game, you little minx. Playing hard to get to make me more interested. That might just work. Now, I expect you up in my room after you finish your shift. Knock gently, so no one else hears. We don't want to alert my brother-in-law or his cousin to our little tryst. They might want a go with you, too.' He laughed once more.

Edie's skin crawled, but she had no time to reply to this request when Charlie appeared through the staff door.

Lord Fernsby walked away, calling, 'It had better be quick, or I'll have something to say to that jumped-up arse of a manager.'

Charlie walked over slowly as the man disappeared back up the stairs. 'See, I told you they called the manager names. If only he knew.' He emitted a brief sigh, nodding his head. He looked at her with a smile that became a frown. 'What's up? You look a cross between annoyed and, I dunno, worried.'

She didn't dare tell Charlie what he'd said; she didn't want him confronting Fernsby and getting into any bother. No, better to keep quiet. She had no intention of going to the man's room, and what was the pompous prig likely to do about it? He couldn't exactly complain about lack of service. Surely even Bygrove would draw the line there.

'It's just Lord Fernsby, playing his status card and being so rude. These people!' *Of which she was one*. But she wasn't. And not all of her class were like him.

'Manners maketh the man, as my old nan used to say. Don't take no notice – he's just a privileged nincompoop. I'd better get back to my position by the desk.'

Privileged nincompoop! Oh dear, is that what he'd think of her if he found out the truth? *When* he found out the truth. It didn't bear thinking about.

Oh, what a tangled web we weave,
When first we practice to deceive.

The lines from Walter Scott's poem came to her from her lessons with Miss Langley. The day of reckoning was coming ever closer, she could feel it.

Chapter Seventeen

'I swear the Earl of Middlesbrough's lot are getting worse!' Fanny complained as she stomped into the staff dining room.

'What have they done now?' Edie asked, regretting the question immediately.

The relationship between her and Fanny had inevitably become even more strained since the incident with the pearl necklace. They'd had to apologise to her for a second time, and had got into tremendous trouble with Helen and Mrs Leggett, with final, *final* warnings from Mr Bygrove, who was presumably loath to get rid of them with the present staff shortages.

Gertie had, at least, been a little more contrite than Fanny. This had convinced Edie that Fanny had been the brains behind the deceit, and that Gertie, as was often the case, had been carried along with it.

'More untidiness.' Fanny's mouth went down at the corners. 'But now they're saying it's because *we* didn't tidy up and clean well enough in the first place. 'Specially that Lord Fernsby. But Gertie and me's good at our job.'

Edie couldn't deny that; they were meticulous. 'The live-out maids have complained about them too. I wonder if they're like that in their own homes. I pity their servants.'

'Huh! The ones they've left behind to look after their houses must feel like they're on holiday. I worked at a place like that once, and they weren't even no lords and ladies, just business owners. Didn't stay long, I can tell ya.'

Edie thought back once more to Lord Fernsby's suggestion two days ago, that she visit his room. She gave a small involuntary shiver at the thought of it. She'd seen him only once since then, first thing this morning as he'd passed the desk. He'd considered her with a glare. Being in company, he must have thought better of saying anything.

Mrs Leggett walked into the room with a tray of sandwiches. Phoebe wasn't long behind with pots of tea. The table was already laid.

'Where's Gertie?' said the housekeeper. 'Not behind on her cleaning rota, I hope.'

'No, she ain't,' said Fanny with a sigh. 'Lord Fernsby's made a real mess of his bathroom since she cleaned it earlier, and he's insisted she clean it again. He says she didn't do it right before.'

Mrs Leggett clattered the tray onto the table. 'How dare he! I inspected it myself this morning and it was perfectly fine. I've a good mind to have words with him. I've had enough of his false complaints.' She became still for a moment, as if to calm herself. 'No, I'd better speak to Mr Bygrove.' She walked out of the room.

'Good luck with that,' said Phoebe. 'It's like Charlie said before, he'll only make a fuss if money's involved. Like when Sir Reynard Strong didn't want to pay the bill for the days he was cancelling.'

'Hm! Never mind us working hard all hours,' said Fanny.

Edie wondered whether Fernsby's latest tantrum was her fault, due to her failure to turn up for his hoped-for assignation. She should have told management about it. She'd do it later on today.

–

Gertie mumbled several words under her breath that would have been unsuitable for polite company. She wiped the dry cloth around the bathroom that was in Lord Fernsby's suite. What the blazes had he been doing during his bath? Throwing the water around the room? Even the walls were wet. Mucky devil. And as for the suggestion that she hadn't cleaned it properly in the first place… There'd be no sandwiches left for her at this rate.

When she finally got downstairs, she was going straight to Mrs Bygrove to complain. No point telling the housekeeper, and Mr Bygrove probably wouldn't even agree to see her.

There, that should do it. She wrung the cloth out over the WC, dropped it in her bucket and pulled the chain. Carrying the bucket back into the bedroom, she jumped and came to an abrupt stop at seeing Lord Fernsby sitting on the end of his bed. She thought he'd gone out. He had on only a dressing gown, as far as she could tell, with his legs bare and his hairy chest on show. The bedcovers were pulled down and crumpled. And after she'd made the bed, too!

She looked away, not wanting to stare it his partly exposed body.

'All done, I hope.'

'Yes, all done, m'lord.' How she hated having to be so civil to this ungrateful sod. She turned to leave the room, but before she'd gone two steps, he'd jumped up and stood between her and the door.

'Where are you off to so hastily?'

'It's my dinner time, m'lord.'

'That's fortunate. You can spend it with me.'

She panicked, not wanting to endure this man's company a moment longer, but not knowing how to convey that politely.

'That's not allowed, m'lord,' she decided upon. 'And I'm hungry. And the housekeeper wanted to talk to me during the break, too.' It wasn't true, but he wasn't to know that.

'You can tell her you had to clean the bathroom on my order.'

'But I've already finished it, m'lord. I'll get into trouble for taking so long.'

He grabbed the bucket off her, dropping it on his other side. 'This hotel owes me a favour, since that little minx at the desk didn't come to visit me on Saturday evening, as she was supposed to.'

Edie? Had she something to do with this? And what on earth did he want? To show off? To belittle her? To talk politics like that silly old fool of a major often did? Perhaps that's why he'd asked her to visit him. Yes, Edie would be better at that kind of chit-chat. She couldn't blame her for not turning up for His Lordship.

'M'lord, that's because we're not supposed to, to – fraternise with guests.' Yes, that was a good long word to use, *fraternise*. She'd heard Mrs Leggett using it.

'I'm sure your pompous manager would be more than willing to keep his guests happy in any way he can, being the sycophant he is.'

She didn't know what a *sycophant* was, but it clearly wasn't a compliment. The only option she had now was to leave. She managed to take hold of the handle of the bucket and hurried towards the door. 'I'll just get rid of this and I'll be back.' Not that she would, no thank you. And if he complained, let him.

Before she reached the door, he'd caught up and grabbed hold of her, making her drop the bucket once more.

'Oh no you don't.' He turned the key in the door, put it in his pocket, then picked her up, carrying her across the room almost upside down as she struggled.

What on earth? But as they approached the bed, his intention became crystal clear. How had it not occurred to her before?

She pummelled his leg with both hands. 'Put me down! Put me down *now*!'

'Keep the noise down, you little harlot. It's a good job my brother-in-law and cousin have gone out.'

He dropped her on the bed, on her back. Before she had a chance to recover and get up, he was straddling her, a combination of coffee and cigarettes on his breath making her want to cough.

'Let me go! I'll report you, I will.'

'And who'll believe you, a low-born menial?'

'Let me go!' Her hands hit out at him, with the added anger provoked by his insult, but he grabbed them tightly, making her grimace at the pain.

'You're not comely like that receptionist, but since she's disobeyed my order, you'll do. And I'm rather partial to fillies with flaming-red hair.'

She tried screaming, but her voice caught on the first word and it came out as a strangled cry. He pinned her down with his arms and legs, continuing to grip her wrists.

'Any more noise, and I'll make sure you suffer even more discomfort.'

Releasing one of her wrists, he undid the cord of his dressing gown. She closed her eyes once more, determined not to see his naked body. He flipped her onto her front, causing her to gasp with the abrupt movement. She was afraid for a moment that he was going to smother her.

'Now, let's get this apron and dress undone and see what we have underneath.'

If only she hadn't been persuaded by Fanny to abandon her old corset in favour of the more modern liberty bodice. It had seemed like a wonderful idea at the time. The corset would have been much harder to remove. Despite what he said about hurting her, she tried once more to scream, but it came out as a sob instead, as the tears fell.

Having succeeded in undoing the apron and the dress buttons, he turned her roughly onto her back once again.

'That's better. Access will be easier now.' He emitted a low laugh.

This was all her fault. She shouldn't have been so mean to Edie, lying to get her into trouble. Now she was being punished, and who among the staff would feel any sympathy for her? All the fight in her was gone. She closed her eyes once more and accepted the inevitable.

–

Mr Bygrove was tapping the pencil on the desk impatiently and it was starting to irritate Imogen.

'If the maid hasn't performed the job properly, then the guest has every right to demand that she redoes it. And you, Mrs Leggett, need to make sure that she does it to the correct standard.' He stressed each word with a tap of the pencil.

If he didn't stop that soon, she'd be tempted to grab the offending item off him and break it in two.

'I inspected Gertie's work, and she *had* done the job satisfactorily, but that Lord Fernsby made a mess of the bathroom once more.'

'Which is his prerogative,' said Bygrove. 'He's paying good money to do so.'

'But it shouldn't take up her whole lunch break. She needs to eat to do her job properly. And I have to say, the Earl of Middlesbrough's group have been nothing but trouble since they arrived in December. I'm not sure we *should* have to put up with it.'

'Like I said, they're paying good money.'

Imogen was beginning to wonder if that's all he cared about. 'But if our staff are mistreated, they may leave. A lot of women are finding alternative work for the war effort, on the land, at the railway, even as policewomen.'

'What, that lot? Their only talent is skivvying.' He emitted a false, high-pitched laugh, as if the idea of their having any other skills was utterly ridiculous.

Imogen had clung onto the idea that Mr Bygrove was a good manager, convinced that the thriving business of the hotel had been down to him. But it was becoming increasingly obvious that its achievements were *despite* his presence. What he was good at was taking all the credit for its success.

'Very well, sir. I'll let you get on.'

He made no reply as she exited the room. Her retreat had nothing to do with her accepting the situation. No. This was something she needed to take to Mrs Bygrove. She *would* do something about it.

–

Back on duty at reception, Edie wondered what had become of Gertie, who never did appear for her lunch. If something wasn't done about this unruly party soon, she could see staff leaving. As if the shortages weren't bad enough, what with all the male staff members who'd enlisted. And the other guests might be put off by the Middlesbrough party's increasingly selfish behaviour. Then where would the hotel be?

Stanley Morris was on porter duty, Charlie having gone for the late lunch sitting. She was disappointed she wouldn't see much of him today.

Mrs Bygrove appeared through the staff door with Mrs Leggett, as the Earl of Middlesbrough's group entered the foyer from outside, chatting noisily. Helen reached the desk first, asking hurriedly, 'Have you seen Gertie?'

'No, madam. She's still cleaning Lord Fernsby's bathroom, as far as I'm aware.'

'We'd better check she's not been made to do anything unnecessary.'

Helen and the housekeeper hurried to the stairs, ahead of the guests. It was unusual for them to take this route to the first floor, rather than the staff stairs. Stanley stepped towards the desk once they'd all disappeared, leaning on the counter.

'At least that lot haven't stopped to insist on some errand, or order, or other. We might get a bit of peace for the afternoon.'

'We can always hope,' Edie laughed.

–

'What should Gertie be doing now, Imogen?' Helen asked as she and the housekeeper reached the first floor.

'Dusting and sweeping the two rooms at the end here, ready for guests arriving this evening.'

'Then she may have already started. Let's check there first. She really shouldn't have missed a meal.'

At the specified area, they checked a room each, coming together in the hallway to agree that Gertie was not in either. The earl's party, meanwhile, had retired to their various rooms, along the corridor from Lord Fernsby's. Their staff and the children had taken the next staircase up to the second floor.

Helen shook her head. 'Unless she's unwell and has gone to bed, I can only imagine that Lord Fernsby still has her cleaning his room.'

'Fanny checked their quarters, and she wasn't there.'

Helen gripped her hands together, furious with Fernsby, the worst of his party so far. 'Right, we'll try His *Lordship's* room next.'

If Gertie was indeed still there, she'd have words with him, despite what her husband had said. It wasn't unreasonable for guests to have a code of conduct they should abide by.

Helen knocked lightly on Fernsby's door. With any luck, he'd gone out and she would be able to extract Gertie without any fuss.

When there was no reply, she knocked again, louder this time. 'Lord Fernsby? Miss Green?' Still nothing.

Losing her patience, she rapped on the door more insistently. After a short pause, when no voice or person was forthcoming, she turned her hand so that the end of her fist was banging on the door. This was more to do with her frustration at the situation than anything else.

The door to the next suite along opened and out came Viscount Stockton.

'Is something wrong? You've been knocking on my brother-in-law's door a while.'

'One of our maids has gone missing, My Lord,' said Helen, 'and she was last seen doing work in this room, beyond that which she was given, on the unreasonable insistence of Lord Fernsby.'

'I'm sure any demand he might have made would be with good reason.'

'What's going on?' said Lady Elliot, appearing beside her husband.

Helen, losing patience completely now, thumped on the door with one hand, turning the handle with the other. It was locked.

–

Edie was vaguely aware of someone knocking several times on a door, or doors, upstairs. Could they not locate Gertie still?

The door to the staff area opened, revealing Mr Bygrove. Edie jumped off her stool, making herself ready in front of the reception desk.

'Where is my wife?' the manager barked when he reached her.

'I believe she was looking for Gertie Green, sir.'

'One of the scullery maids told me that the housekeeper went to my wife, complaining about Lord Fernsby.'

'I have no idea about that, sir.'

'But have you seen them?' He was starting to shout now.

'Mrs Bygrove and Mrs Leggett did pass through the foyer and headed upstairs.'

Bygrove grumbled something she didn't catch, making for the stairs. Once he'd disappeared, Stanley said, 'Someone's in trouble.'

–

Gertie wasn't exactly sure what was happening. Her mother had never been very forthcoming about the details of the 'marriage bed', as she'd put it. She'd only been insistent that you shouldn't let anyone but your husband see to his *needs* and do things *down there*. All she knew was that Lord Fernsby was trying to do something between her legs while pushing and growling the odd 'Damn it, get in!' and 'Stop moving, you whore.'

But she wasn't moving. She was stiff with fear.

Her hopes were raised when she heard chatter outside in the corridor. She tried to make a noise, but again, she couldn't get anything out.

She suspected that what Fernsby was trying to do was what made babies happen. Oh Lord, babies! She'd never really understood what it was all about, how the baby got into a woman's stomach. She'd talked to Fanny about it once, but she'd laughed at her ignorance and had used it to make fun of her ever since.

'Please, please, stop,' she managed in a strangled whisper.

'Shut up, you bitch. You'll do as you're told.'

She thought at first it was her imagination, the faint knock on the door. Wishful thinking.

When the knock came again, louder this time, followed by Mrs Bygrove's voice saying, 'Lord Fernsby? Gertie?' a spur of hope shot through her.

Fernsby stopped what he was doing. 'Don't say a thing. She'll go away when there's no reply.'

Her heart was pounding and her breath came rapidly, making it impossible to voice any words.

The next knocks were louder still.

When all became silent once more, Fernsby continued, still cursing. 'When are they going to bugger off?'

There seemed to be a male voice now, joining Mrs Bygrove's, but Gertie couldn't distinguish the words. Sweat was pouring down her face, her breath hitching as she dreaded the voices disappearing and leaving her to her fate. She tried to call out once more, but instead broke out in a fit of coughing.

–

'Did you hear that?' said Helen. 'A woman, coughing.'

'I'm sure—' Lord Elliot began, only to be interrupted by Douglas, running along the corridor.

'Helen, get downstairs this instant. And you, Mrs—'

'No.' Helen rattled the door handle, but the door was locked. 'You see, there is someone in there.'

'Heeelp!' came a voice from the room beyond.

Imogen came forward, lifting the keys from the chain attached to her belt and selecting one to unlock the door.

'You can't do that!' roared Lord Elliot.

'I jolly well can, and I will!'

'Give me those keys now!'

'I will not!'

'Mrs Leggett, step away from the door,' shrieked Bygrove.

Helen came to her aid, pushing Bygrove away, giving the housekeeper time to open the door.

'Gertie!' Helen called, when she saw what was happening.

In her attempt to escape the bed, Gertie pulled the quilt off with her, maybe to conceal her dishevelled state.

'Mrs Bygrove, he pulled me into the bed and tried to do things to me and threatened me.' Gertie was sobbing now.

Helen ran to her, helping her to cover up while Imogen stood in front of them, as if to guard them.

'Clifford!' the viscount shouted. 'How many times have I told you not to do such things on your own doorstep?' He twisted round to his wife. 'Leave the room, Beatrice!' She did as she was told.

'It's all nonsense,' said Fernsby. 'She was perfectly willing, for a florin.'

'No, he made me. He said, he said he'd h-hurt me.'

'Mrs Leggett, call the police,' said Helen.

'Now let's not be hasty,' said Lord Elliot.

'Of course, Mrs Bygrove.' The housekeeper rushed off.

'There's no need for that,' Douglas bawled, finding his voice once more. 'It's clear the maid was complicit.'

'I dunno what that means,' Gertie cried, 'but I didn't let him do nothing. He forced himself on me.'

'Clifford, get out of there and get dressed,' the viscount roared.

'Not with the hoi polloi here.'

'Come on, Gertie, let's get you out of here and tidied up.' Helen helped her to the door as she clung onto the quilt.

In the corridor, she could hear Bygrove back in the room saying, 'I'm sure we can sort this all—'

'Get out!' Fernsby yelled.

She didn't see what happened next, as they hurried to the door to the back stairs, and she helped Gertie up the winding steps to the staff quarters.

Chapter Eighteen

Edie wasn't entirely sure what was going on, only that something had happened upstairs involving the earl's party, Mrs Leggett had rung the police and the earl had been down to demand that all their invoices be prepared. So far they had settled them once a week, but it had only been a day since they'd paid the last one. She was glad that none of the lunch guests had passed through the foyer during this time.

It wasn't until Charlie marched out into reception, his eyes narrowed, that she and Stanley found out what was going on.

'That bloody Lord Fernsby – pardon my French – but he only went and assaulted Gertie. You know, tried to have his way with her.'

Stanley gasped. 'He did what? He didn't succeed, though?'

'Nah, thanks to Mrs Bygrove and Mrs Leggett. Mr Bygrove was no bleedin' use, of course.'

'Oh no,' said Edie. She shook her head, cursing herself for her own stupidity. She laid her forehead on the counter. 'Oh dear, oh dear.'

'It's not your fault.' Charlie put his hand on her shoulder.

She lifted her head. 'But I might have been able to prevent it, if only I'd spoken sooner.'

'What d'ya mean?'

She explained what had happened on Saturday, how Fernsby had insisted she go to his room that evening.

'Why didn't you tell Mrs Bygrove? Something could have been done.'

'I don't know. I suppose I thought that Mr Bygrove would get involved and nothing would be done, so what was the point, and that I'd just not go and that would be an end to it.'

'It didn't occur to you that Fernsby might pick on another member of staff?' She could tell he was irritated with her.

'No, I suppose not.'

It should have done. Sir Roger, the past acquaintance of her father's she'd been reminded of a couple of days back, had harassed several young women on his staff, and had got two of them pregnant, that they knew of. It was one of the reasons her father had ceased any dealings with him. Because of her father's reaction, she'd thought it had been the exception rather than the rule at the time. Increasingly she could see how sheltered her life had been.

'I'm gonna get Mrs Bygrove. You need to tell her so the police know it's not just Gertie. He's saying she went along with it for money, but the state she's in, according to Fanny and Mrs B, I doubt it.'

How stupid of her. She should have thought it through. 'I'm so sorry. Charlie, if you could take over reception for a few minutes, I'll go and find Mrs Bygrove and tell her myself.'

'That might be better. Stanley, go back to your place.'

–

'And you didn't think to tell us this before, you stupid girl?' Mrs Leggett stood over Edie in the staff dining room, while Helen sat opposite her.

'I'm sorry, I thought it all best forgotten. It didn't occur to me he'd trap a maid in his room. We've never had anything like that here before.' Her words were aimed at Helen, resentful as she was for the housekeeper's presence.

Mrs Leggett humphed. 'Not in your time, but it's not unprecedented, I can assure you.'

'Though it was slightly different circumstances and a few years ago now,' said Helen. 'Let us not dwell on that, for it has nothing to do with this. We cannot know if Edie reporting this would have made any difference.'

'Of course it would have. Lord Fernsby could have been warned not to bother the staff.'

'So it's *your* fault,' said a high-pitched voice, as Fanny burst through the door. She must have been standing outside, listening, as was her habit.

Mrs Leggett glared at her. 'Fanny, what have you been told about eavesdropping?'

'She should be punished, she should. I bet she told Lord Fernsby to pick on Gertie instead.'

Helen stood, almost knocking the bench over. 'That is enough, Fanny! The only person who is to blame for this is Lord Fernsby.'

'Um, begging your pardon, madam.' Stanley stuck his head round the door frame. 'But the police are 'ere. And you ought to know that the earl's been on the telephone to someone. Some superintendent, I think.'

'I'll deal with this,' came Mr Bygrove's voice from the corridor, leaning up over Stanley.

'No, you will not,' said Helen. 'At least, not on your own. Stanley, show the police into the private dining room, and then inform the viscount and Lord Fernsby that they are here. Mrs Leggett and Edie, you will also come to speak to the police. Fanny, tell Gertie the police have arrived and that they will want to speak to her shortly.'

As they left the room, Lili came in from the hotel dining room. 'What on earth's going on? One of the customers said they spotted the police coming in, and another said they thought they heard some shouting earlier.'

'There's no time to explain now. Keep the dining room door shut and do your very best to make sure the customers are happy. Pass that on to Phoebe and Mr Smithson.'

'Very well, madam.'

They carried on, Bygrove rushing ahead, no doubt wanting to get there first to try to belittle the seriousness of it all.

Edie only hoped other people weren't going to blame her, too.

–

In the private dining room, Edie, Helen and Mrs Leggett were standing together by the window, while Mr Bygrove paced up and down the room. DI Davis and Sergeant Gardner were sitting at one of the tables, listening to Gertie's halting and humiliating version of events.

When she got to the part where he had her in the bed, her words became choked and she started to sob. Helen stepped forward to place her hands on her shoulders.

'She's not the only one to have been bothered by Lord Fernsby,' she said. 'Miss Moore here was also approached by him.'

Edie came forward. 'The day before yesterday, he ordered me to go to his room. I didn't go, of course.'

'Ordered you?' said Davis.

'Yes. He insisted I should go to his room that evening. I was to do so quietly, otherwise the viscount and earl would also – and I'm using his phrase here – *want a go* with me. It was clear what he meant.' It was embarrassing to have to repeat his words, but it had to be said to show what a cad he was.

'I see.' The detective inspector made a few notes in a small jotter. 'Gardner, would you go and see what's happened to Lord Fernsby? He should be here by now.'

'Right away, sir.'

The sergeant opened the door, only to find Stanley leading the Earl of Middlesbrough, Lord Armstrong, to the room, with another man in police uniform. He had on a cap, rather than the helmet that the sergeant wore. Edie hadn't seen him before.

On seeing the group, the inspector stood up. 'Superintendent Crooke, sir.'

'Davis.'

'To what do we owe this honour?'

'Lord Armstrong here gave me a call. Said that the local constabulary had been called in over a misunderstanding. We don't want to be arresting the Earl of Scunthorpe's son for no reason, now do we, Davis?'

Bygrove stood to attention, his nose in the air. 'That's what I said.'

'It ain't for no reason,' Gertie said crossly. 'Is it, Mrs Bygrove?'

'Don't worry, Miss Green, we'll handle this. Inspector Crooke, is it?'

'Superintendent Crooke! I'm from the Arundel police station and I'm in overall charge of Littlehampton. And since this is a matter involving the nobility, *I* will be taking charge.'

'Lord Fernsby needs to come to the station to answer some questions about assaulting Miss Green here. He hasn't shown up yet,' said Davis.

'That won't be necessary. As I said, I will be taking charge. I shall take him to Arundel and question him there and will decide if any action needs to be taken. In the meantime, we will keep this alleged incident to ourselves, is that clear?'

'*If* any action needs to be—' Gertie started. Helen placed a hand on her shoulder and she went no further.

'Thank you, Inspector,' said Lord Armstrong. 'I knew I could rely on your discretion.' He turned to Bygrove. 'We have tired of this place and its inadequate service. I think it's high time we went home, so I trust you have my instruction about getting our invoices ready?'

'Yes, of course. They're being prepared now.'

That wasn't true, as Edie had not had a chance to tell anyone about the request.

'I think that, in light of the terrible inconvenience we have suffered, some discount is owed to us.'

Helen strode towards the earl. 'You have had nothing but the very best service, Lord Armstrong. It is *we* who have been inconvenienced with your unreasonable demands and your chaos.'

'Helen, that's enough,' said Bygrove. 'What my wife means to say, Lord—'

'What I mean to say is what I've said. You have been the most unpleasant guests we have ever had the misfortune to serve in this hotel. It is *you* who should pay *us* more for the extra work. And now with the abuse of our chambermaid, we will be glad to see the back of you.'

'Mrs Bygrove,' the superintendent started, in a condescending tone.

'And you, sir,' she said, pointing at Crooke, 'are complicit. I have no doubt you will let Lord Fernsby get away with it.'

'Let us go,' said the earl. 'Clearly the woman is unstable, as they all seem to be here.'

'I'd rather be unstable than a rapist.'

Lord Armstrong turned. 'I would be careful what accusations you make, lest you find yourself in court for slander.' Then he did an about-turn and departed.

Superintendent Crooke looked around the room at them all. 'I've taken this over now, and I suggest you keep your mouths shut. Do you understand?'

'Yes of course, of course,' said Bygrove, following Crooke out. His words, 'And if you ever want a meal in our restaurant, you can...' faded and disappeared.

'I knew no one would believe me.' Gertie slumped in the chair.

'We do,' said Helen. 'And be sure we will be on our guard so this doesn't happen again. We will have a meeting with the rest of the staff later, and make sure everyone is aware that they must report the least little harassment.'

A wave of guilt washed over Edie once more. If only she had... Too late to do anything about that now. She'd just have to make sure to do the right thing in future.

Chapter Nineteen

May had arrived, and with it some warmer weather. It was like the hotel had breathed a sigh of relief after the Middlesbrough nobs had left, Charlie considered as he listened to the singers at the bandstand, sitting in a deckchair on the edge of the crowd. Even so, the mood had been a little sombre, and the staff more reserved, what with Gertie so withdrawn, Fanny all upset for her friend and Mr Bygrove angrier with everyone, especially his wife. It had been hard to keep cheerful for the guests, but they all seemed to have managed it.

There was no question in Charlie's mind that, thanks to that creep Superintendent Crooke, Lord Fernsby would get away with it. And had no doubt done so many times in the past. Superintendent Crooke! He was well named.

He looked at his wristwatch. Edie was due to meet him here once she was ready. They were taking a boat trip up the River Arun to Arundel. He'd been looking forward to this, having her to himself.

The song ended. Charlie was clapping with the few other people there, when he felt a hand tap him on the shoulder. He turned, smiling, anticipating Edie's arrival, but it wasn't her. Dread enveloped him as he saw before him an old acquaintance he'd hoped never to lay eyes on again.

'Charlie Cobbett, as I live and breathe. You're difficult to get hold of. Been lookin' round for you, I have.'

'Frank Steel. Thought you'd moved out of the area.' At least, he hoped he had.

The man before him had aged beyond his thirty-eight years, with his hair completely grey and deep lines set into his face.

'So I did, for a bit. Came back a coupla months back and I thought, I know, I'll find my old mate, Charlie.'

Frank took the deckchair next to him. Charlie looked beyond him, to the common, hoping Edie wouldn't turn up just yet.

'Waitin' for someone, are ya?'

'Could say that. And I'm not sure I'd call you a mate after what you did, buggering off like that and leaving me to take all the blame.'

'Water under the bridge, surely, old pal.'

'I'm not your pal. Now, while I've enjoyed this little catch-up with you, if you don't mind, I've got a life to get on with.'

'Not so quick, Charlie lad. You 'aven't 'eard why I've been lookin' for ya yet. Got a nice little job for you, I 'ave. Good money. Dunno what you're doin' right now, but this could set you up.'

He didn't seem to know that Charlie was working at the Beach Hotel, so that was something. The last thing he needed was him coming to the hotel looking for him, causing trouble and making him look bad.

'That's what you said last time, Frank. Good money. It'd set me up. Set me up was about right. Look what happened! Nah, I've paid me due. And I'm not doing nothing else for you.'

'You owe me, Charlie boy.'

'I don't owe you nothing, Frank. If anything, it's the other way around. What happened to that money? Weren't in a hurry to keep any for me, I bet. Not that I'd take it.'

Frank stood as the next act started on stage. 'You might regret that decision, pal.'

'Goodbye, Frank.'

'Not goodbye, Charlie boy, *au revoir*, as the French say. Till we meet again.'

He watched as Frank strolled away, whistling along to the tune, in the direction of South Terrace. That's all he needed,

Frank Steel back in his life. Nah. Whatever happened, he wasn't getting involved with him again.

As he was contemplating this, he felt a hand on his shoulder once more. The little rat hadn't returned, had—? 'Oh, Edie. Am I glad to see you.'

She looked perplexed. 'You say that as if we hadn't planned this.'

'I know. But I've been looking forward to this trip out, that's all.'

'Me, too.' She leant over and kissed his lips lightly. 'Come on then.'

–

On the motorboat, Charlie and Edie sat holding hands, watching the warehouses as they glided past them, with the dozen other people aboard. He felt a warmth envelop him, despite the cool breeze. It was being with Edie, away from the hotel. It must be a relief for her, too, what with the accusing frowns she was still getting from some of the staff, particularly Fanny.

'It does get prettier than this,' he said. 'Once we get past the bridge and a little further on, past the town.'

'I know it does. We've walked along the bank there.'

'So we have.'

'You've been quiet since we met. Are you all right?'

'I'm enjoying the peace after all the bustle at the hotel,' he said.

'Trade has improved in the last week or two. It makes me wonder whether rumours of the unruly Middlesbrough party had spread and people weren't coming.'

'Maybe. It's good to be back to normal. If you can call it that, after what happened. 'S'pose it doesn't feel normal for Gertie. Got to feel sorry for her, even if she is a pain in the proverbial the rest of the time.'

'Yes, I agree.'

As they approached the bridge, Edie tipped her head back, looking up at the people leaning on the ledge who were gazing downriver. She gave a little audible gasp.

'What's up?' said Charlie. 'You look like you've seen a ghost.'

It was a few seconds before she lowered her head and replied, intent as she was on looking at the bridge.

'There was a woman up there who looked familiar. It took me a few seconds to think who it might be. But no, I must be mistaken.'

She wasn't seeing unwelcome old friends, too, was she?

On the other side of the bridge they spied a cargo steamer, moored on the right. It was being loaded with goods of some kind. Edie pointed to it.

'I wonder if those supplies are going to France.'

'Maybe.' Charlie felt uncomfortable, seeing it there. Supplies going to France, where some of his old colleagues were fighting, or soon would be. The stories in the newspapers every day were dreadful. And here he was, on a boat trip, enjoying a day out with his sweetheart.

Guilt, that's what it was, that uneasy feeling. Yet how would he cope in a trench, in a confined space? Look what had happened when Alex and Jim had shut him in the store cupboard. He had thought of joining the Civil Guard, to do nightly patrols. Yes, he'd definitely have to look into that.

He'd only be a liability in the army.

Chapter Twenty

Edie and Charlie could hear the commotion of the fair before they saw it, passing the bottom end of Pier Road, close to the quay, on their next half-day off.

'We struck lucky.' Charlie squeezed her arm affectionately where it was linked through his. 'Getting our time off from Easter Monday today couldn't have worked out better. Look at the weather.' He pointed up to a completely blue sky. 'Been a coupla years since I've been able to get to the fair.'

'It only comes for the day, someone said.'

'Yep. Twenty-sixth of May, every year.'

'Fanny wasn't very pleased, I can tell you. I heard her having a good moan about us getting today off. She said she hadn't got to the fair in five years.'

'I'm sure that can't be true. She hasn't even worked at the hotel for five years. I bet Gertie had a thing or two to say, too.'

'No. She's been very quiet since… you know.'

'Ugh, don't set me off on that again. Got away with it, did that Lord Fernsby. And that won't discourage him from doing it again.'

'I know.' That would have been the one good thing about her privileged position, if she could have got him punished for what he tried to do to Gertie, the rotten scoundrel. 'Anyway, Fanny also said she'd heard the fair wouldn't be as big as usual because of the war.'

'We'll see. Still seems to be something on the Fisherman's Quay, down by the Britannia, by the sounds of it. We'll look down there afterwards.'

As they rounded the last corner of Pier Road, where it led on to Surrey Street, there was the roundabout ahead of them on the wide road there, which had been shut to traffic. There were many more people milling around there than she'd ever seen in the town. The sound of the music, the machine's engines and the people shouting to be heard above it was almost deafening.

'Fanny's right,' shouted Charlie. 'There isn't as much as usual. Wonder if it was the same last year. Still, there's a galloper, and I enjoy one of those.'

Edie looked over to the roundabout. 'I've never been on one before.'

'Why on earth not?' Charlie looked flabbergasted.

It wouldn't hurt to share this simple fact. 'My mother considered them too—' About to say *common*, she changed it to, 'dangerous.'

'Nah, not if you're sensible. You don't wanna be mucking about on one, that's all. I did see someone come to grief once doing that.'

'Please, don't tell me any details.'

He grimaced. 'I wasn't going to. Let's have a look what's here before we go on anything,' he said.

They crossed the road, over to the motor car garage, passing shop windows with various war posters encouraging men to enlist. The dominant one had a picture of a father sitting on a couch, with two children. On the bottom were the words, *Daddy, what did YOU do in the war?*

Charlie poked his thumb towards it accusingly. 'Spent my time not killing people, would be my reply.'

'My brother would agree.' She added a hasty, 'Probably.'

'You have a brother?'

'I do. Freddie.'

'You've not mentioned him before. What's he do?'

'Oh, helps my father in his wood business.' That was true. 'Do you have any siblings?'

'A sister, older. She moved to Kent a few years ago with her husband. Come on, the galloper's coming to a standstill. Let's get on.'

He paid the man there then helped her onto a horse. She sat side-saddle, as she would have done on her own horse when she was younger. He got up onto the one next to her, on the inside. 'Gee up, Dobbin!'

As the roundabout slowly rotated, Edie found herself gripping on tight. It would be easy to slip off and be tossed to the ground, despite what Charlie had said.

'You all right?' he called.

'Yes.'

'You don't sound it.'

'Just a bit nervous.'

'You'll be fine. Faster, Dobbin!' He clapped his heels against the pretend horse's haunches.

His obvious delight began to rub off on her and she found herself relaxing a little and enjoying it. After all, she'd ridden real horses, which were a lot more dangerous.

At the end of the ride, feeling a little dizzy, she allowed Charlie to help her down.

'So, what d'ya think of your first go on a galloper then?'

'It was fun.'

'Told you it would be. Let's go and see if the swingboats are on the Fisherman's Quay.' He took a deep breath and sighed it out, adding a chuckle at the end. 'This is the life.'

About to head around the corner to the river, they found themselves surrounded by a group of four women. They were each holding a bunch of feathers in one hand.

'Why aren't you in the army, young man?' said one who couldn't have been much older than them. Her heavy brown coat was done up to the top, despite the warm day.

''Cos I 'aven't enlisted,' Charlie replied. 'I don't 'ave to. And I'm going to join the Civil Guard to protect our shores, I am.'

This was the first Edie had heard of it, but she admired him for the idea.

'There are old men aplenty for those duties,' said another woman. 'You're just a shirker and a coward.' She thrust a feather into his hand and they all marched off to find another potential victim.

He looked down at the feather, brow creased. 'Who the hell do they think they are, poking their noses into my business?'

'Don't worry about it, Charlie. They're just troublemakers and will get into bother with someone, if not the police, soon enough.'

He considered her, the hurt in his face obvious. She'd have hugged him had they not been in such a public place.

'Called me a coward, they did.' He tossed the feather to the ground.

'Look, Charlie, that man's family are having a row with them. They're picking on people randomly, without finding out their circumstances. For all they know, you might have had a condition precluding you from fighting. Like flat feet.'

'But I 'aven't, have I? You know what, I've lost my enthusiasm for the fair, what with the busybodies and these blinking posters.'

'Oh, Charlie.' She slipped two arms through one of his. 'Shall we go for a cup of tea instead?'

He nodded limply and she led him away.

–

He couldn't have been sure, but Charlie thought he spied Frank in the crowd when he'd peered behind, as he and Edie had walked the long way back to the hotel that afternoon, down the promenade. That would just about make his day after what had happened at the fair earlier.

'Why do you keep looking behind you?' Edie asked, as they passed the coastguard station, near the pier.

This wasn't the time to explain about his erstwhile colleague. 'Thought I spotted an old friend in the crowd, but it's just someone what looks like him.' With any luck.

'Do you want to go and make sure? I don't mind.'

'Nah, it's all right. We've been lucky with the weather today, haven't we? Shame there wasn't more to the fair.' Not that they'd seen all that was there after those white feather women had had their say. They'd seen them pass the café they'd escaped to, but luckily they hadn't come in.

He knew he'd been a bit quiet, and hoped it hadn't spoiled Edie's day. She'd spent much of the time trying to cheer him up with various amusing stories about the guests, and he loved her all the more for it.

His insides did a weird thing – a cross between a jolt and a melting sensation. It was that word: love. Yes, as much as he hated to admit it, he was pretty sure he did love her. He puffed his lips out with a breath as he considered this.

'What's wrong now?'

His head jerked round. 'What? Nothing. Why d'you ask?'

'You looked like you'd just realised something, or lost something.'

'Nah. Just appreciating the calm sea. Look how green it is, with the sun shining on it.'

No, he hadn't lost anything, more like found it. But he wasn't sure how it helped him. It was wonderful, yet impossible, him and Edie. Yes, they were walking out, but how could he ever keep someone like her content, a bright and intelligent woman?

'Let's cut across here to the hotel.' He pointed towards the fountain, halfway between them and their destination.

Another day off over. If only he could spend the evening with her on their own, not sharing space with a pile of other people. Especially the likes of Fanny and Gertie.

Entering the scullery, they were aware of lively chatter in the staff corridor.

'What's going on?' he asked the young porter, Leslie Morris, as he pushed the next door open. He'd been relating something to a group of female staff there, including Lili.

'The White Feather Brigade have turned up at the hotel and are pestering the guests and a row's broken out. Mrs Bygrove and the major have tried to calm things down, but now Mr Bygrove's turned up and all hell's been let loose.'

'Not here, too!' Charlie growled. 'All hell *will* be let loose when I get hold of them.'

He stomped off towards the foyer door.

'Charlie,' Edie called. 'We shouldn't get involved.'

He knew she was right and that he should turn back, but they'd ruined his afternoon and now they were poking their noses somewhere else they shouldn't be. When he didn't turn back, Edie followed him, as did Leslie and Lili.

In the foyer, the argument was still raging, guests on one side, with Bygrove standing in front of them, yelling. The white feather women were shouting abuse back. Mrs Bygrove was standing a few feet away with the major, both shaking their heads. At the desk, Richard Watkins was looking on, agog.

Edie took his arm. 'Please, let's leave them to it.'

'Not likely,' said Lili. 'Most exciting thing that's happened all day, it is.'

'They need a telling-off.' Charlie carried on, not at all sure what he was going to say, but he knew he had to do something.

Both sides were talking over each other now, as Charlie shouted, 'Not you lot again. Didn't you cause enough trouble in town, at the fair? We should get the police on you. You're troublemakers.'

'Mr Watkins has already telephoned them,' said Mrs Bygrove, with regret in her voice.

'I'd advise you to get yourself gone,' said the manager. 'Invading the conservatory and bullying my guests, trying to foist your disgusting feathers on them.'

'Yes, it's abominable,' said Mr Perryman, the timber yard owner who was a regular and valued guest. 'Ruining afternoon tea and throwing accusations of cowardice at people you don't even know.'

'That's right!' said a woman Charlie didn't recognise. 'My son has been convalescing after a bout of whooping cough and is still unfit, and you have the temerity to call him a coward. How dare you!'

'Oh, we dare,' hollered the woman in the brown coat, who appeared to be the leader. 'Because for every man with a genuine excuse, there'll be ten who are simply shirkers.'

Edie came from behind Charlie. 'Do you not think that there might be some more edifying way by which to achieve your aims?'

She was really putting on that posh voice of hers again. Probably what they needed, someone who sounded like they were in charge.

'You were with *him* at the fair,' said the leader. 'You're a bit above his station, aren't you? Or do you like them low-born and rough?' She emitted a brief, sneering laugh.

'You are entirely disrespectful,' said Edie. 'You clearly think you're entitled and you need to learn some manners. You don't hear of politicians insulting people to get them to enlist. Men will have many different reasons why they have not enlisted. And until they bring in conscription, if they ever do, it is not your business to police who enlists and who doesn't. There are still jobs in this country to be done.'

Edie had a calming voice, which Charlie had some hope would bring this charade to an end.

'Talking of police, where the devil are they?' Bygrove moaned. 'They need to drag off these harridans.'

The women's leader held up a fist. 'Who are you calling harridans?'

'You, you stupid mares!'

That was the end of that hope, thought Charlie.

The leader came forward to shove Bygrove, causing him to stumble backwards, just as Sergeant Gardner walked through the front doors with four constables. Apparently not spotting them, Bygrove delivered a mighty slap to the woman's face.

'Douglas!' Mrs Bygrove hollered.

All four of the white feather women surged forward to hit and slap at Bygrove, while he held up his arms to protect himself. 'Get off, get *off* me, you silly mares!'

Mr Perryman was pushed during the onslaught, along with his wife, causing him and another guest to push the women back in turn.

'Stop this immediately!' Gardner shrieked. The constables surrounded the group, bringing them to a standstill.

'I've had several complaints at the station about you causing trouble in the town,' said the sergeant. 'You've been harassing old men, and even off-duty coppers! I'm arresting the lot of you.'

'But he slapped me!' the leader wailed, pointing a finger at the manager.

'After much provocation, I've no doubt. Now you'll all come quietly, or my men will be forced to handcuff you.'

'I'm sure there's no need for that, Sergeant,' said Edie.

'I 'ope not, miss.'

The leader turned to her group. 'Ladies, we will go quietly, so all may see what martyrs we are.'

'Martyrs?' said Charlie. 'Trying to persuade men to sign up to be killed? It's those ill-trained soldiers what are martyrs.'

'That's enough, Mr Cobbett,' said the sergeant. 'We'll deal with this now.'

The staff and guests gathered, watching quietly as the police led the women away.

'Back to work, you lot,' said Bygrove, flicking his hand towards the members of staff there. On seeing his wife go to speak to the guests, he quickly followed on, talking over whatever she was saying with a loud apology.

Lili went ahead to the staff dining room. Charlie stopped at the top of the corridor and held Edie back.

'Oh Charlie, you look upset. I'm sorry you had to encounter them again.'

'I've been thinking. Maybe I should enlist. Lorcan and Jasper and the others have gone to do their bit. It's probably only a matter of time until I have to go. Better to jump than be pushed.' Even as he said it, the very thought of going made him queasy.

She took his arm and leant against it. 'Don't do anything rash, Charlie, please. There may never be conscription. Or the war might end before you finish training.'

'You're right. No point doing nothing rash.' He held onto her for a few seconds, more thankful than ever to have her in his life. 'Let's go and see what's for supper, eh?'

Chapter Twenty-One

May had been a busy month at the hotel, especially the Whitsun holiday the week before. It had given Charlie little time during the day to think about Frank Steel, the White Feather Brigade or to ponder the letters that had come from Joseph Norris. His mother had been keen to read them out at mealtimes, detailing the training at Bexhill, where those who'd enlisted into one or other of the three South Down battalions still were. He'd moaned about the discomfort and the inferior food, garnering sympathy for him and the others at the hotel who had enlisted. *Our poor boys*, as Mrs Norris had referred to them.

Night-time was a different matter, and had him tossing and turning, as all these concerns weighed heavily on him. But the biggest worry involved his own secret that he'd kept from Edie, a burden that gnawed more at his insides with each passing day that he didn't tell her.

'Will you be long?'

He was roused from his reverie by her now, standing at the staff gate of the hotel as they left on a day off.

'Shouldn't be. Sounds like a simple job. I'll meet you in the Harbour Tea Rooms in an hour.'

She looked at her wristwatch. 'A quarter past two then.'

'Yep.'

'It's good of you to agree to do the motor car repair for your friend.'

'Not exactly a friend. A former customer of me dad's, who fell out with him over the cost of his last repair. My father did charge a bit over the top, figuring Mr Edwards could afford it. But then, we was good mechanics, the pair of us.'

'Won't he tell your father he's seen you?'

'Nah. I told him we'd fallen out. I was lucky to bump into him just when he needed a repair. It's a bit of extra spending money. Anyway, quicker I get going—'

'Of course. I'm going to walk on the promenade, and maybe have a detour to the bandstand to see what's on.'

She headed off in the direction of the sea. He watched her for a while, before he went in the opposite direction, on his way to Fitzalan Road, off South Terrace. Charlie rubbed his hands together. Maybe Mr Edwards would recommend him to his friends. If he could make some extra on the side like this, his savings would grow a bit quicker and he could… What? Leave and set up his own business? Unlikely, but it was nice to have a dream. It was a pity the hotel's garage didn't offer repairs, as it would have been a good job for him.

On Fitzalan Road, he found Mr Edwards's house and opened the gate. The blue Austin was parked on the road looking clean and shiny. He was surprised how much he was looking forward to getting his hands oily again, even if it was just a small job. It had been a while, nearly three years, but he was sure he hadn't forgotten what to do.

Before he had a chance to knock on the door, Mr Edwards opened it.

'Ah, Charlie. I'm sorry, I didn't know how to get hold of you, but I've had the repair done at the garage on Surrey Street. My wife wanted to go on a trip, and so I needed to get it fixed as soon as possible.'

'Not to worry, sir.' Charlie smiled even though he was bitterly disappointed. 'At least you got it done.'

'Thank you for being understanding. And if you ever set up your own business, let me know.'

Charlie touched his cap. 'I will that, sir. Good day to you.'

He sloped back down the road. At least he'd get longer with Edie. If he headed up to the prom and walked down, he'd soon find her.

–

The sun was shining brightly today, making Edie wish she had a parasol with her. She had three at Downland House, but they were the last things she'd planned to pack when she left. And how would it have looked, a hotel staff member walking along with a parasol like she was, oh, the Honourable Edith Moreland or someone? She chuckled to herself. That person seemed so very far away now. Maybe today she'd tell Charlie. Maybe.

Passing the Punch and Judy show, she stopped to watch for a while. She'd never been keen on them, even as a child. About to pass on, she heard a voice calling her name.

Charlie was early? No, not Charlie's voice. She looked into the crowd to see a familiar face rushing towards her, hand in the air to get her attention.

'Dan?' He was sporting a cream suit with a thin blue stripe, and a boater.

'Edie, I'm so glad I found you. I went to the hotel to ask if you were there, but the woman on the desk said it was your afternoon off and that I might find you on the promenade. I was so pleased, as I remembered you writing that you often have Mondays off at the moment.'

'Oh Daniel! I don't want people at the hotel questioning why a young man of breeding is asking after me.'

At least it had been the more discreet Mrs Bygrove on the desk, not Watkins or worse still, Bygrove himself. But even so…

'I know, but I did tell her that I was the uncle of your old charge, and since I was passing by you might like news that he was getting on splendidly at his school, thanks to all your hard work.'

'Oh my, you did think that one through.'

'See, I remembered what you told me at Freddie's, about your reference from Lady Evelyn.'

'It sounds like you were taking notes,' she joked. 'But I'd rather you hadn't added to the – the fibs.'

'Since it is your day off, could we do something?'

'I'm afraid I have already arranged to do something with, um, a friend. I'm meeting them in—' She glanced at her wristwatch. 'Fifty minutes, at the tea room on Pier Road.'

'Then I will walk with you until then, and escort you to the tea room.'

She hesitated. 'Come on, then. You can tell me what you've been up to.'

They strolled in the direction of the pier, taking a brief detour towards the wetter part of the shore to watch a sand artist form a knight on horseback with sticks and combs. Dan threw a few coins into his bucket.

Back on the promenade, Edie asked, 'Did you really just turn up in Littlehampton on the off-chance I'd be having an afternoon off?'

'Yes, I did. I know it's mad, but I thought to myself that if you weren't on a day off, I'd simply enjoy a few hours by the sea.'

'You could do that more quickly and easily in Brighton.'

'True. But it is a little different here. More green. And it has the river.'

'Aren't you afraid people will think you're walking out with someone beneath your station?' She thought of the white feather woman's words and felt sad once again on Charlie's behalf.

Dan looked her up and down, putting on a mock-pompous smirk. 'You're looking half-decent today. I think you'll pass muster, my little filly.'

'That's so kind of you to say, sir,' she replied, mimicking Gertie.

'You do that voice too well. I fear you are indeed turning into one of that class.'

She came to a halt by the pier and glared at him. 'Dan, I never had you pegged as a snob. What an awful thing to say – one of *that* class. And I thought you were a supporter of unfranchised lower-class men getting the vote, as well as women, and for workers' rights and unions.'

'You know I am! It was a joke, Edie. I have had battles with my own father over this matter in our business. Decent wages and proper time off. A happy worker is a productive worker. And everyone has the right to happiness.' He looked down at her, his expression unfathomable.

'Yes, they do. You're a good person at heart, aren't you, Dan?'

She put her hand loosely through his arm, as she would do a friend.

'I try to be. But not good enough for you, apparently.' He pulled a funny face at her.

She chuckled. 'Oh Dan, don't say things like that. Now tell me, have you seen my brother and Lucia since I was there last month?'

'Only once.'

'Tell me all.'

–

When Charlie reached the common he veered off toward the bandstand, since Edie had mentioned popping in to have a look. The musicians were taking a break and so the audience was thin, allowing him to see quickly that she wasn't there. In that case, he'd go back to the prom by the hotel and start from there, so as not to miss her.

Almost at the pier, he spotted her hat first and quickened his pace. As the throng ahead parted, it became apparent that she was not alone. Beside her was a young man, clearly well-to-do, sporting a boater. Could it be one of the hotel guests who she'd met and fallen into conversation with? They were discouraged from engaging with guests outside of the hotel, but if they talked to you, you could hardly be rude.

He didn't recognise this one though. He'd catch them up and all would be made clear. But as he started to close in, his heart jolted. She'd put her hand through his arm. Didn't she say she had a brother? Yes, but he wouldn't be posh, like this bloke.

She laughed at something he said; it was the laugh of someone who knew their companion well.

Charlie continued to follow them, but not as quickly now. Could *he* be the real reason she'd left her last job? Not because of Lord Whatever-his-name-was, Stansfield? But because of his, what? Older son? Younger brother? Cousin? Such relationships happened, of course, but they were frowned upon.

Was he back to claim her? Charlie came to a standstill. That being the case, his appearance would be as welcome as a dose of cholera.

He stemmed the urge to cry, an urge he hadn't felt since his father had thrown him out of the family home. He turned, going back in the opposite direction. He should go and see his mother. Dad had said she didn't want to see him before, but maybe she'd have changed her mind by now.

He hardly registered the walk back, floating through the crowd and across the common, on his way to Western Road, where his parents lived, one road back from South Terrace. As Edie had said, there he was, working at the hotel, hardly any distance from his parents, yet they didn't even know he was there.

He ploughed on down Western Road, determined to see this quest through. A figure appeared on the pavement ahead, next to his parents' house. His father. Charlie took a deep breath for courage, but instead lost his nerve. He did an about-turn and marched back to Norfolk Road. He hadn't gone two steps around the corner when he spotted Frank Steel, looking in the window of the post office. Had he seen him come onto the road and assumed he was in one of the shops? He scooted back into Western Road and flattened himself against a wall, checking Frank's position every few seconds.

When Frank disappeared into the shop, Charlie looked at his wristwatch. One fifty-five. Still thirty-five minutes until closing time. He took the opportunity to run straight across the road and into the New Inn. He could do with a couple of pints.

–

Edie checked her wristwatch as she and Dan stood on the pier, watching a cargo steamer motor from the River Arun into the sea.

'I don't suppose there are many ships with sails now,' said Dan. 'Especially since the war started.'

'Hardly any. I remember there being a lot when I came here as a child.'

'Me too. Such a shame. They are so much more elegant than the modern ships.'

'Dan, it's nearly ten past two. I need to walk down to the tea room now.'

'Very well. I'll accompany you.' They started off down the river path that passed the Kursaal and the windmill.

'Do you have to accompany me?'

'Are you ashamed of me?' he quipped. 'Or afraid your friend will take a shine to me?'

'My friend take—? Oh, I see. No, my friend is a male member of staff who has the same day off. We agreed to meet for afternoon tea.' That was sufficient explanation.

'Either way, I'm sure he'd appreciate me escorting a single woman safely.'

He wasn't going to give up. If they met Charlie along the way she'd say he was an acquaintance of Lady Evelyn's, using Dan's story to Mrs Bygrove. Perhaps. Or tell him the truth?

As they passed the Nelson public house, he blurted out, 'Have you thought about what I said, when you were at Freddie's?'

'The answer is the same,' she replied, rather too shortly.

'Sorry. I'm sorry. Of course. But I will keep on hoping.'

They reached the tea room door. Edie glanced inside but couldn't see enough to know if Charlie was there. 'It's been nice chatting to you, Dan, but please, don't ask for me again at the hotel.'

'Could I come and have tea with you and your friend, please? I'm sure he wouldn't mind, if he's just a friend.'

'Your superior class would make him feel awkward, so no.'

'Doesn't your superior class make him feel awkward?'

'No, because he doesn't know about it and I play it down.'

He widened his eyes. 'A good job he is only a friend then. Farewell, Edie.'

'Farewell, Dan.'

He leant forward and she thought for one awkward moment that he was going to kiss her cheek. If he had intended that, he thought better of it, bowing slightly instead before heading off down Pier Road.

A weight fell off Edie as she entered the tea room and saw that Charlie had not yet arrived. She may not have been able to see much looking in, but he would have certainly seen them outside. The sweet aroma of the cakes and pastries put her at her ease. She would enjoy this afternoon, despite the interlude with Dan.

She was shown to a table for two, telling the waitress that she was awaiting a friend and would order a pot of tea for one in the meantime.

A quarter past two came and went. As did two thirty. The motor car repair must have taken longer than anticipated. Just after three, she ordered a piece of Victoria sponge and more tea.

It was coming up to half past three when Edie had to admit that Charlie was not coming. And if he did turn up now, he would surely understand when she wasn't there. She apologised to the waitress and asked for the bill.

What would she do now? All of the ideas she'd had felt dull now Charlie wasn't going to be part of them. She'd go to the bandstand and see what entertainment was on. It was something she'd mentioned to Charlie, so if he did come looking for her, with any luck he'd find her there.

–

Edie hadn't stayed long at the bandstand. Despite the sunny day, it might as well have been gloomy without Charlie. Had she come to depend on him too much? He made her feel good about herself, about the world, even if recently he hadn't been quite the optimistic and cheerful chap he normally was.

Walking by the sea again now, she envied those people brave enough to bathe. It had been an activity she'd enjoyed as a child and young woman, but not for many years. She imagined herself floating in the green water, her cares melting away.

It wasn't quite as busy as earlier, but there were still plenty of people around. The nannies, children's nurses and their wards stood out, familiar as she'd been with that world. She took her mind back to those days, remembering Nanny Street bustling them along when there was an entertainment she considered not suitable. Like the young woman singing on the edge of the promenade at this moment. It was a song that was innocent on the surface, but there was a reference or two that Edie knew to be improper. Not that she'd have realised as a child. Nanny Street hadn't approved of her and Freddie watching the Punch and Judy show either, declaring it 'intemperate'. It's probably where she'd got her own dislike of it from.

These memories were not enough to banish her concern about Charlie's whereabouts. Silly, really; he was probably perfectly fine, but just delayed. And being Charlie, he'd be worrying about her worrying about him, because that's what he was like. She smiled. Her dear Charlie.

She was fast approaching the last bench before the main road turned the corner and came up to meet the promenade. Relief flooded her: there he was, on a bench. He looked glum, almost certainly because he hadn't found her.

'Charlie! Am I glad to see you.'

When he looked up, he didn't seem relieved. 'Are you sure about that?'

She sat next to him, but he looked ahead, not at her. 'Of course I am. I waited an hour and a quarter at the tea room. I suspected you'd been held up, doing the repair.'

'Mr Edwards didn't need me to do it after all. I went to the New Inn, to have a coupla pints. Then I went for a walk.'

'But why?' She was starting to feel cross now, at his easy abandonment of her.

He didn't reply for several moments, then slowly turned his head to look at her. 'You clearly didn't need my company, since you had the arm of a posh bloke.'

Oh dear, Charlie must have seen her with Dan after all. This was a disaster. Where had he seen them?

'Your silence says everything. I saw you walking onto the pier with him, as I'd come to look for you, having finished early. You obviously didn't expect me to catch you.'

'No, Charlie, it's not like that, really it isn't.' She tried to take his hand but he moved it away.

'What is it like then? Is he the one who you were involved with at your last job, and why you had to leave?'

'You don't believe that nonsense of Gertie and Fanny's, do you?'

He shrugged.

This was it then, the day she'd dreaded. The only thing now was to tell the truth, otherwise the untruths and half-truths would get even more tangled.

'Daniel, for that is his name, is a childhood friend of my brother's. And mine, I suppose.'

'What, a posh bloke like him? What's he done, gone up in the world? Or are you, as I said all along, middle class? Mind you, he looked a bit more than—'

'It's time to explain, though goodness knows where I shall begin.'

He considered her with narrowed eyes, the hurt in his face still evident.

'It is true, that I taught Lady Evelyn Stansfield's son for nine months before he went away to private school. His governess had left, and my parents wanted to find some way of occupying me, so I didn't get into any more bother.'

'Bother? You were in trouble with the law?'

'No, of course not. Only with my parents, thanks partly to my brother, though he claims he did it to make them see they were being unreasonable.'

He shook his head. 'I don't get it.'

'I'd been attending suffragist meetings and talks behind their backs. They disapproved. They'd already put a lot of restrictions on my life, wanting me to marry well, as they put it.'

'Like I said, middle class.'

'One day they caught me out in a fib. I'd told them I was going with my friend, Henrietta, to a play in Brighton. Unfortunately, they came across her parents at a function, who, not knowing otherwise, mentioned the suffragist meeting we were actually attending. Her parents approved, you see. My parents had read in the papers about the marches and destruction caused by Mrs Pankhurst's suffragettes, not to mention poor Emily Davison being killed at the Epsom Derby when she jumped in front of the King's horse. They assumed that was the kind of thing the suffragists were doing, too. But they weren't. They only had peaceful protests.'

Charlie all the while had remained silent, leaning forward, his mouth slightly open. As she paused to draw breath and continue, he said, 'But what's that got to do with you being a governess and then coming to work at the hotel?'

'I'm getting there. My parents came to the hall where the meeting was taking place and dragged me away in front of everyone.'

'That must have been embarrassing.'

'It was *humiliating*. Back home, I was told to go to my room like a child. What made it worse was that Freddie, who knew I'd been going to the meetings, told them I'd been going for ages without getting into any bother, and that they were out of date and should be proud of me. They'd assumed it was the first time I'd deceived them and had planned on being lenient. Discovering I'd been doing it for months had them threatening to lock me in my room until a suitable husband could be found. Or worse, have me declared mentally unstable and placed in an asylum.'

'What?' Charlie looked horrified.

'I don't think they would have gone that far, but they wanted to frighten me into submission. But who knows? It was then that Lady Evelyn Stansfield came to my rescue and offered to take me on as a governess to her son for the nine months he had left at home. She had heard from Freddie what had happened and was sympathetic.'

'Right. And then?'

'When my charge went to boarding school, I had to go back home. The house was then inundated with "suitable men", as my mother put it, around for dinner, or afternoon tea, all of them boring, or too old, or very strict, or all three! Oh, just not the kind of people I'd want for a husband.'

'Right.'

Edie wished he'd have a bit more to say for himself than these sharp, accusing phrases.

'By May last year, I'd had enough. That's when I planned my escape. As I said, Lady Evelyn was sympathetic, agreeing as she did with the suffragists. I told her I needed to escape, though I was half joking, but she offered me a reference and I thought, why not? So, with Jenny's help, I planned my getaway.'

'Jenny? Who's she now?'

'Oh, our, um, maid.'

'You had a maid. And knew a lady. See, like I said, middle class.'

This was getting harder. 'No, Charlie, I promised you I wasn't middle class, and I'm not.'

'Eh? I don't get it. You'll be telling me next that you're not really Edie Moore.'

Did he really not understand by now? She was going to have to spell it out.

'I am Edie, short for Edith, as you're aware. I suppose you could say Moore is also short for my surname, Moreland.'

'Edith Moreland?'

'Yes. In fact… the Honourable Edith Moreland, is how I used to be referred to.'

He stared at her like she was some horrific apparition.

'My father is Baron Howard Moreland, Lord Moreland, the owner of the Moreland and Buckley timber company. Lady Evelyn Stansfield is actually my godmother.'

'You're – you're – an Honourable?'

'Was. I've given it up.'

'And you lived – where?'

'Downland House. In the Downs, north of Rottingdean.'

He rested his elbows on his splayed legs and looked out to sea. She said no more, waiting for him to speak. He didn't seem to have taken it too badly. They could talk all about it now, and he'd see it didn't matter that she was different.

–

She was an 'Honourable'? She'd said she wasn't middle class, so she hadn't lied. But this was worse. She was a member of the nobility! Or aristocracy. He never had worked out the difference. He couldn't take it in. He looked out to sea, at the light glinting on the water. On the beach, children were running around, a couple of them throwing a ball to each other. It was like any other day. Except it wasn't.

The daughter of a baron, a lord. The Honourable Edith Moreland. Moreland and Buckley. It was a well-known company with warehouses in several towns. Owned by Lord Moreland.

'How did nobody guess who you were? Or recognise you? Your family is prominent in Sussex.'

'It's amazing how different you can look when you're not dressed up, and your hair is not arranged in the latest style, and you don't have to wear face paint. My parents didn't report my disappearance because the maid saw me leave of my own volition, and they didn't want a scandal. In fact, I was spotted, by Daniel, at the hotel, back in August. He told my brother and sister-in-law, who told my parents I was fine. I've been lucky, not to come across any of my parents' set at the hotel, probably because they have places aplenty to frequent in the Brighton area.'

She was going on and on, like it was an ordinary conversation, like he hadn't been dealt a severe shock.

'I'd rather have been honest with you, Charlie. I was afraid to tell you, because of the obstacle it would cause in our relationship. I didn't want to lose you.'

Despite her words, he couldn't help but be convinced he'd been convenient to her. Who'd think she was anything special, walking out with him? The Honourable Edith Moreland, pretending to be little Edie Moore, a former governess from a working-class family. She may not have said she was working class, but it had been implied. His sense of numbness disintegrated, and instead a massive rage rose inside him.

'You've used me for your little charade.'

She took his arm in both her hands.

'No, Charlie, no.' Her raised voice gained stares from those who passed by. She lowered her voice to say, 'I really haven't, Charlie. I thought long and hard before letting myself get involved with you.'

He removed his arm from her embrace. 'Don't be daft. This ain't no Shakespeare play where people pretend to be other people and it all works out in the end.'

'But, but I care for you, Charlie,' she whispered on a strangled breath.

He turned his body on the seat to face her more fully. 'And how would that have worked out, eh? You, the daughter of aristocracy, and me a, a porter, and the son of a motor car mechanic?'

'I've left my old life. I don't belong there anymore.'

He stood up and peered down at Edie. Her face was a picture of misery. It broke his heart, but there was nothing he could do about that. 'You don't belong 'ere either. Now, if you don't mind, I want to be alone. Or maybe I'll go and visit my *lower-class* family.'

He stormed off, hoping his final sentence would prevent her from following him.

It did.

–

Edie watched as Charlie walked away, down the promenade towards the pier, wanting to run after him, plead with him. It would do nothing, though, except make fools of the pair of them. She needed to give him time to come to terms with it. When he'd thought it over, he'd see she'd acted with the best of intentions, and that she really wasn't part of that world anymore.

She should have told him about Dan's offer of marriage, and how she'd turned him down. That would surely make him see that she didn't want her old life back. Or would he see it as another deceit?

Her eyes stung as the hurt welled up, threatening to choke her. She needed to cry, but she couldn't do that here. She stood up and ran away from the promenade, across the edge of the common. People stared at her as she went, probably thinking how unladylike it was. Who cared? She was sick of being ladylike.

Where could she go? Not back to the hotel. She looked at her wristwatch: a quarter past four. Would Julia be back from school by now? She kept running, the tears trickling down her cheeks.

Reaching Norfolk Road, she was relieved to see Julia approaching the house where she had her rooms. Her friend spotted her, a look of delight brightening her face, until she realised what a state Edie was in.

'What on earth is wrong?'

Edie came to a sudden halt next to her. The tears were flowing now.

'Please, can I come in and talk to you?'

'Of course you can.' She led her upstairs to her rooms.

'Sit down. I'll get some tea.'

'Afterwards, please. I need to tell you – now.'

Julia sat next to her on the settee. 'Whatever is it?'

'You – you might be quite shocked by – by what I have to say.' She took a handkerchief from her handbag and blew her nose, then sobbed a few times.

'Oh dear. All right. I'm your friend, and I'm here for you.'

'Thank you. I'll begin at the beginning.'

She told her the story in much the same way she'd told Charlie. Julia didn't interrupt at all, letting her get it all out, as she did at some speed.

When Edie had finished, she looked at her friend, her chin still wobbling.

'Well, that is quite a story. I can't say I'm totally surprised about the Honourable Edith Moreland part. Hmm.' Julia stood up. 'Let me get that tea now. You look like you need it.'

–

Edie had found great relief in telling Julia her story, finally leaving her rooms at five past six, in time for the middle supper at the hotel. The delay would have given Charlie time to cool down as well. Perhaps, after the meal, they'd be able to talk sensibly.

But Charlie didn't turn up for supper, prompting several questions from Fanny, which Edie tried to answer simply, but all it did was produce a cross-examination.

'You say Charlie went to see his family? He's never mentioned them being close by before. I thought he came from Portsmouth.'

'He doesn't sound like someone from Portsmouth,' said the stillroom maid, Hetty.

'He isn't,' said Edie. 'He worked there for a couple of years, that's all.' It had never occurred to her that the others didn't know he had family on Western Road.

'Why doesn't he live with his family then?' Fanny persisted.

'He is a grown-up, pet,' said Mrs Turnbull. 'Maybe he thinks he's too old.'

'So you didn't spend today together?'

Lili thumped the boiled potatoes onto the table and sat down. 'Is it your business, Fanny?'

'Yes, we did,' Edie said, all the same. 'But he left during the afternoon and I went to see my friend, Julia.'

'How is she?' Lili asked. 'Still enjoying living in Mrs Bygrove's cousin's rooms?'

'Yes, she much prefers it to the guest house.'

'What did you and Charlie do today then? Did you have an argument, and that's why he went to see his family?' Fanny smiled, presumably at the idea of them falling out. She was not going to let this go. It was like she'd taken over the lippiness and confidence that Gertie had once had, who now only sat quietly, head down.

Mrs Leggett entered with a platter of fried flounders. 'Miss Bullen, I believe you've already been told by Miss Probert to mind your own business.'

'Aren't we allowed to have a conversation no more?'

'Not when you are annoying other members of staff. Now, I'm sure Mr Cobbett will either turn up for late supper, or he'll have it with his family, and there's an end to it.'

Fanny stabbed a fish on the platter that fell apart when she tried to lift it up.

'Use the server, Miss Bullen, for pity's sake!'

'All right, all right.' Fanny scooped up the pieces of fish and scattered them onto her plate.

'Any more of your cheek and you'll be sent upstairs without any supper.'

Lili nudged Edie and grinned. Edie attempted to smile back, but she wasn't convinced it hadn't come out as a grimace. She surveyed the food on the plate before her. It was well cooked, prepared to perfection by Mrs Norris and her staff, but she had no appetite.

Please come back soon, Charlie.

She picked up the cutlery and began on the meal regardless, otherwise someone would make a comment about that too.

-

Edie and Lili spent the remainder of the evening in the dining room, in one corner, while the rest of the middle supper staff returned to their shifts. The pair of them chatted with the late supper staff as they knitted gloves. The wool had been unravelled from old jumpers, cardigans and blankets collected by Mrs Bygrove from a local appeal, to encourage her female staff to knit items for the soldiers abroad. Even Mrs Leggett was taking part, declaring it 'calming'.

'I do like the idea of being able to contribute to the war effort,' said Lili, not for the first time, as she completed a purl row and turned the knitting around.

'It'll be getting a bit warm for them thick gloves now,' Stuart Coulter, the desk clerk, called down the table.

'But we'll have plenty to send to the soldiers when they do need them,' said Lili. 'Cold it'll get, in them trenches.'

Edie glanced at her wristwatch. Five past nine.

'Keep looking at the time, you do. You worried about Charlie?'

'I thought he'd be back by now.'

'Just be having a chinwag, he will, with his family, especially as he doesn't seem to see them very often.'

'Hm.' Edie normally enjoyed knitting, being able to chat and knit with whoever else was in the room. But tonight, she'd dropped several stitches because of her worries, and just wished the evening would come to an end.

When the clock on the dresser chimed ten, she placed the knitting down. 'I must get to bed. I'm exhausted.'

'Nobody'd think you'd had a day off,' Lili joked.

'No, they wouldn't. Good night. If I'm asleep when you come up, I'll see you in the morning.'

'If Charlie gets in before I go to bed, do you want me to give him a message?'

She thought about it. 'No, that's fine. I'll see him in the morning, no doubt.'

They wouldn't have much chance to talk tomorrow, but she'd have to make the best of the time they did have.

–

A new month, a new start. Yet another one. As Edie dressed the next morning, she decided that things would be different between her and Charlie, that they'd start June being absolutely honest with each other. It was the only way to go. She'd tell him the whole truth about Daniel, too. The sun was already shining through the partly opened curtains, bringing the promise of another fine day.

Lili had gone down to breakfast before her, saying she was starving, and Edie headed downstairs the second she was ready.

In the dining room, she was disappointed to see that Charlie hadn't arrived yet. She hoped he hadn't been drinking too much the night before and developed a hangover. Phoebe and Annie brought in two plates of breakfast each and served those already sitting down. She'd taken only two mouthfuls when Mrs Bygrove came into the dining room, holding what looked like a note in her hand.

'Edie, could I have a word, please.'

She rose, wondering what bad news Helen might have received, by the look on her face, and whether she'd be asked to take over a few other shifts in various places. She didn't mind when there was some extra money to be had. She'd be able to buy a few more pieces of clothing with it.

In the corridor, she handed Edie the note. 'This was left on the kitchen table for me this morning. I don't know whether you're aware of this, so I thought you ought to be the first to see it.'

It was folded and had 'Mrs Bygrove' written on one side. It looked like Charlie's writing. Opening it confirmed this. She read it quickly, taking in a sharp breath and holding it until she came to the end of the short missive.

'No, oh no. Charlie!'

'I'm truly sorry, Edie. I understand you'd been walking out. He doesn't seem to have been himself since the incident with the White Feather Brigade. I dare say that's what at least part of this is about.'

'But to enlist, and not even tell anyone beforehand.' What she meant was, *not even to tell me*. The tears came quickly.

'You're in no state to do your shift on the desk this morning. I'll cover for you. Go and finish your breakfast and then, I don't know, go for a walk maybe.'

'No, I will do my shift. But I couldn't finish my breakfast,' she said, sniffing regularly. 'I'll go to my room now and get ready.'

'If you're sure. I shall go and tell the others what's happened.'

Edie ran up the staff stairs to her bedroom, collapsing into a heap on her bed and sobbing. A few minutes later, Lili came in and sat beside her.

'I'm so sorry, Edie. Is there anything I can do?'

'No,' she croaked, wanting to say, *you can leave me alone*, but appreciating her friend's concern too much to be rude to her.

'I wish I knew what to say, but being in the same position, like, I know there's nothing'll make it better, except a bit of time to get used to it. So I'll leave you now and see you later. I'm on breakfasts, and need to finish my own, see.'

Edie didn't reply and was relieved when Lili had gone. She wasn't convinced time, or anything else, would help her get used to this.

–

Edie wasn't sure what was worse: the sad looks of sympathy from most of the female staff, or the look of resentment, yet glee, on Fanny's face. She'd no doubt that Gertie would have had the same expression, had she not given up conveying any emotion. At the early lunch, which Edie fancied no more than she had breakfast, she said little as those around her chatted about the situation.

Stuart Coulter picked at his food, looking glum. 'I'll be last man standing at this rate. I thought Charlie was dead set against enlisting.'

'Me too,' said Mrs Turnbull. 'It were a right shock, that note of his.'

'Mrs Bygrove's got Gertie in a porter's cap and stuck a jacket over a waitress's dress, so I can have me dinner. Mr Bygrove did his nut, but there ain't a lot of choice, until Stanley and Morris come in later. Gertie weren't best pleased neither.'

Edie had been witness to that, just before Mr Watkins had taken over from her at the desk. He would give her short shrift if she kept that glum expression up for the guests.

'And I 'eard the major tell Mr Bygrove that there's been an air raid on London by one of them Zeppelin things,' said Stuart.

'Lord help us!' Mrs Turnbull clutched her hands in front of her face, as if in prayer.

Talk of the raid faded into the background as Edie thought instead about Charlie. What else could she have done, to stop the situation ending up like this? Told him right from the start? Then he probably wouldn't even have been her friend, let alone anything else. And maybe that would have been better. *Better to have loved and lost, than never to have loved at all*, Lord Tennyson had written. But right now, she'd rather not have fallen in love with Charlie than to have this terrible heartache. She put her knife and fork together, despite there still being food on her plate.

'You not gonna finish that?' Stuart asked.

'No, you're welcome to it, if you want it.' She pushed her plate along.

'Not 'alf.'

'You all right, lass?' the storekeeper gave her that sad look she'd already tired of.

'I'll head to the dining room, to see if anything needs doing before the lunch guests start arriving.'

And she could be alone there, for a short while.

Chapter Twenty-Two

The last three weeks had dragged by for Edie, filled with misery as they were. Her first half-day off after Charlie's departure had been so plagued with sadness that she hadn't bothered with the next two, asking Mrs Bygrove if she might hold them in lieu, in case she needed to visit her family again. Helen had readily agreed, adding that Douglas 'didn't need to know'.

And now had come an opportunity to escape the hotel and its memories for a while, an opportunity she'd never have taken three weeks ago. But at this moment, the invitation to Freddie's twenty-eighth birthday celebration was welcome. As luck would have it, his birthday fell on a Monday, and he'd decided to celebrate it then, not at the weekend, which, it being the summer season, Edie would never have got off.

As the train she was now sitting in left Falmer station and headed for Lewes, she pondered the irony of running away from the hotel to Freddie's. If only she could have shared that with—

She sighed. Charlie. But if he'd been there to share it with, she wouldn't be going. He'd written again to Helen, telling her he was training at Bexhill, like most of the others, part of the 11th Service Battalion, known as the 1st South Downs.

The countryside of the gently sloping downs became town once more as the buildings of Lewes loomed into view and a small hope burned in her. Dan had picked her up in his motor car last time. To have the company of someone she'd known many years, and who cared about her, would be welcome, even if she saw him as a dear friend, not a lover. Freddie and Lucia cared for her too, but if she were honest, they were more bound up in their own little world than anyone else's. Perhaps she'd even tell Dan about Charlie, so he'd understand why she couldn't be with him. No, that would be cruel.

She stepped off the train, looking around the platform. No Dan, as yet.

'Miss Edith Moreland?'

She twisted around to locate the voice. A man walked towards her, tall with sandy hair under a grey homburg, looking to be around his early thirties. His brow was creased, as if he were trying to work something out.

'Yes, that's me.' Though it felt strange to be addressed as such.

He held out his hand. 'Hilary Cranford. How do you do?'

She shook his hand. 'How do you do?'

His smile melted her initial fear, that he might be here on her parents' behalf, about to abduct her and return her to them. How absurd she was!

'Freddie asked me if I would pick you up.'

'That was kind of you. Is Daniel not around?'

'Daniel?'

'Obviously not.' She laughed, though disappointed.

He showed her to his motor car, a small and oldish Humber with only two seats and a fawn cloth top that made it look a little like a perambulator. She had no choice but to put her bag on her lap.

Once off, she set out to find out exactly who this man was. It occurred to her too late that he could be anybody, and not there on her brother's request at all. She'd not heard Freddie mention his name before.

'How do you know Freddie?'

'I met him playing tennis at a local club. This is the first time I've been to one of his parties, though I'm told they're notorious.' He raised his eyebrows as he glanced at her. He was clearly hoping they would be, whatever he thought people meant by that.

'Notorious? I wouldn't know. I've been to his new house only once, and it was quite sedate, with only three other guests.'

He chuckled. 'We can only hope.'

She wondered what exactly they'd told this Hilary Cranford about her. Nothing, hopefully.

'So, what do you do, Miss Edith?'

'A bit of this and that, you know.' It was certainly true in the hotel at the moment.

'Oh yes, I know.' He nodded sagely. He maybe assumed she flitted between social events and charity work, like many of her class.

'And what about you, Mr Cranford?'

'I'm a writer.'

'How interesting.'

'It certainly can be, when the right story presents itself.'

'When inspiration comes, I suppose.'

'Something like that.' He swung the car round a bend as town became country once more.

Little was said after that, apart from a couple of observations about the scenery, the warm weather and the gathering cloud. She was relieved when they arrived. She didn't know what to make of this new friend of her brother's.

After effusive greetings from Freddie and Lucia, she was ordered to the bedroom she'd slept in last time, to change into something more appropriate. As before, clothes from her old life were laid across the bed, with a couple of other outfits hanging on the outside of the wardrobe. Lucia must have been raiding her old room again.

Back downstairs, in the garden room, there were about a dozen people there for her brother's dinner party, including Clotilde and Percy.

'Happy birthday, Freddie.' She kissed his cheek and presented him with a card. 'I gather Dan wasn't able to make it.'

'Ah.' He and Lucia looked at each other.

'Now is as good a time as ever. I'll go and get it.' Lucia left the room.

'Get what?' said Edie.

Freddie gave her that look of sympathy that some of the staff at the hotel had given her after Charlie's departure. She had a sense of foreboding.

Lucia returned and presented her with a letter, with only her first name on the front. A lump formed in her throat. This felt too familiar.

She opened it, walking away to the garden. Reading it quickly, the inevitability had her sighing long and deep. Dan had enlisted too. Furthermore, the battalion he mentioned was the same as Charlie's.

Although not possessing the deep emotions for him that she held for Charlie, it hurt to know he was another friend putting himself in danger. And was this likely her fault as well? Had he done this because she'd refused him, in the same way Charlie had done because she let him down?

Lucia came up behind and placed her hands on Edie's shoulders.

'He's not the only one in our group to have enlisted. Another four of them have, including George.'

'Oh dear. Another of Freddie's old school friends.'

She wondered how many of them would return, immediately pushing the thought from her mind.

'You were fond of Dan, weren't you?'

Edie folded the letter up and returned it to the envelope. 'Fond, yes. But nothing more. I've known him a long time.'

'Come, meet the rest of the party. Not everyone could come, but you'll know a couple of Freddie's other old school chums.'

'I thought they looked familiar.'

'Remember, Dan is only training and not yet in any danger, nor will he be for some months.'

Lucia was right. And the same thing applied to Charlie.

She took her sister-in-law's arm. 'Come on then, introduce me to your friends.'

–

The evening consisted of conversation, and some argument, about the war. Much wine had been drunk, though not by Edie, who had stuck to one glass. Most had ventured out into the gardens, standing and sitting in groups, with almost the lightest evening of the year being upon them. At least half had taken a turn in the punt on the large pond. She had mainly stuck to Freddie or Lucia, though had fallen into conversation with the other two of her brother's old friends, who had stayed at their house a few times in their childhood.

Despite the outward appearance of joining in, Edie still felt apart from these people, most of whom didn't know of her escape to another life. She was thankful that neither Freddie, Lucia, Percy nor Clotilde had made any reference to it. She got by in conversation by asking questions or speaking of the war, or the arts, or the theatre, never once having to refer to any part of her own daily life.

Freddie, and some of his house guests, had retired to bed by eleven thirty. All those who were not staying had left. So much for this notoriety Mr Cranford had spoken of. Lucia was still up, playing poker with Clotilde and a young couple. Edie and Hilary sat a few feet away on the pink Chesterfield sofa, half watching. Staying up this late felt indulgent to her, who, having to get up so early each day, was normally in bed by this time. Even so, she wasn't yet ready to settle down with nothing but thoughts of Charlie, and now Dan, to haunt her.

'I've heard about your mad adventure,' said Hilary, out of the blue.

'My what?' But even as she said it, she knew that it hadn't been kept as quiet as she'd thought. She cursed whoever had told him.

'I overheard Freddie talking to Percy about it. So I'm afraid I was nosy and asked questions. Is it true? Are you working as a chambermaid?'

'Shh, keep your voice down. Really, Freddie shouldn't have even been talking about it.' She'd have words with him in the morning.

'Are you afraid I'll spill the beans?' He seemed highly amused, which annoyed her all the more.

'To whom, exactly? Not my parents, I hope. And I'm not a chambermaid, I'm a receptionist.' Why she had to make it sound more respectable she had no idea. She also waited in the dining room and conservatory from time to time, and helped with other things, too, but she didn't need to mention those.

'Excuse me for getting it wrong,' he laughed. 'Trying to see how the other half live, are you?'

'The other half? More like the other ninety per cent. Perhaps more people in the so-called middle and upper classes should spend time living as the working classes do. They might learn a thing or two.'

'Are you some kind of philanthropist, doing a study?'

'No, I'm just tired of being bossed and bullied by my parents, and all because I attended a few suffragist meetings.' Not that they'd been any better before. It had just been the last straw.

'I admire you, in a way. It can't be easy to put privilege to one side and live an ordinary life.'

'I'm not sure I'd call it ordinary. You said you were a writer. What do you write?'

'A variety of things. Whatever takes my interest – or I think will take my readers' interest.'

'You've been published then?'

'Yes, I've been published.'

'I'll have to look out for you in the bookshops.'

He grinned and looked away.

'I don't want my story coming out in some novel, by the way.'

'It would make for an interesting premise. But I already have a project I'm currently working on.'

'Good.'

'If you're so keen to get away from your privileged life, you could do war work, you know. As a VAD nurse, for instance.'

'It has crossed my mind.' Especially since Charlie's departure. She was grateful that this Hilary Cranford knew nothing of that. 'And who knows, maybe I will. Though I am doing my bit for the war effort. I'm knitting for the men abroad, and I've been involved in raising money for them, you know, for smokes and the like.'

'Very noble of you.' He didn't sound like he meant it.

'You've not thought of enlisting yourself?' Since he was being so judgemental.

'I did try, but I have flat feet. I'm unable to walk any great distance without much discomfort. Who knew such an insignificant encumbrance could deprive one of serving one's country.'

'Indeed, who knew.'

'My straight flush wins!' Clotilde shouted in triumph. She pulled the coins on the table towards her.

'Oh, do let's have one more game,' said the female guest at the table.

'Yes, one more,' Lucia pronounced.

Edie rose. 'I think that's my cue to retire. Good night, Mr Cranford.'

He nodded his head. 'Madam.'

She waved a good night to the poker players and left the room. Although her body was tired, her head was still whirring, but if she didn't go to bed now, she'd surely fall asleep on the Chesterfield.

-

Edie had enjoyed a good night's sleep, despite her various worries. Something she did miss at the hotel was a comfortable bed and having a room to herself, with all its various luxuries, including soft sheets. And a proper bathroom. Lili was a good companion with whom to share; she could certainly have done worse with Fanny and Gertie, but it wasn't like having her own space.

Having dressed and packed her bag ready for her departure later that day, she ventured forth onto the landing, tempted there by the faint aroma of a cooked breakfast.

About to head downstairs, Lucia passed her on the landing, sporting a silk negligee.

'Good morning, Edie, and what a beautiful one it is.' She seemed cheerful about something. 'I'm just off for a bath. Smells like Mrs Riddles has started breakfast for the early risers.'

'Is Freddie up yet?'

She put her hand to her lips and chuckled. 'You know what a lazybones he is.' She waved as she moved away and entered the bathroom. 'Anon, anon!'

Freddie would be alone now, so it would be an ideal opportunity to give him a good talking-to about telling Hilary Cranford her secret. She had a vision of sitting on the end of his bed, trying to get him up, as she so often did in their younger days.

She knocked on his door and waited. Getting no reply, she guessed he was still asleep and entered without knocking a second time.

'Rise and shine,' she announced as she shut the door. 'I want a word with— Oh, oh. I'm, I'm sorry – I—'

'Do you always enter people's bedrooms without being invited?' Percival croaked, lying on the side of the bed nearest her, a sheet draped over just enough of his naked body to make him decent.

Freddie's head popped up on the other side. 'Edie!'

'I'm so sorry. Excuse me.'

She ran from the room, red-faced, stopping at the top of the stairs to catch her breath.

Why was she surprised? She'd long suspected it, at the back of her mind, before Freddie had married Lucia. That's why she'd been surprised when Lucia had told her of the impending wedding. What to do? The breakfast scenario, having to make small talk with those she barely knew, did not appeal to her now. What an idiot she'd been, just walking in! Even if Percy hadn't been there, Freddie might have been naked, or getting dressed, or, well, who knew?

What she needed was a walk, and the garden was the best place for that.

She ran down the stairs and out through the front door, hoping to meet no one, least of all Mr Cranford. Reaching the pond, she headed around to the other side, near the punt, where there were two wooden seats and a bed of blossoming pinks.

She wondered, not for the first time, if their parents had had any notion about Freddie's… preferences. They surely hadn't, otherwise the recriminations for him would have been worse than for her after the revelation of her suffragist activities.

She'd been sitting there for a while, pondering these matters, when Lucia appeared and sat on the other seat.

'Edie, I'm sorry you had to find out like that. Did you have no clue?'

'I think I already knew, deep down. That is, I knew he was attracted to men. Or I thought I did, until he married you. Then I thought I'd imagined it. I can't say I understand. If you knew, why did you marry him?'

'Oh Edie, life is not that simple. He wouldn't be allowed to marry another man, any more than I would be able to marry a woman. It was the ideal solution.'

'You, marry a—? So, you're attracted to women?'

'Don't sound so surprised. It does happen. The only difference is that although I can't marry a woman, it's not illegal for me to love one.'

'Doesn't the law cover both?'

'No, it doesn't. I suppose the powers that be don't imagine in their wildest dreams that *women* would do something so *depraved*. Huh! So ironic, when some would pay good money to see it acted out.'

'They what?' Edie had a feeling that she'd turned into Alice in Wonderland and had fallen down a rabbit hole to another world.

'Well, never mind that. The fact is, it's illegal for Freddie to love a man, and it's most certainly frowned upon for a woman to love another woman. Freddie and I have a great deal of affection for each other and rub along nicely together. It seemed the perfect solution, for us to marry, to allay any suspicions, so we could carry on our preferred lives behind closed doors. The friends we invite to stay understand, and a couple have the same – situation – as us.'

'What about that Hilary Cranford? He's new. Does he know?'

Lucia chuckled. 'I suspect Mr Cranford is that way inclined himself, by some of the things he has said. But we have tried to be subtle on this occasion. Percy and Clotilde have a room each on either side of ours, so it makes things easier.'

'Clotilde?'

'Why of course. Clotilde is my lover.'

It made sense, now she thought about it.

'Lucia, I would be careful of Hilary Cranford, all the same. I can't put my finger on it, but there's something about him I don't like.'

'He seems harmless enough. He's a writer, you know. Perhaps he even writes of such things.'

'Do Percival and Clotilde live here all the time?'

'No, for that would look strange. But they come to stay often. Freddie and I are trying to persuade them to get married, but they are not as keen on the idea.'

'What about the servants? Do they know?'

'Part of a servant's job is to keep quiet about their employers' lives, you know that.'

But they don't always, thought Edie. 'I think I might be ready for some breakfast now. I will have to leave straight after luncheon, as I have to do an evening shift on the desk.'

Lucia raised her eyes and tutted. 'We all have things in our lives that would seem abnormal to others, I suppose. Hilary has already agreed to give you a lift back to the station, as it's on his way back to his home in Lewes. I hope you don't mind.'

She'd rather not have spent any more time alone with him, but she supposed it was kind of him to offer.

'It's not like it takes long to get there, so it will be fine. Thank you.'

'Come then, for I am ready for my breakfast, too.'

Chapter Twenty-Three

Edie's turn on the desk had just finished and she'd never been gladder. She stretched and alighted from the stool as Richard Watkins approached to start the evening shift.

'Seems a bit quiet for July,' he said, lifting the counter to enter. 'Especially as it's warm and sunny.'

'It's been a slow afternoon altogether, with few queries or requests, and no telephone calls whatever. Afternoon tea was quiet, too. But it is Monday. How was your mother today, Mr Watkins?'

'A bit brighter, I felt. Thank you for asking. I'd go and stay with her if she didn't live in Lancing. It's a bit far to get to work each day, especially with the different shifts.'

'It is rather,' she agreed.

He leant towards her to whisper, 'How's Miss Green been today?' referring to Gertie, who was standing by the door into the dining room, hands linked behind her back, looking serious.

Unable to find a male replacement for Charlie, but able to acquire a new chambermaid, Mrs Bygrove had commissioned two uniforms with a long skirt for Gertie, who now looked, to everyone's surprise, quite smart, taking care with her hair for a change.

'Efficient, but not chatty.'

'You get off to early dinner now, Miss Moore. I'll see you when you take over for my dinner hour. I presume Stanley-should be here to take over from Miss Green.'

'It's not six fifteen yet, Mr Watkins. I dare say he'll be here soon.'

As she was about to enter the dining room, Edie experienced that small jerk of excitement she still got at the anticipation of seeing Charlie at mealtimes. As always, now, it melted into disappointment. She still couldn't quite get used to the idea that he was gone.

Jack the cook was placing a plate of pigs' trotters on the table. 'I'm telling you, they wouldn't be passing no act about national registers unless they intended to round up the rest of the men to enlist them.'

Lili was sitting at the far end of the table. 'Don't say that. I don't want my brothers being hauled off, or "rounded up", as you put it. And anyway, it's men aged fifteen to sixty-five what they're requiring to register, isn't it, and they won't be taking the old men, and surely not the fifteen- to seventeen-year-olds.'

Edie sat next to Lili. 'Let's hope not.'

Mrs Leggett was clattering down the cutlery. 'Of course not. *And* they want women to register. They're hardly going to send *them* off to war.'

'They might do if Mrs Pankhurst has her way,' said Phoebe, placing two teapots on the table. 'In the newspaper it said she led a "Women's Right to Serve" demonstration last Saturday, in Trafalgar Square.'

'Well, that's just *ridiculous*. Who'd do the jobs at home, the children?' Mrs Leggett laughed mirthlessly.

'I believe it's to do with war work in general,' said Edie, 'not going to war.'

'I should think not. Miss Probert, help me fetch the rest of the food before everyone else arrives.'

Lili left with the housekeeper as Gertie entered. She removed her peaked hat and slumped onto a bench. She was followed by Fanny.

Mrs Leggett doubled back. 'Miss Green, Miss Bullen, fetch the plates off the dresser and put them out.'

Gertie grunted but did as she was told.

Fanny was not so compliant. 'How come you ain't been told to do nothin'?' She glared at Edie.

'I've no idea. I'm quite happy to help.' She got up to give them a hand.

'Oh no, ya don't! I'm not havin' Mrs Leggett sayin' I'm not doin' me job.'

Edie lifted her hands in a mixture of surrender and exasperation. 'Fine!' She sat, lifting a letter from her skirt pocket.

'I s'pose that's from Charlie,' said Fanny.

'No, it's from… a friend.' How else to describe Daniel?

'Have you 'eard from Charlie?'

Phoebe returned at this point with two pots of coffee.

'I haven't heard from Charlie,' said Edie, 'but the letters he's sent to Mrs Bygrove say he's training at Bexhill.'

'I know that. How come Charlie ain't written to you then?'

'I don't know, Fanny.'

'He musta realised you wasn't for him.'

'Don't be mean,' said Phoebe. 'The men training and away fighting are busy. My auntie's lucky to get a letter every two months from my cousin. Even Günther, at his camp, only writes once a month.' She looked sad.

'At least Günther won't get killed,' Gertie mumbled.

But what kind of life would he have in England after the war, Edie wondered?

Phoebe didn't reply, maybe thinking the same, and left the room once more.

Edie put the letter away as others filtered in to take their places at the table. She already knew what the letter said, but liked the reassurance of it, as something especially for her from someone she was fond of. Dan was training to be a lieutenant, he said, no doubt because of his status and education.

Lili returned with a bowl of peas.

'We're talking about letters,' said Gertie. 'You 'eard from that Norman of yours?'

Lili's expression suggested she was about to tell Gertie to mind her own business, but softened as she sat. 'As it happens, I've got a letter to read over breakfast.'

The meal began and the chatter centred around the new Registration Act and Mrs Pankhurst's demonstration. It wasn't until the maids were sent to the scullery with the dirty plates that Lili pulled a letter from her pocket and opened it.

'It's a bit of a short one today,' she muttered. She started to hum as she read it.

Edie waited to see if Lili would tell her more, but when her eyebrows drew together and she bit her bottom lip, Edie felt compelled to whisper, 'What's wrong, Lili?'

'Norman. His… his battalion, they're due to go abroad on… Oh no. The letter must have taken a while to get here. They left, they left two days ago.' Her head fell forward onto her chest and a sob escaped her lips.

Edie curled her arm around her friend. 'Oh Lili. Can I do anything?'

Lili shoved the letter back in her pocket, whispering, 'I've got to be alone for a while. Tell the others I've gone to the lavvy if they ask.' She swung her legs over the bench and got off it.

'All right.'

–

It was a busy lunchtime on the desk, with Edie making several telephone calls to book theatre tickets for guests and welcoming three new rooms of people to the hotel. It had picked up from the week before, and Edie was glad of the activity to take her mind off worrying about Lili.

Her friend had rallied and carried out her job as efficiently as she always did, but she had been down at mealtimes and had cried herself to sleep every night since receiving the letter. Edie had tried not to think about how she would feel if Charlie were sent abroad. *When* he was sent abroad. The war was unlikely to end before his training was finished, yet the prospect seemed unreal. She turned her attention back to the desk and picked up the telephone to make yet another call.

Gertie was also being kept busy. Despite her moans and moods at break times, she had become more cheerful as a porter. Edie wondered whether she felt more content, knowing she didn't have to enter bedrooms and risk being put into another frightening situation. And she no doubt appreciated the tips.

How cynical of me. Edie smiled to herself while waiting for the operator to connect her to the Theatre Royal in Brighton, so she could book tickets for a young couple staying the week.

Having made the booking, she welcomed Lady Blackmore and her companion, Cecelia, who had been awaiting her attention.

'We were just passing, and thought we would pop in to book afternoon tea today for the earliest time you have.'

'Of course, My Lady.' Edie pulled the restaurant booking register in front of her. 'Here we are. Three o'clock?'

'Splendid. I was saying to Cecelia, if it wasn't for the supply ships in the harbour and the occasional man in uniform, you'd hardly think there was a war on, wasn't I, Cecelia?'

'Yes, My Lady. And the fact that the businesses have more and more women taking over, as they are here.'

Lady Blackmore pinched her lips in and looked askance at Cecelia, as if disapproving of her opinion.

'That's all booked for you, My Lady.' Edie grinned, resisting the urge to mention the raised prices and the increasing number of men heading off to the Front. Maybe she had no loved ones signed up and in imminent danger.

'I suppose the women who have taken over the men's positions in the hotel have made a reasonable fist of it,' Lady Blackmore conceded. 'But I think—'

She was cut short by someone swinging open both front doors and entering in a most dramatic manner. Edie was shocked to see Lucia rush in, out of breath. She put one hand to her chest and hurried over.

'Are you not going to shut the door after you?' Her Ladyship complained.

Gertie, arriving back in the foyer, called, 'I'll see to that, m'lady,' and moved briskly to the doors.

'Welcome, Lady Moreland,' Edie called, so that Lady Blackmore would realise she was dealing with at least an equal.

She could tell by Lucia's bearing that all was not well. Her heart beat wildly as she sent up a prayer that it was only her sister-in-law being dramatic, as usual.

Lucia reached the desk, glancing at the other two guests. 'I'm so sorry for my abrupt arrival, but I had the feeling I was being followed by a scoundrel, who maybe wanted to steal my handbag.'

Lady Blackmore stuck her nose in the air. 'It's the weather, and the crowds. It brings out the pickpockets.'

'Quite so,' Lucia agreed.

'Let us away, Cecelia. Come along.' She beckoned her companion as one would a dog.

Edie and Lucia watched as they strolled away. Gertie rushed to open the doors for them.

'Thank goodness, I thought they'd never leave,' huffed Lucia.

'Shh. Not a word while Gertie's here.'

Two guests arrived to book in, occupying Edie for some minutes. Lucia waited to one side, having graciously allowed them to go first, at least for show.

As soon as Gertie had disappeared up in the lift with the guests and suitcases, Edie said, 'What are you doing here, Lucia? You know this is awkward.'

'It's Freddie and Percy.'

'They've signed up?'

'No. It's worse.'

'Worse? Oh my Lord, have they had an accident?'

'No, no, it's that so-called writer, Hilary Cranford, who wangled his way into our house.'

'Wangled? I thought he was invited.'

'So did we, but, but… Oh Edie, he's a journalist. He must have befriended Freddie on purpose, to bring him down.'

'But why? And how?'

'Because he'd heard – he'd heard things about Freddie and Percy. I don't know who could have told him. But he's going to write an article in the local newspaper about it, and say how we're enjoying an elaborate and debauched lifestyle, while others enlist or help the war effort or are suffering shortages. As if speaking our minds on current matters and inviting our guests to add to the decoration of our house is debauched! And he's going to tell his readers that Freddie and Percy are homosexuals. He says he's also going to report them to the police. They have never been open about that, except among friends who are sympathetic. Edie, you didn't tell him about finding Freddie and Percy together, did you?'

Edie was quiet for a few moments, taking this all in. 'No, of course I didn't tell him anything. And I told you I didn't trust him, if you remember. He said he was a writer, but didn't mention being a journalist. And Freddie told him about my 'adventure', as he put it, so he might write about me as well.'

She was afraid and angry all at once, tempted to toss the reservations register in front of her across the foyer in frustration. If only she hadn't gone to Freddie's that weekend, he may never have found out.

'Don't be so selfish, Edie. At least you won't be arrested.'

'I know, Lucia, but I will be exposed and hauled away by my parents. Of course I'm worried about Freddie, and Percy. Does Cranford want money? Is he blackmailing you?'

'He hasn't said so.'

'We'll think of something.'

'Could you come with me now? I've got the motor car. Freddie is in such a state, and you've always been the sensible one. Well, apart from this.' She pointed at the desk.

Her sister-in-law really did live in a different world. 'I can't just leave my shift, Lucia. Would you let one of your servants run off for the day? I have tomorrow afternoon off. I'll come then. But only for a couple of hours.'

Lucia looked down, her face filled with sadness. 'All right. It's better than nothing. Freddie will have to plead another day off ill to your father. Your parents, of course, have no idea what's happening.'

Edie heard the staff door close. 'Oh no, it's the manager. Please, look as if you've come to make an enquiry.'

Mr Bygrove straightened his tie and peered over at the desk. Lucia stood upright and put on a smile.

'Why, Lady Lucia Forsyth! What a great honour it is to see you again.' He put on his smarmiest voice. He must have remembered her from when she'd supposedly come to pay back the train fare.

'It's Lady Lucia Moreland now, but thank you. Mr Bygrove, isn't it?'

'That's right, Your Ladyship.' He bowed low, giving Lucia the opportunity to raise her eyes at Edie. 'Is there anything *I* can help you with?'

'No, no. Miss Moore here has been more than helpful, informing me of serving times for dinner. My husband and I may drop by one evening.'

'You would be most welcome.' He performed another bow, even deeper. 'Though it is wise to book in advance.'

'I shall have to talk to my husband first. Now, if you'll excuse me.' She walked away and raised a hand, calling, 'Anon, anon.'

Bygrove considered her receding back with some awe, before coming to and running to the door to open it for her.

Sycophantic old fool, thought Edie, but the belligerent sentiment was immediately overridden by worry for Freddie and Percy. Damn Hilary Cranford! Tomorrow couldn't come quickly enough. She only hoped they'd be able to do something.

Chapter Twenty-Four

'We have several options, as far as I can see,' said Edie, sitting in the garden room of Bergenia Cottage.

Freddie and Lucia were huddled together on a Chesterfield, holding hands, while Percy and Clotilde sat in separate armchairs, both looking gloomy.

'You could offer to pay Hilary Cranford off,' Edie continued, 'for this may just be a blackmail attempt.'

'That will make us look guilty,' said Freddie, 'and we've told him, in no uncertain terms, that he is mistaken. And blackmailers are in the habit of coming back for more, so I've heard.'

Percy stretched his legs. 'Besides which, he has no proof. The birthday party he came to was not debauched, as he put it, or even particularly lavish, and our other guests will attest to that. Yes, we may be a little bohemian, but so are many others. And where is his proof that we are homosexuals? We're not exactly overt.'

'So where did he get this information in the first place?' said Edie.

'Supposition? Body language? Wishful thinking?' He huffed a brief laugh. 'I don't know.'

'I can't help thinking he'd come to that conclusion before he arrived,' said Edie. 'When he picked me up in the motor car, he mentioned he'd heard your parties were *notorious*. I told him I hadn't experienced that, and I'd been once before. He also implied that he hoped they were.'

'It's almost like he was trying to trick you into revealing something,' said Lucia.

Edie looked at Freddie. 'He told me he met you at the tennis club. Could you have done or said anything there that might have made him suspicious?'

'No, nothing. Like Percy said, we've never been overt about it when among the general public, you know that. You just can't be.'

'It does seem that he already knew something then.' Edie let out a laboured sigh. 'Do any of you know other journalists, or someone who could show Mr Cranford up as a liar, who could threaten him in return?'

'If he publishes, we could sue,' said Percy. 'For we'd have many witnesses on our side, and he'd have none.'

'You don't want it going that far, if you can avoid it.' She wondered if their parents would be of any use in tackling Mr Cranford. They may not want to, though, in case it went badly for Freddie and implicated them, too. But then, it might still reflect badly on them, even if they didn't get involved.

There was a loud, insistent knock at the front door. Edie rose to answer it, what with the other four being so down, but Lucia took her arm. 'One of the servants will get it.'

Of course. Servants.

They heard voices, then a rapid knocking on the garden room door, before Mrs Riddles, the cook, entered without waiting for a reply.

'Sir, Lady Lucia, the police are here,' she said in a panic. 'They're in the entrance hall, insisting on speaking to you, Mr Moreland and Lord Percival.'

Edie's stomach plummeted and she felt sick. Judging by the faces of the other four, they felt the same.

Lucia stood. 'Show them in, Mrs Riddles.'

Edie had a shock when Inspector Davis marched through the door, followed by a constable she didn't recognise. She bolted up. 'Detective Inspector Davis, what on earth are you doing in this neck of the woods?'

Davis appeared equally surprised to see her. 'Miss Moore, I could say the same.'

This was unfortunate. What could she say, and who would he tell? But he was the police and she couldn't lie, for he'd surely find out.

'You see… Freddie, Frederick, is my brother.'

'But if he's your brother, you must be the Honourable… someone. Not Moore. Ah. Moreland.'

'Yes, the Honourable Edith Moreland. I can't explain now. Tell Julia I give her permission to tell you, for she knows about it.'

'Does she? Anyway!' He became upright and stern once more. 'Who you are, or aren't, isn't why I'm here. They're short of police officers on this side of Sussex, due to enlistments, so I've been brought in to deal with this. So, which of you is the Honourable Frederick Moreland and which Lord Percival Challen?'

'That would be us, old boy,' said Percy, indicating the two of them. 'I'm Lord Percy.'

'Right. I've had reports of the breaking of the Criminal Law Amendment Act of 1885, and have been sent to investigate. You do know what I'm talking about.'

'The act about homosexuality, of course.' Percy flicked his hand, as if to bat the accusation away. 'I suppose it was that hack Hilary Cranford who reported that lie. What a surprise! He has already asked Freddie for money in order not to pass on his lies to the police.'

This wasn't true, and while Edie could see why Percy had made the counter-accusation, she was not at all convinced of its wisdom.

'Is that so?' said Davis.

Freddie stood. 'Yes, it is. Mr Cranford befriended me at the tennis club, and I made the mistake of inviting him to our home. But he came only to find something that would sound plausible with which to blackmail me.'

'But he's a journalist. He claims he was following up on a tip he received.'

'That's either a lie,' said Percy, 'or someone else thought they could make a bob or two from this travesty.'

'I'm sorry to have to inform you that a report of the goings-on here, and of your homosexuality have, today, been printed in the Lewes *Recorder*. So it's now on record, and the latter accusation is a matter to be dealt with by the police.'

Percy thumped down into his chair. 'For pity's sake!'

Clotilde rose to speak, the first time she had offered any contribution that afternoon. 'How can you say zees when you 'ave no evidence, Inspector? My poor Percy! Do you not think I would know if he was… what you are accusing him of?' She knelt down by his chair, leaning her head on his lap and taking his hand. It was a performance worthy of Lillian Gish at the picture house.

Percy stroked her hair. 'Clotilde, my love.'

'Constable, would you wait by the front door for my instructions, please?'

'Very well, Inspector.'

When he'd gone, Davis said, 'Look, I personally don't care who you have a– a liaison with, in your private lives. Whether the accusation is true or not, because it's now a matter of public record, I've got to do something. I have a couple of options for you. First, I can arrest you and let the courts decide whether Mr Cranford is lying or not. But I warn you that he apparently has a witness from this household, a member of staff.'

Lucia, Freddie, Percy and Clotilde gasped. Edie was not surprised.

'However, the Chief Constable is of the opinion that such court cases are a waste of resources in the current climate. He therefore offers an alternative.'

The other four leant forward, their expressions hopeful. Edie, however, was almost certain she knew what was coming.

'The Chief Inspector will ensure that the newspaper prints a retraction and an apology, as will Mr Cranford, on the basis that the information was incorrect and gained from a source that has been proved unreliable. If Mr Cranford doesn't agree, he will be charged with defamation.'

Percy and Freddie slumped back with a sigh. Lucia's head flopped forward, as if with relief. Only Clotilde, of the four, stared ahead with no expression, as if guessing what Edie already suspected.

'Then that is the solution,' Freddie announced.

'However,' Davis continued, 'the Chief Inspector will only ensure this is the case if you two… enlist.'

Edie had been right.

Freddie's mouth opened in shock. Percy groaned and placed his head in his hands on his lap. Lucia's hand shot to her face and her eyes closed in grief.

'To be honest, I don't think it will be too long before you have to enlist,' said the inspector. 'Word has it, that's what this national register is all about.'

'What if Freddie and Percy are conscientious objectors?' said Lucia. 'I've heard that such people are working with the medical staff, as stretcher-bearers and the like.'

'I don't think that will be acceptable in this case. They'd have to face a tribunal, and they'll still face a court case for homosexuality.'

'But—'

Freddie put his hand on Lucia's arm to silence her. 'All right, Inspector. Just tell us where to go, and when, and we'll comply. As you say, it's probably only a matter of time anyway. And to be honest, although I abhor this war, I will stand up and be counted with the rest of the men fighting, if that's what our government wants.'

'I suppose I have no choice then,' said Percy, his mouth set hard.

'Thank you, gentlemen. I think you have made the right decision.' He took a sheet of paper from a pocket inside his jacket. 'This is your nearest enlistment office.' He handed the sheet to Freddie. 'Now, I'll bid you all good day.' He lifted his homburg.

Before he had a chance to leave, Mrs Riddles ran into the room. 'Sir, My Lady, I've just caught Lottie packing her case without a by-your-leave. Reckoned she had enough money to marry her sweetheart now, so was off. She tried to get out the front door, but your constable stopped her on account I was shouting at her.'

'I think you might have your informant, Mr Moreland,' said Davis.

'Oh, Lottie!' Lucia groaned. 'How could she? I will see to this.'

'I will show you out, Inspector,' said Edie.

They walked past the crying maid, shrieking cook and an unhappy Lucia, leaving through the gate that led on to the road. The constable got into the police motor car.

'Thank you, Inspector. I understand you are in a difficult position, and although the solution is not ideal, it is a solution, all the same.'

'It gives me no satisfaction to have to deliver such an ultimatum. I have no urge to arrest men for this so-called offence. However, I am still intrigued about your situation, Miss Moore.'

'As I said, Julia will explain. But I do implore you to keep my secret, Inspector.'

'As far as I'm aware, Miss Moore, there is no law about members of the aristocracy working in a hotel. I'm sure you have your reasons. Cheerio for now.' He lifted his homburg once more.

'Farewell, Inspector.'

Edie watched the motor car drive away down the country lane. The emotion she had been bottling up since the inspector revealed his 'solution' finally burst free and tears spilled down her cheeks. Now there were three men she cared about imminently in danger. And Freddie would cope even less well with the rigour and discipline of army life than either Charlie or Daniel.

She pulled a handkerchief from her skirt pocket, to wipe the tears and blow her nose vigorously. She had a couple more hours at Bergenia Cottage. She needed to be the strong one and give what comfort she could.

Chapter Twenty-Five

A couple of weeks later, Edie was on the reception desk in the morning, with the prospect of a shift at afternoon tea later.

'There you are, sir, the key to Room 206, on the second floor.' Edie handed over the item. 'Gertrude will show you to the room and assist with the luggage. There is a lift over there, should you prefer it. Luncheon is served from twelve o'clock until one forty-five.'

By the time she'd given them this information, Gertie had picked up their cases and was leading them to the lift, probably because she preferred not to haul the luggage up two flights of stairs. Edie couldn't really blame her.

Gertrude. It still made her want to laugh. Edie had realised that must be her full name, but it didn't suit her. After a couple of weeks of being referred to as Gertie in her new role, Mr Bygrove had interfered and pronounced that the name was not 'dignified' enough. But Edie could tell that Gertie disliked her full name.

She looked over at the grandfather clock. Eleven fifteen.

'Good morning, Edie.'

'Good morning, Mrs Bygrove.'

'I thought you'd like something to read during lunch.' She held up a letter and handed it over. 'Charlie sounded a little more cheerful in this one.'

She wondered if Freddie and Charlie's paths would cross, being in the same battalion. Freddie wouldn't have a clue who Charlie was, but Charlie might guess that the Honourable

Frederick Moreland was her brother. What a strange situation it would be.

'It's good that so many of our former employees write to one or other of us, or that someone they're enlisted with does, so at least we have news of most of them.'

'I do wonder,' Edie started, but hesitated. This was her employer she was talking to, or at least, his wife.

'You wonder what, Edie?'

'Whether we should all go into more—' She was going to say 'worthwhile', but didn't want it taken the wrong way. And it wasn't quite what she meant. 'More war-related work. Mrs Pankhurst did have a point with her protest.'

'There are many women who are already in such jobs, such as the munitionettes. And we do our bit with the knitting and raising money. Perhaps we could do more of that at the hotel. There is plenty of room.' She turned in a circle, taking in the whole foyer. 'And you know, Douglas doesn't get much right, but he is correct about keeping people's spirits up.'

But only those of the upper and middle classes, thought Edie.

'Mind you, he only says that over and over because he's afraid conscription will come in and he's getting it ready as an excuse to be excluded. Sorry, I shouldn't be saying that to you and making you feel awkward,' said Helen.

'Would he have to fight at his age?'

'He's only thirty-nine. I know he behaves like a stuffy Victorian.' She laughed.

Edie raised a smile, not wanting to seem amused at her employer's expense.

'I have been wondering,' said Helen, 'about the keeping up of people's spirits, whether we could introduce some initiative, you know, to do something, for those who can't afford to stay or dine here.'

Now Edie did smile. 'You must have been reading my mind. I was thinking something very similar.'

'Then you should have said! I always welcome your contributions. We are getting some of the locally billeted officers in now, but maybe we could have an evening for the ordinary soldiers. Though I can't see Douglas wanting to pay for that.'

'We could have a charity event to raise money for it, like we do when we want to send parcels abroad to the soldiers.'

Helen clapped her hands together. 'Yes, what an excellent idea. You see, I said you'd be an asset.' She had a faraway look in her eyes as she said, 'If Douglas does ever get conscripted, and I'm left as manager, I would be more than happy to offer you the job of under-manageress.'

This prospect excited Edie, but she didn't want to seem too eager. After all, it would depend on Bygrove being sent off to war.

'Not that I'm wishing my husband away to danger.'

'No, of course not… The thing is, before I would consider such an elevated position, I do have something I should tell you. But only you, not Mr Bygrove, or anyone else. I guess today is as good a time as any.' The need to come clean to Helen had only just seized her.

'How intriguing,' she said, though she looked worried. 'Come and find me around five thirty. I've got to go and speak to Mrs Norris now.'

As Helen left, Edie wondered what on earth had possessed her. Was she ready for this confession? But Helen had been good to her, and she deserved to know the truth.

The bell on the desk was tapped twice, making Edie jump.

'Oh, Major, I'm so sorry. I was miles away.'

'That's all right, m'dear. I often feel like that myself. I just wondered if you could help me.'

'Of course, Major.'

–

Helen leant forward, placing her elbows on the desk in the office and linking her hands. She pressed her lips together, but otherwise displayed no other facial expression.

What had Helen made of her tale? Edie sat back, exhaustion enveloping her after her rushed, yet long explanation of who she was and how she came to be at the hotel. She added how Charlie had most likely left because of her confession to him.

'Well,' Helen finally said. 'I suppose I always suspected you had some breeding, and that your family had maybe found themselves in reduced circumstances, so you'd had to find work. But I'd never have guessed your actual story. How incredible.'

'I'm sorry I wasn't honest in the first place. I assumed nobody would be willing to take me on, knowing who I actually was.'

'You're probably right. Though it is strange, in a way, for you and I aren't so very different.'

'In what way?' Edie was eager to find out.

'I myself was the daughter of Sir Ronald Wright. Our family was reasonably comfortable, until my father gambled the money away and I ended up marrying Douglas, instead of someone further up society. Not that I didn't love Douglas, and he was a different man then, still ambitious, but more considerate. He was the manager of a local hotel, a much smaller one than this, though he didn't own it. We were able to buy this one with the last bit of the family fortune, the part that my mother managed to keep from my father when she sold her own late mother's substantial property.'

'So, this is your inheritance?'

'Except it's in Douglas's name, not mine.'

'Was that wise? I'm sorry, it's not my business.' It was as if the opportunity to confess had been turned around, and she was now listening to Helen's story. 'It's just that married women are now allowed to own property. Or it could have been in your joint names.'

'Douglas wouldn't hear of it. He reckoned he would be emasculated if it were in both our names. And also that my father's creditors wouldn't be able to get their hands on it.'

It sounded like Helen was trying to convince herself.

'Where are your parents now?'

'Deceased. Father wasn't only a gambler but a drinker. Since their house had to be sold and used to pay the creditors, my mother came to live here, with us. She passed away three years ago.'

'I'm sorry, Helen.'

'It's a dull story compared to yours, but I do prefer to keep it to myself. What do you think you'll do, ultimately?'

'I'm not going back. No, I'll keep on working, and who knows, one day I may find a nice man to marry. If not… I hope you'll still want me to work here.'

'Of course I will. Like I said, Edie, you're an asset. And I admire you, going out into the world on your own, when you could have simply relied on your father, or a rich husband. I had no choice about my fate, but you did.'

'I'm so relieved. Thank you, Helen.'

'And don't worry, I will say nothing to Douglas. Now, I believe you're having an early dinner, so you'd better get to the dining room.'

'First, I'd like to tell Lili my story. She's been a good friend to me.'

'Very well. I will see you later.'

–

Edie had dreaded telling Lili more than telling Helen, expecting her reaction to be similar to Charlie's, but instead, her friend had become excited.

'You mean, you mean, it's a real live "Honourable" I'm friends with?' She danced around their bedroom, singing, 'You've made my day. And it's some cheering up I need, what with Norman being sent abroad.'

If only Charlie had felt like that. But it was a relief.

'You don't mind, then, that I deceived you?'

'You could hardly have told us the truth now, could you? I presume you're telling none of them others though. Some of them wouldn't be so understanding, like.'

'No, I've only told Mrs Bygrove. She doesn't mind in the least.'

'Then why would I mind? It's like one of them novels, with people what turn out not to be who they seem.' She stopped jigging about, looking serious. 'And you know, I'm not going to judge you by your background. You can't help it if you've got the disadvantage of being brought up with posh people.' She grinned.

Edie couldn't help but laugh at the joke. 'You know what, I think you're right. I did feel at a disadvantage in many ways. Leaving Downland House, though it was scary, was liberating.'

Lili lunged at her and they hugged. 'Come on now, else we'll miss supper.'

Mrs Leggett was distributing the late post when they entered the dining room.

'There you are, ladies. You're not normally last to the table,' said Mrs Leggett. 'There's a letter for you, Miss Probert.' She handed it to Lili.

'It's Mam's writing.'

Lili put the letter away until she'd finished her meal, then fished it out of her pocket and opened the envelope, humming to herself.

Edie was chatting to Phoebe, aware that her friend had stopped humming and had slumped.

'Lili?'

'It's bad news. Mam says that my sister-in-law, Jane, has… Oh Lord, she's, she's died, of the consumption.'

Everyone around the table ceased moving or talking. All eyes were on Lili.

'Oh, no, and she's just had a babby too.' Lili pushed her plate away and lowered her head to the table, before starting to sob. 'My poor brother, Morys, what's he gonna do? How's he gonna look after baby Emily?'

Mrs Leggett left the room, soon returning with Mrs Bygrove, who took a crying Lili into the corridor. Edie followed.

'I'm so sorry, Lili,' said Helen. 'Is there anything we can do for you?'

'M-Mam says I should come home for the funeral. It's on Saturday. J-Jane wasn't just Morys's wife, she was my best friend at school.'

Helen put her arms around Lili and hugged her. 'You poor thing. It's such a wicked disease, tuberculosis. Of course you must go back for the funeral.'

'But I don't think I can afford the fare, or the time off, and you'll be even more understaffed.'

'Your welfare comes first. You can go Friday and return on Sunday.'

'What's going on here?' Bygrove barked, striding up the corridor from his office. 'Miss Probert will be going nowhere. We need every member of staff here as the committee of my golf club are coming to lunch on Saturday and will expect the best of service.'

Helen let go of Lili and stepped towards Douglas. 'And we will manage, as we always do, by swapping staff around. Lili has had a death in the family and *will* be going home for the weekend.'

'Home? To Wales?'

'Yes Douglas, to Wales. It's all decided. I will ensure that there are plenty of staff members for Saturday, don't you worry.'

He emitted something between a 'humph' and a groan, then strode on to the kitchen.

'But Mrs Bygrove, I've already said I can't afford it.'

'Don't worry about that,' said Helen. 'I will pay your fare, and I'll make sure you lose no wages. But not a word to Mr Bygrove.' She placed her forefinger to her lips.

'Thank you, thank you so much, madam.'

When Helen had gone, Lili said to Edie, 'This is too much, on top of Norman being away.'

'Do you want pudding, or shall we go for a quick walk by the sea?'

'I couldn't eat a thing. Let's walk. The sea always calms me down.' She took Edie's arm and they left promptly.

–

Edie chose not to have lunch at the hotel the following Monday, her half-day off. Instead, she went to her room to change as quickly as possible, to get out and take advantage of her free hours.

Today was her birthday, but at present only two people in her life knew that. One was Lili, who had returned from Wales yesterday, quiet and sad. She hadn't expected her to remember after her heartbreaking weekend. The other was Charlie...

She did her jacket up and lifted her handbag from the bed. About to open the door, she had to step back, as it was pushed in from the other side.

'I'm glad I caught you,' said Lili, breathless. 'With us having different shifts and mealtimes today, I was afraid I'd miss you. Should have done it first thing. Hang on.' She went to one of her drawers in the chest and took out something wrapped in tissue paper. 'Happy birthday. Sorry it's not in a fancy box.' She handed it to Edie.

'A lace handkerchief. How lovely!'

'Made the lace myself, I did. And embroidered your initial, see?'

'It's beautiful. When did you do this?'

'When we were on different break times.'

'You could do lacemaking professionally.'

'There's not much money in it. My *mamgu* used to do it. She was the one what taught me.'

'Your what?'

'*Mamgu*. Grandmother.'

'Ah. I will take it with me today.' She opened her handbag and placed it inside.

'I won't keep you. See you later.'

Edie had already decided to take a walk first, to clear her head. Later she'd have afternoon tea in the Harbour Tea Rooms. That would make up for lunch and be more like a birthday celebration. She headed out and across the common, to the promenade.

She had not been on the desk this morning, but instead had been interviewing a mix of older men and women for potential waiting staff, porters and chambermaids, with Mrs Bygrove. Mr Bygrove had gone out. How strange to think that it was only just over a year since she'd been interviewed here.

On the promenade, walking towards the pier, she took Charlie's letter to Helen from her handbag and considered sitting to read it once more. No! How many times had she read it already? She put it away. Instead, she'd distract herself with the various stalls along the beach. Maybe even go for a donkey ride. She hadn't done that since she was sixteen.

A figure darted past someone in front of her but was soon lost in the crowd. It was the second time she'd seen whoever it was. Possibly. It was a woman in a long black coat and huge hat, like the one she'd seen on the bridge when she and Charlie had taken the boat to Arundel. There were still plenty of women dressed in the late-Victorian fashions. But usually older women. She hadn't seen this woman's face, but the one on the bridge had reminded her of Pamela Brownlow, who she first shared lodgings with when she arrived in Littlehampton. Though this woman had the wrong colour hair.

She stopped to watch the children taking goat rides on the common, amid much laughter. How she wished she could return to those carefree days.

Walking on, she decided against the donkey ride. She was suffering from too much nostalgia today. Maybe it would have been better not to have come to somewhere associated with her childhood, but to have gone further afield. Then Daniel would not have discovered her and told Freddie and Lucia where she was. And she wouldn't have fallen in love with someone who didn't want to be with her.

Stop it! She was becoming maudlin.

Although the promenade was not so busy, being a Monday, the crowds thickened as she approached the pier. She had the feeling there was someone walking close behind her. She quickened her step, but still felt the presence. Perhaps the black phantom had been a ghost all along, she joked to herself.

Look behind and see. Now she was being daft. It was just somebody too close. *What if it's a pickpocket, waiting to steal your handbag?* She pulled her bag closer to her.

On the pier Edie went to the other side and stopped abruptly, hoping whoever it was would walk past, but no one did. She looked out across the river, where it entered the sea. There was nothing for it but to look back.

Close by, looking down, was the woman in black. The coat was thick wool, too warm for a sunny August day. The huge hat meant that her face was hidden. If she was to move off once more, following the river towards Pier Road, would whoever it was follow her?

About to do so and find out, a black sleeve shot out and stopped her.

'Do you mind?' Edie barked in her most affronted voice.

'Please, just talk to me awhile,' came the strained reply.

Edie pulled her wrist away. 'I'm sorry, I have to go.'

'Please!' The head went up to reveal the face and black hair. 'Please, just listen to what I have to say.'

'Oh my goodness. Pamela? It *is* you!'

Chapter Twenty-Six

Edie couldn't take it in. Pamela really was here? Had she been nearby all the time?

'Your hair, what's happened to it? It was auburn.'

'It's a wig. Let's walk.'

They carried on slowly, by the river, Pamela all the while looking around suspiciously.

'I assumed you'd be far away by now,' said Edie. 'You do know the police consider you a suspect for Mrs Hadley's death, don't you?'

'I thought the police might assume it was me, but it wasn't. I had to leave, because… because I was told to, by my sweetheart.'

'Jim?'

'Y-yes.'

'He's the other suspect.'

'Well, he did disappear, so I think he might have done it. He reckoned Mrs Hadley was an easy target to steal from.'

'No. I saw the thief from the Kursaal leave the house. I'm sure it was him.'

Pamela's eyes widened and she stopped, looking around once more. 'You're mistaken. It would have been Jim, I'm sure.'

'Where have you been?'

'Um, staying with friends. In Clymping.'

'Do they know about all this?'

'Does it matter?' She was getting irritated.

'It does if the police catch up with you.' She pointed over at South Terrace, or Empress Maud Road, as Mrs Hadley had insisted on calling her end of it, towards their old guest house.

'It's still closed up, as they've been looking for Gordon Hadley, Mrs Hadley's husband, who they reckon is still alive, despite what she claimed. Why don't you go to the police station and explain what you know? They'll find this Jim.'

Although she was still convinced it was the Kursaal thief, perhaps there was a connection between the two.

'No! They'd just arrest me. Or I'd be held as an accessory.'

'Oh Pamela, hiding away isn't helping.'

'You must earn good money at that fancy hotel. And that's an expensive handbag. Come on, you must have something you could spare me.' She tugged at Edie's bag, but she held on tight.

'Pamela!'

'I need to get away, otherwise Gordon will find me.'

'Gordon? Do you mean Jim?'

'What? Yes! Jim. I got confused because you mentioned Gordon Hadley.'

Edie took a step back from Pamela, aware they were getting curious glances. 'You need to go to the police.'

'Please don't tell them you've seen me.' Pamela linked her hands together in a pleading mode.

'Edie, is this woman bothering you?'

Pamela's eyes darted in the direction of the voice. It was Dan, of all people.

'No, no, she's an acquaintance,' Edie said brightly, 'with whom I'm catching up.'

'I must go now,' said Pamela, rushing away.

'Bye for now.' She gave a vague wave.

'Funny woman,' said Dan, drawing up beside her. 'She's young, yet dressed up as if she's older than my grandmother.'

'What on earth are you doing here, Dan?'

'Well, I've hardly deserted in uniform.' He laughed. 'I'm on leave. I'm staying with my parents, but since it's your birthday, I decided to come and see you. I went to the hotel and asked at the desk if you were around.'

'Dan, I told you *not* to do that.'

'I'm sorry, but I just *had* to. It was the same woman on the desk as the time I came before, and she remembered that I was supposedly the uncle of your old charge. She told me it was your day off and that you'd most likely be heading to the promenade. Anyway, happy birthday, Edie. Twenty-five, isn't it?'

'That's right. Look, I was heading to the Harbour Tea Rooms for afternoon tea. Are you able to join me?'

'Absolutely.'

As they took a seat in the tea rooms, Edie recalled that the last time she came here was with Charlie. Was it truly over with him? It must be, otherwise he'd have written to her.

'Is it just you on leave, or are there a few of you?' She was thinking of Charlie again.

'I dare say there'll be a few. I don't know who, though. Were there any at the hotel who are in the 11th Battalion, then?'

'Well, yes. Charlie Cobbett is in that one, along with Peter Smith and Alan Drew. Most of the others are in the other two South Downs battalions.'

'The names aren't familiar.'

Would Charlie have bothered coming to Littlehampton if he had been on leave? It wasn't like he was talking to his parents.

They chatted about his training until their order arrived.

'Dan, did you hear what happened with Freddie and Percy?'

'Yes. Freddie wrote to me. I'm sorry about the way it worked out. That Hilary Cranford deserves a punch in the face.'

'It's unusual for you to express such aggression, though I confess I feel that way too.'

'At least there was a way out, even if it wasn't ideal. A criminal record and time in prison would have ruined the pair of them.'

They'd finished the scones and cakes, being left only with their tea, when Dan piped up, nervously, with, 'I have something to say, Edie. And I want you to listen until I've finished. All right?'

'Yes, all right.'

'My father is unwell. I fear he will not last long.'

'Oh Dan, I'm so sorry.' She took his hand.

'What did I say?' He looked at her as if she were a naughty child.

'I'm sorry. Carry on.'

'You know we own much land and housing, leased to various farmers and occupants. When Father is gone, it will all pass to me. If you became my wife, you'd have money, and I would treat you well. Very well.'

She had no doubt about this, but it would always be under his rules.

'I adore you, Edie, I really do.' He took a box out of his pocket and pushed it towards her. 'Happy birthday.'

She opened the box hesitantly, suspecting she would find something she would have to give back straight away. She shut it without completing the act and put it down. 'I don't love you in the way a woman should love a husband. I do love you in a way, but as a dear, dear friend.'

'That would be a good start to any relationship. However, I think you may have mistaken my intention on this occasion. Although I'd love you to think about it, an actual wedding is not something I would consider right now, when I may be away some time. But at some point in the future, when we can do it properly.'

She lifted the box, and this time opened it fully. Inside was a pair of silver flower drop earrings with garnets. She considered giving them back for a moment, but did not want to hurt him when his intentions had been kind.

'They're lovely, Dan, thank you. They are beautiful.' It was a shame that she'd have to hide them away for the most part, maybe only taking them out to wear on days off.

'You deserve beautiful things. As for the future, I can understand why you might balk at marriage when it would limit your freedoms.'

'I don't want to do the vacuous things wives in my position normally do.'

'I'm not sure it would be any worse than being married to someone lower down in society. You'd be the housewife, the drudge, doing the chores.'

'So maybe I will never marry.'

'If you don't want to do the vacuous things, as you call them, think about what you would like to do. You'll have plenty of time while I'm away. I'm open to suggestions.'

She nodded, having nothing to add.

'I had better get back.' He looked at his wristwatch. 'There's a train soon.'

'Of course.' She rose. 'I'll walk you to the railway station.'

'No, you stay and finish your tea. And enjoy the rest of your afternoon off.'

'All right.' At least, that way, she was less likely to come across Pamela again.

–

Why had he bothered to come back here, thought Charlie, as he looked at the decorative items in the window of the fancy repository shop on Norfolk Road? He wasn't interested in anything there, just taking time to build up the courage to do something he would no doubt back out of. Again. He could have taken some leave back at Bexhill, had a walk around the town. It's not like he had anywhere to stay here. He'd probably end up getting on the train and going back to Bexhill this evening.

He'd come with the idea that he could put things right with his parents, or at least with his mother.

'Come on, Charlie boy. Just do it, or get the train back.'

'I thought it were you, Charlie,' called Mr Johnson from the dairy, as he brought his cart to a halt. 'You look right smart in your uniform.'

'Thanks, Mr Johnson.' He waved as the dairy cart drove away.

'Right.' He marched off, like he would on parade, taking the corner onto Western Road with an about-turn.

Halfway down he came to a halt, looking up at the window above his father's garage, where his family's rooms were. Should he go down the alley and knock on the door? At least his father didn't seem to be around.

He looked back down towards Norfolk Road. It might be better to forget it. He'd only be disappointed if she didn't want to see him.

'Charlie! Oh, my Charlie.'

Turning back, he spotted his mother running down the alleyway.

'Charlie!' She threw her arms around him, her head jamming into his chest. She was around a foot shorter than him. He hugged her in return.

She pulled slightly away to look him up and down. 'So you enlisted? That's where you've been some of the time?'

'Only recently. I was head porter at the Beach Hotel until June.'

'Head porter! You did do well. But you've only been around the corner, and you didn't come to see your old mum?'

'Dad said you didn't wanna see me.'

'He said that? Oh my Lord, I shall have words with him. He's out delivering a motor car back to a customer.'

'I nearly came before, in May, but I lost me nerve.'

'I wish you had. Come inside and I'll put the kettle on and you can tell me what you've been up to.'

She dragged him up the stairs, into their kitchen, pushing him into a chair. 'Now, tell me all about what you've been doing.'

He started with leaving Portsmouth and the argument with his father, then being taken on at the hotel, following it with a potted history, up to the time he'd enlisted.

'You got a sweetheart then?'

'I… sort of had one. But we parted when I enlisted.'

'That's a shame. Should be settled down by now, you should.'

'Well, I *might* go to see her. She's at the hotel too.'

They heard footsteps outside, then the door was pushed open, revealing his father. This was the bit where he got thrown out, but at least he'd got to see his mum.

'Charlie.'

'Hello, Dad.'

'You're in the army?'

'That's right.'

'Come 'ere, my boy. I'm that proud of you, enlisting to help your country.' He held out his arms.

Charlie wasn't sure about being accepted back into the fold just because he'd joined the army, but at least his father had forgiven him. He got up and put his arms around his father tentatively. His mother joined them, and all three embraced.

–

Even though it had only been two months since Charlie had been in the hotel, it felt strange. Mrs Bygrove was at the desk, head down, writing something in a register. He started off across the foyer. He probably should have gone the back way in, but blow it, he wasn't staff anymore.

'Charlie! Am I glad to see you, old chap.' The major hurried across the room and took his hand to shake it vigorously. 'You're looking dapper in your uniform.'

'Thanks, Major. We've only just got them.'

'Charlie, how lovely of you to pop in,' said Mrs Bygrove. She came out from behind the reception desk. 'Are you on leave?'

'Yep. Three days, staying with my parents.' He felt the glow that thought gave him once more.

'You've made up with them, then.'

'Yep. I'm actually looking for Edie. Is she available?'

'Saw her heading off to the beach earlier.' The major pointed his thumb in the appropriate direction.

'It's her afternoon off,' said Helen. 'And, um, another young man came in asking for her, shortly after she left. A relative of the boy she used to be governess to.'

'I'd better go. I'll come back to see everyone, probably tomorrow.'

'Come in time for early lunch and you can have some food with us.'

'Will do, Mrs B. Thanks.' He ran out of the door. With any luck he'd find Edie walking by the beach, or the river. Or maybe in the tea rooms. How long ago had she left? He should have asked.

And who was this young man? Was he actually this friend of her brother's again, or someone else? What a fool he'd been, getting cross about her secret, especially when he had a whopper of his own.

Across the common and down the prom, he couldn't believe the attention he was getting. Looks of respect from the men and admiration from the women. So different to when he'd sported a porter's uniform, or his civvies.

He passed the coastguards' cottages near the pier. Where would she be? If she'd gone into town, he'd never find her.

'All right now, Charlie boy, calm down,' he muttered to himself.

He'd walk down to the tea rooms. She liked going there, sitting watching the river. And it being her birthday, she might have gone to treat herself.

Then he remembered: that's where he'd stood her up. More fool him.

Reaching the tea rooms, he marched straight in. No point dilly-dallying.

'Charlie!'

There she was, sitting alone, no sign of this other bloke. Perhaps he hadn't found her. She rose and ran to him, stopping just short. The other customers looked on with curiosity.

'I'm *so* happy to see you,' she said.

'Me, too. I could do with a cuppa meself.'

'Sit down. We'll order another pot. If you like.'

He noticed there were already two empty cups on the table. Maybe she'd explain in a bit.

'Yep, I'd like that very much.'

Chapter Twenty-Seven

Charlie took a long draught of the tea. 'So, that Daniel bloke came to see you 'cos he has leave?'

'That's right. He has shown some interest in me, though.' She looked uncomfortable.

His breath hitched. How far had it gone?

'But I'm not interested in him, not like that. I've known him since I was a child, and I only think of him as a dear friend.'

A *dear* friend. Even so, he was jealous.

'I'm sorry, Edie, I've been a fool.'

She looked out at the rapidly moving river, causing him to do the same.

'No, Charlie, it's my fault. I couldn't have told you my story when I first came to the hotel, but I could have told it to you when we started getting involved. I *should* have told you, so you had a choice.'

'Yes, maybe when we started getting serious. But Edie, I'm just as bad. Worse.'

'What, because you left without talking to me? No, Charlie, I understand.'

'Let me finish. What you did, at least it wasn't illegal.'

'I don't follow.'

'Why would you?' This was even harder than he'd imagined. Telling himself earlier to *just get on with it* wasn't helping now. 'The reason I was in Portsmouth, well, you see—'

'Was to work. Yes, you said.'

'No, Edie. I spent two years there – in prison. That's why my father didn't want to see me. Not simply because I left his business.'

She stared at him, wide-eyed, her lips parted, such pretty lips, in an expression he couldn't fathom. Amazement? Disbelief? Disgust?

'A friend of mine, or not a friend, as it turned out, persuaded me to take part in a robbery.'

Her hand went to her mouth. 'A robbery?'

'It'd be easy, he said, to break into the business, an ironmongery that also sold all sorts of other things. Reckoned the owner kept a pile of cash in his safe, 'cos he didn't trust banks, so he'd heard from one of his staff. The owner, he weren't a nice man, always rude to customers, mean to his staff. Nasty to his wife.'

He looked at Edie, whose expression hadn't changed. He stared at his cup as he continued. 'Frank Steel, that was my accomplice's name, reckoned it'd set me up in my own garage. I thought it'd be a lark, make me some easy money and pay back Mr Billington for being a rotten human being.'

'Oh Charlie!'

'Nah, I know. It's no excuse. And nothing's that easy, is it? Just after we'd stolen the money, the police turned up. Frank scarpered with the cash, leaving me to take the consequences.'

'Didn't you tell them he was involved, too?'

He blew a breath out between his teeth. 'More than my life's worth. Nasty piece of work, is Frank Steel. Anyway, when I came out two years later, me dad refused to take me back. Neither of me parents had been to see me in prison. Mrs Bygrove took a gamble on me, said she wanted to give me a second chance, and took me on while Mr B was out, so he never knew my background. I was upfront with her, 'cos I had no reference. It worked in my favour because I was honest with her. Hmm! I should have remembered that lesson.'

'So, where is this Frank now?'

'Still around, though I didn't know that until he approached me, that day we went on the boat to Arundel. Thought he must have skipped the county, especially with that money. Then, that day I was waiting for you, at the bandstand, our last day, he turned up a bit before you did, telling me I had to help him with a job, and threatening me.'

'You should have told me then!'

'Maybe. I saw him that evening, too, in the New Inn. Dunno if he'd been following me around. He made the same threats. It was what partly persuaded me to enlist, to get out of his grasp. And I was afraid he might do the same to you, if he knew we were connected.'

'I thought I'd driven you away.' She closed her eyes as if in pain.

He caressed her hand. 'That was only partly the reason. And being in prison was the main reason I didn't rush to sign up, even if I weren't keen on the war.'

'What had prison got to do with it?'

'Made me claustrophobic, didn't it? Being locked up. The day I came out, I thought: I'm never doing nothing to put me in that position again. And when the war started, the thought of being huddled together in a hole, with a pile of other men, it sounded too much like prison. I didn't even know about the trenches at the start.'

'So that's why you reacted so badly to being locked in the store cupboard?'

'Yep.' He ended the story there, taking a few more gulps of tea, waiting for her verdict.

There was a long silence, during which she removed her hand from his and gazed at him. Was she waiting for him to tell her more? Or waiting to deliver the blow?

'Charlie.'

'Yep.' *Here it comes.*

'It doesn't make any difference to me what you've done in the past. The Charlie I know is caring and funny and wouldn't hurt a flea.'

The relief had him relaxing his muscles, which he now realised had been tensed, ready for disappointment. He grinned.

'What about handsome?' He lifted his chin and turned his head sideways in a pose.

She chuckled. 'That goes without saying.'

He took both her hands now and they considered each other for some while.

She broke the silence with, 'My brother enlisted last month.'

'He isn't by any chance the Honourable Frederick Moreland in our battalion, is he?'

'Ah, you've met him.'

'Not exactly. Seen him in training and heard the way he spoke. Then someone said he was the son of a baron. I thought they'd have been training him up as an officer.'

'Oh dear, that's another story. I dare say some of it has filtered through to the army, and that's the reason.' She frowned.

'I've got time.'

'The last time I went to visit, there was a guest there called Hilary Cranford…'

He listened, not commenting as she told him about the birthday party and the upshot of it. At the end of her tale, he shook his head and tutted. 'Them newspaper reporters should mind their own business.'

'You don't disapprove of Freddie's situation then?'

'What's it got to do with me? He hasn't done no harm to no one else, as far as I can tell. We've 'ad them in the hotel, masquerading as chums having a few days away together.'

'You can tell?'

'You get a bit of an instinct for these things in my job as a porter. Little signs. But I've never found them nothing but decent people. If you prick them, do they not bleed?'

'Shakespeare, eh?' She looked surprised.

'Here, I might be working class, but I'm not an ignoramus. I've seen a coupla Shakespeares at the theatre.'

She leant towards him and stroked his cheek. 'Charlie Cobbett, I have never thought you an ignoramus. You have more intelligence and insight than most other men I've known. And common sense.'

'Except went I went robbing a shop.'

'That's history.' She took hold of his chin and kissed him lightly on the lips.

'Do you mind?' called a middle-aged man two tables away.

The Italian manager walked by, a long white apron tied around his middle. 'I think we can let the lovebirds off thees one time, don'ta you? In these uncertain times, is good to display *l'amore*, no?'

The complainer's wife agreed. 'It's so romantic, dear, and he's clearly on leave.'

The man raised his eyes heavenward but said no more.

'That may be our cue to depart,' Charlie whispered. 'Oh, but first...' He took a small package from his pocket and put it in her hand. 'Happy birthday. Go on, open it.'

Inside was a small wooden trinket box, with a mother-of-pearl heart in the middle of the lid.

'That's beautiful. Thank you.' It would be worth a lot less than the earrings Dan had given her, but to her it was worth so much more. She kissed him once again.

'You're welcome. Let's take a walk on the promenade. I've missed that, being banged up in the camp.'

'Has it been that bad?'

'Not as bad as I thought. But then, it's just the dress rehearsal so far. Come on, I wanna forget about it for a while and enjoy my time with you.'

-

'We've come to the finish of this end of the promenade – unless you want to walk on to Rustington,' said Edie, as they reached the part where the main road curved away from South Terrace and around to follow close to the beach.

'Nah. I'd rather walk back to the pier. Take advantage of it while I'm still here.'

Edie knew he meant still on leave, but a quite different, more finite, meaning brought her down to earth.

A middle-aged gentleman strolled past whistling, sporting a nautical outfit, complete with captain's hat.

'Mr Janus! Hello there,' said Edie. 'I don't know if you remember me.'

He stopped, with some surprise on his face. 'Of course I do, Miss Moore. You were the one who helped Brenda when the thief broke into the Kursaal last year.' He came forward, hand outstretched. 'How are you m'dear?'

She shook his hand. 'Very well, thank you, sir. I found a job at the Beach Hotel.'

'A very lovely place to work. Used to come in for breakfast from time to time, but haven't done it for a while.'

'This is Charlie Cobbett. He works there, too. Or he did.'

'Ah, yes, I remember you. A porter, weren't you?'

'That was me, sir.'

'I see from your uniform that you're in the army now.'

'That's right, sir. And may I say how much I've enjoyed your shows over the years, with the Pierrots and the like.'

'Why, thank you, lad.' He shook Charlie's hand. 'Out for a walk, are you?'

'That's right,' said Edie.

'Me too. Lovely to see you again. And remember, I still owe you that favour.'

She chuckled. 'Thank you, sir. Enjoy your walk.'

'You, too.' He did a quick salute then strolled off, hand in pocket, greeting people along the way.

As they watched him walk away, Charlie said, 'Do you mind if I use the WC while we're here?' He pointed across, to part way down the road, to the public lavatories between the trees.

'Of course not. You're wriggling around like young Arthur Bygrove does.'

'Won't be long.'

'I'll wait in the first shelter back down this way.' She pointed back towards the river.

Before she reached the shelter, she took a moment to admire the sea, the sun glinting off its ripples. She perused the area, taking it all in, her world now, with the Beach Hotel prominent in the background, the bandstand beyond and further still, the coastguard station and cottages beyond the common, and the windmill. Footsteps came up behind her as she enjoyed the scene and the warmth of the sun.

She turned to say, 'You were qui—' only to find it wasn't Charlie.

She drew in a horrified gasp and went to move away, but the man there grabbed her arm and shoved something into her back.

It was the ruffian who'd robbed the Kursaal.

The one who'd almost certainly killed Mrs Hadley.

Chapter Twenty-Eight

'Ah, Charlie, didn't you find Miss Moore?'

He was coming out of the public lavatories when he spotted the major coming towards him.

'I did, thank you, Major. She's waiting for me now up on the prom.'

'Glad to hear it, old boy. So, how's the training going? I imagine it's a bit different to my training days, with all the new-fangled weapons and whatnot.'

Charlie wanted to get back to Edie quickly, but the major had been good to him over the years, giving him tips and singing his praises to the manager. The least he could do was indulge him with some information.

'Let's walk up while I tell you.'

Charlie gave him a rundown of their days at camp, but the major strolled leisurely, hands behind his back, nodding at different points.

Ah well, they'd get there eventually.

–

'Keep your gob shut, and I won't stick this in you. Been waitin' for you to be on your own.'

Edie's heart thumped as she felt the point of something against her back. Was it really a knife, or something sharp but harmless? She wasn't going to risk finding out.

'Now walk towards that shelter, and I'm warning you, if you alert anyone, it'll be the end for you.'

She walked unsteadily in the direction indicated, beads of moisture forming on her forehead. People must think them sweethearts, so close together. Once in the shelter, he stood just behind her, as she faced the sea. He stank of stale tobacco and dank sweat.

'I've been following you, waiting for this opportunity.'

How had she not spotted him? Probably the complete change of style: a smartish suit and homburg that hid his distinctive hair.

'I saw you, talking to Pamela, and knew it was you, the woman what saw me at the Kursaal, and then at Honor's.'

'Honor's?' She could barely breathe. She pressed her sweaty palms together in front of her.

'Honor Hadley, ya silly cow. Your landlady.'

Of course. She recalled the funeral. Honor Ivy Hadley. He knew her name, then.

'My good-for-nothing wife found my substantial ill-gotten gains hidden under the floorboards in our house in Southsea while I was in prison. Late wife, I should say.' He laughed darkly.

His wife? So *he* was Gordon Hadley?

'Thought she'd get away with taking the cash and moving away to buy somewhere. Guess she thought I'd never find her when I got out.'

Why was he telling her all this? She could pass it on to the police. Despite his claim that he wouldn't stab her if she kept quiet, she feared this could only be leading one way. Where was Charlie? She tried to look sideways but the blade, or whatever it was, was edged into her side, causing her momentary pain.

'I turned up at the house, three years back, but there were too many guests and she told them, and the police, I was some stranger, harassing her, so I bided my time.'

She recalled Helen saying there'd been some trouble at the guest house. Why hadn't Mrs Hadley told the police who he was? Of course: because the house had been bought with the stolen money. They'd probably have worked it out and she'd have lost it all.

The scene ahead of her, the bathers in their costumes, the children building sandcastles, blurred a little.

'I sent Pamela there, cheap tart that she was, with the promise of lots of money, so I had a way into the house. For all the good it did. There was no money left after Honor had bought that ridiculous edifice.'

'Th-the police s-said she'd left you the h-house in her will. But they c-couldn't find you.'

'She what? You're lying!'

The point jabbed at her once more and she emitted a small yelp.

'Shut up!' he growled. 'All the good it would have done me anyway, if I'd turned up to claim it. I'm sure the first thing you did was describe me to the police.'

It was true, she had, but she wasn't going to admit it. *Oh Charlie, hurry up.*

'And now I have no choice. Pamela ran away from me in Portsmouth. I had to find her. Moved in with some man, she had, in Clymping, one of her old clients. She'd become a liability. I had to get rid of her.'

Did he mean he'd killed her? That didn't bode well for her.

'You'd better do as you're told or you'll go the same way. Now come along quietly. I need a replacement for Pamela, a new whore to make money from. Jim'll meet me soon, and we'll make sure you're locked away good and proper, so there'll be no running away.'

She felt sick. If Charlie didn't come back soon she'd be gone and he might not find her. Did she have anything to lose in that case, fighting him? And it would alert others. If she wasn't killed first.

He jabbed the object, which she was convinced now was a knife, into her side once more. 'I'll put me arm around you and we'll pretend we're sweethearts. Right?'

The thought of having that relationship with him turned her stomach. He must have felt her flinch as he grabbed her around the waist with his other hand, snarling. 'You little bitch. You wait till we're alone. I'll give you more than you bargained for. Always fancied something a bit posh like you.' He pushed his groin into her hip so she could feel his arousal.

She couldn't help it; the groan of disgust left her mouth before she could stop it.

This was it; she'd gone too far. Before she knew what was going on, she'd been pushed to the ground. What was he doing to her here, in front of everyone? She was lying on the promenade, surrounded by people shouting and screaming.

'I recognise you, you scoundrel! Stay where you are!' A hand went out to help Edie up. 'Sorry, m'dear, I didn't mean to push you over, too.'

It was Mr Janus, frowning with concern.

Hadley, in kneeling position, pulled himself up. 'Dunno who you think I am, but you're—'

There was the sound of a crack. She thought at first that she might have broken her knee or elbow, but nothing hurt. There was just a dizziness.

'You bastard! You'd try to harm my girl?'

What? What? She was confused. Gordon Hadley was on the floor, whimpering. She looked up to see Charlie, clutching his own fist, screwing his face up in pain. He must have punched Hadley. He delivered an almighty kick to the man's stomach.

Mr Janus took Charlie's arm. 'That's enough, lad, though I understand why you'd want to knock seven bells out of him.'

The major came running towards them, lithe for his age. 'Miss Moore, are you all right?'

'Yes, yes, Major.' She straightened her back. 'Charlie, thank goodness. It's the man who killed Mrs Hadley, the one I saw robbing the Kursaal.'

'Yes, I recognise him from the robbery,' said Mr Janus.

'And it turns out it's… it's her husband, Gordon Hadley.'

She ran out of breath and stumbled forward. Charlie caught her and held her to him. 'Someone get the police,' he said.

'I'll go back to the hotel and get them to ring the station.'

'Thank you, Major,' said Charlie.

'And I'll stay with you,' said Mr Janus. 'If he comes to, he'll have Private Cobbett here and me to contend with.'

'Are you sure you're all right, Edie?' Charlie held her closer to him.

'I am now, Charlie, I am now.'

–

Edie sat in the staff dining room at the hotel, Charlie and Mrs Bygrove standing behind her. Detective Inspector Davis and Sergeant Gardner sat on the other side of the table from her. She'd told them all she knew.

'So you think he did away with Miss Brownlow?' said Davis.

'He certainly made it sound that way, Inspector.'

'We shall comb the area for her, since it's likely she'll be nearby.' Davis rose and put his notebook back in his pocket. 'And don't worry, Miss Moore, Gordon Hadley will be going away for a long time. He'll be granted no bail, I'll make sure of that.' He considered Charlie. 'And well done, Private Cobbett, for being brave enough to tackle the rogue. I dare say you'll be an asset to the army.'

'Thank you, sir.' Charlie saluted him. 'Mr Janus played his part, too.'

'I know. And his identification of Hadley as the Kursaal thief will certainly help.'

After Davis and Gardner left, Helen said, 'Sit down, Charlie. You two could do with a little something for the shock. I shall fetch you both a large brandy.'

'Thank you, Mrs B,' Charlie called.

Edie only smiled, not liking to admit that she wasn't fond of the spirit.

As Helen left, Richard Watkins stuck his head around the door. 'Just heard all about it. Hope you're all right, Miss Moore. Well done, Mr Cobbett. You're something of a hero.'

When he'd gone, Charlie shook his head. 'Well, there's a first for everything. What's happened to that miserable old blighter?'

'He's all right when you get to know him.'

Charlie looked unconvinced, his forehead crinkled. 'Watkins?'

'He just needs a few kind words – like most people. His mother has been ill and I've asked after her. He's appreciated it and been very nice to me since.'

'Miracles will never cease!'

–

An hour later, as Lili was laying up the staff table for early dinner, fussing around Edie at the same time, Mrs Bygrove led Inspector Davis and the Sergeant back into the room. Julia, just behind them, ran past to hug Edie. 'You poor thing!' She sat next to her, on the other side from Charlie.

'I'm afraid to inform you that we found Miss Brownlow,' said Davis.

The way he said it, Edie knew he didn't mean alive and well.

'She was in the alley, behind Pier Road.'

A cold shiver ran through her. It might even have happened while she was in the tea rooms, not many yards away.

'I have to apologise to you, Miss Moore,' said Davis. 'For doubting your word after Mrs Hadley was killed. If we'd done a little more digging at the time, as we have now, we would have found that Gordon Hadley had been in prison in Portsmouth, like he told you.'

Charlie looked awkward. She took his hand.

'Of course,' said Sergeant Gardner, 'not everyone who ends up in prison is a bad 'un at heart. Sometimes they just take a wrong turn.' He glanced at Charlie.

'Quite so,' said Davis.

'But Hadley was a bad 'un. His last spell in prison was for robbery, but he'd been in before, twice, for aggravated assault.'

'Will I have to come and identify Pamela?' Edie asked.

'No, I'll do that,' said Julia. 'You've been through enough today.'

The door flew open and in charged Fanny, brandishing a bunch of letters in one hand, tied with a ribbon. Gertie came up behind her, followed by Mrs Leggett. Edie recognised the letters at once.

'I knew it! So the police have come to arrest you for pretending to be someone you're not,' Fanny shouted in triumph. 'These letters prove it.'

Gertie pulled on her shoulder. 'Stop it, Fanny.'

'No, I won't. She's the daughter of a lord and is probably here to spy on us. See, Charlie, you should keep well away from her.'

'Oh, that?' He shrugged. 'Known about that for ages, I 'ave. I'm no snob. She can't 'elp it if she's had a disadvantage in life.'

'But, but—' Fanny looked around at the others in turn, as if to get their support.

'Don't look at me,' said Lili. 'Edie told me, oh, ages ago.'

'I already know, too,' Helen admitted. 'And I think you have some explaining to do.'

'Inspector, surely—' Fanny started.

'That's old news,' said Davis. 'And what exactly do you imagine I would arrest Miss Moore for?'

'Impersonating, well, someone ordinary.'

'That's not a crime.'

Fanny looked behind at Gertie, who was removing her porter's hat.

'To be honest, Fanny, does it matter? Edie's been a good worker and has never looked down at us, even if we haven't always been nice to her. Now give 'er the letters back.'

'Don't think I will.' She placed them into her armpit.

Mrs Leggett came forward and wrangled them off her. When she'd succeeded, she placed them in front of Edie. 'Fanny, you have been warned about taking things from people's rooms. If Mrs Bygrove has faith in Edie, then that's good enough for me. You should be fired, but that's up to Mrs Bygrove.'

Mrs Bygrove, not Mr? The housekeeper had certainly changed her tune.

'What do you want to do, Edie?' Helen asked her.

'Fanny is a good worker. I think she should have *one* more chance, especially as we're short of staff, but she really has got to be honest and not underhand anymore.'

'I agree. Do you hear that, Fanny?'

'Yes,' she said glumly, before exiting the room.

Edie felt the relief of people knowing at last. Well, maybe not quite everyone yet, but they soon would. And the people who mattered were on her side. She could move on now, from feeling that there was always someone going to find her out.

'I'm glad that's sorted,' said Gertie. 'It's about time we served supper, innit?'

'I think that's our cue to leave,' said Davis.

About to leave the room, the pair of them stepped back as Phoebe rushed in.

'Mrs Bygrove, there's a Lord and Lady Moreland in reception, and they want to see Edie.'

Chapter Twenty-Nine

'Here she is, at last.' Lady Agnes Moreland stepped away from the window as Edie closed the door to the private dining room. 'Go and pack, Edith. You're coming home.'

'So, you found me.'

'Frederick told us,' said Lord Howard Moreland, leaning against the wall in a pinstriped three-piece suit. 'He felt, things being as they are, that we should know.'

Whatever that meant. It wasn't as if 'things' had changed since she'd run away. Unless Freddie was referring to his own situation.

'Yes, Frederick is in the army now,' said Agnes. 'Probably the best place for him, given what was put in that shabby local newspaper. Oh, we heard. Several people delighted in telling us. At least the newspaper apologised and sacked that reprobate, Hilary Cranford.' She pursed her lips as she brushed who knew what from her striped silk dress. She was dressed fashionably, as always, sporting a turban-style hat with tiny velvet pansies and ostrich feather tips. 'Though running away to the army is only going to serve to make him look guilty.'

Cranford had been dismissed then. Served him right. It sounded like her mother knew nothing of the choices given to Freddie by DI Davis. She wondered what exactly he and Lucia had told her parents.

'Not that I ever liked that Percival Challen. Too avant-garde and unconventional. Too bohemian. It's probably his fault the rumours spread in the first place.'

'Mother, they are all "bohemian". That's the crowd they mix with.'

'They're setting a bad example, the lot of them, making the upper classes look... irresponsible. Now Frederick and Percival have gone, I shall endeavour to prise Lucia away from that crowd. And from that Mademoiselle Clotilde Dubois. She's a bad influence. Now get your things and be quick about it.'

Her father had said nothing since his initial sentence. Mother had taken over, as usual.

'Mama, I have a life here now, which I find more rewarding than my life with you.'

'Do – not – be – ridiculous! Of course it's not more rewarding. Howard, tell her.'

'Edith, come along now. Your mother is right, this charade is ludicrous.'

'We do not want to get the police involved.' Agnes came towards her and went to grab her arm, but Edie darted away.

'By all means, you can try. I think they're still here, on another matter. I'm sure they'd be happy to help you force me to go. After all, we all know there's a law about an adult leaving the family home.'

'Your sarcasm is not appreciated!'

'Anyway, Detective Inspector Davis already knows who I am and why I'm here, and he hasn't felt the need to arrest me thus far.'

'We will get the doctors to say you are not in your right mind then.'

'You see, this is a perfect example of why I left home in the first place.'

The door opened. Edie was relieved to see Victoria Harrison, her former governess, enter the room.

'Miss Langley, what on earth are *you* doing here?' said Agnes. 'This is a private matter.'

'I came to leave something for Edie, but when Mrs Bygrove told me you were here, I thought I had better make sure everything was all right.'

'So even *you* knew she was in this godforsaken place? You should have told us.'

'It is far from being a *godforsaken place*. And since you're not fond of keeping in touch with old staff, to the point that you didn't give my letters to Edie, I don't see why I would have told you.'

'Now you're here, tell her to come to her senses. She always took more notice of you and Nanny Street than me. She's a Moreland, a member of the aristocracy. It is unthinkable that she should live like this any longer.'

Victoria put a wrapped present on one of the tables and went to Edie, putting an arm through hers. 'Why not? After all, Lady Moreland, you set a precedent, did you not, in changing your life and your station?'

This was going very differently to the way Edie had expected. 'What do you mean?'

Agnes waved the words away. 'Do not listen to her ravings. Always a little too free she was, with her affection for the children, and lacking in discipline. And always inclined to take your sides, just like Nanny Street.'

'And you, Mama, were a little too mean with your affections, and too harsh in your discipline. Now, would someone tell me what this changing life and station thing is about?'

'Do you want to tell her?' said Victoria. 'I think it's about time someone did. After all, there are other people who know. How do you think I found out? Gossip among the staff, who know the staff of people who are aware of your history. Someone is bound to tell her one day.'

Agnes turned her back on them. Howard leant up from the wall and walked to the middle of the room.

'It's better that she hears it from us,' he said. 'Miss Langley is right. Someone is bound to mention it to her one day.'

Agnes did not move.

'Very well, I suppose it had better be me.'

'No, Howard.'

'Yes, Agnes. We have no choice now anyway... Your mother was originally from farming stock. They worked a farm, north of Rustington. As a young woman, seventeen, I think, wasn't it, dear?'

Her mother was from around here? She'd claimed to be from Petworth, and that all her family had passed on.

Agnes remained silent.

'Yes, I'm sure it was seventeen. She caught the eye of a solicitor in Littlehampton, in his thirties, well established, nicely off. They married, but he was killed in a freak accident after only two months of marriage.'

Her mother went back to the window, putting a hand up against it as she stared out. Edie wondered if she'd loved the man, or whether it had been about security.

'She inherited everything and sold the business. She then married a shipyard owner, Oliver Haydon.'

'Haydon?' Edie interrupted. 'A couple of the guests, the Perrymans, once told me I reminded them of an Agnes Haydon. That was you? And they now own Haydon's.'

'That's right,' said Howard. 'How strange they should remember your mother after all this time. Oliver Haydon was forty when they married. He died two years later, of a heart attack.'

Edie did a quick calculation. Her mother would only have been, what, twenty-one or twenty-two by then.

'Again, she inherited the business, and it was through it that we met. She offered to sell it to me as I had a timber business that was already selling wood to Haydon's, but I didn't want it. But I did want to marry her.'

He went to the window, placing a hand on Agnes's shoulder. 'I found a buyer for her – the Perrymans, of course. We married and had you and Frederick.'

A meteoric rise indeed, thought Edie. Farmer's daughter to a baroness in five years.

Now Agnes did turn, removing Howard's hand from her shoulder. 'And I didn't go through all that just to let my daughter go backwards and ruin her life. Or my son. I didn't bring you both up for that.'

'Brought us up?' said Edie. 'Nanny and Victoria – who is actually Mrs Harrison now, by the way – brought us up.'

'In that case, it is maybe her fault that you both turned out the way you did, you with your socialist ideas, and Frederick a bohemian.'

'You give me far too much credit, Lady Moreland,' said Victoria. 'And Freddie is still your son. It's not as if he's killed anyone, or stolen money. Even if the claim is true, all he would have done is love another man.'

'Exactly! Poor Lucia. It's her I feel sorry for. And her so rich she could have had anyone.'

Edie and Victoria glanced at each other. Her mother was clearly ignorant of the whole situation, but then, only Freddie and Percy had been exposed in the newspaper.

'Enough of this! You will pack your bag and return home with us. You can leave most of these – *clothes* – behind. We will buy you some of the latest fashions in Brighton.'

Edie considered her mother. How best to bring this situation to an end?

–

Charlie stood to attention, next to the wall in the foyer, close to the door of the private dining room, as if on guard. It was probably the uniform that had prevented Bygrove from telling him to get lost when he'd come across him. At least Mrs Bygrove was on reception, maybe to keep an eye on the situation with Edie.

He couldn't hear anything from out here, and didn't want to. It was Edie's business. He was surprised there hadn't been more of a scene, though there was still time.

A few of the regular guests passed through, greeting him with surprise. They asked how he was, and a couple of the women told him how handsome he looked in uniform. Even in here the tables had been turned, with all the respect and admiration being given to him.

Mrs Harrison, a friend of Edie's, who he now knew had been her governess when she was young, came into the hotel and went over to the desk. Charlie could see Mrs Bygrove was explaining things to her with frantic hand gestures, before pointing to the dining room. Mrs Harrison hurried over, glancing at him with a worried expression as she entered the room.

He could hear distant voices, but nothing clear enough to make out what was being said. What would be the upshot of all this? Despite what Edie had said to him, would she go back to her old life, for they were surely here to fetch her back?

His spirit sank. After all that had happened today, getting Edie back, he couldn't bear the thought of losing her again. He felt a tingling at the top of his nose, sniffing it back and giving a little cough. *Not here, Charlie boy, not here.*

–

There was only one way to do this, thought Edie. Short and to the point. 'No, Mother, I am not coming home, and that is *that*.'

'You should be proud of what Edie has achieved,' said Victoria. 'You might think it's the opposite of what you did, but all she's doing is starting at the bottom and rising on her own merits. Mrs Bygrove here has even told her she might become under-manageress if Mr Bygrove has to enlist, isn't that right?'

Edie had told Victoria this the last time they'd met for tea. 'Yes, it is a possibility.'

'She's a chip off the old block, I'd say. And all done *without* a man, I have to add.'

'You have one more chance,' said Agnes, ignoring Victoria. 'Come home now or forever be an outcast.'

'Agnes!' said her father.

'No, Howard. I am not having it. She will be dead to us if she refuses.'

When Edie didn't budge, Agnes strode past her and left the room.

Her father followed, but before leaving, said, 'You won't be dead to me, Edith. But do think about your future. What can you achieve here, ultimately? If you want to do something, like help with the war effort, I will support you. I can understand why you don't want to sit around all day looking pretty, for you have a brain in that head. It's a shame you are a woman, for you would have made a better prospect as a future owner of the timber business than Freddie.'

He waited for her to speak, but she said nothing.

'Farewell, Edith. For now. I think one day you will come round, when you realise what you are missing.' He left.

Although Edie felt a hole where her family had been, she knew she'd have been emptier still had she gone with them.

–

The door opened and Charlie stood straighter, inching a little closer. Lady Moreland exited. She twisted her head towards him. She looked him up and down, her expression suggesting she'd swallowed some sour milk. Did she know about him? Unlikely, as he'd probably have been given what for by now.

'Who do you think you are looking at, Private? Don't be so impertinent.'

He was unsure how to react to that, after all the admiration that had come his way today. It proved you shouldn't take anything for granted. But he was darned if he was going to apologise, even if she was Edie's mother. No wonder she'd run away.

Lady Moreland moved on, followed not long after by Lord Moreland, who looked too preoccupied to notice him. When they'd left the hotel, he went into the room.

'I'll leave you to it,' said Mrs Harrison. 'There's your present, Edie. Open it when you feel more in the mood. Happy birthday, anyway.'

As soon as she'd gone, Edie ran to Charlie, which wasn't what he was expecting at all. She threw her arms around him. He hugged her in return.

'I suppose they've come to fetch you home?'

'Yes. Freddie told them where I was. I think he thought he was helping. Again.'

'Are you going?'

She leant back a little. 'I'm still here, aren't I, Charlie?'

'Don't mean you're not going to pack and follow on.'

'Of course I'm not. Oh, Charlie, I don't think they even remembered it was my birthday. Not even when Victoria came in with a gift.'

'So, you're staying? Yer not going home?'

'Charlie, this is home. *You* are my home.'

'Aw, you've made me come over all unnecessary.'

'Well, when you return to being necessary again, maybe you'd like to kiss me?'

'Your wish is my command, the Honourable Edith Moreland.'

Epilogue

19th August 1915

Three days later, Edie and Charlie were walking onto a platform at Littlehampton railway station. As they reached halfway down, the train came chuffing in, the smoke puffing and billowing from the engine's chimney.

'It's strange, coming here to see you off. It's where my new adventure began. I might even have come in on this train. And now, you'll be leaving on it.'

'Yep, but not for good, I 'ope. I'm not going to start a new life, just to have a little interlude in my present one. And I'll be back 'ere on my next leave.'

'It was good to meet your parents. I'm not sure what they made of me, mind. We will have to tell them sometime, about my background.'

'I know. Maybe next time. Or the one after that. But they was impressed with you. "Done yourself proud there," my dad said. And me mum thought you very sweet and proper. "Like a lady," she said. Hah, if she only knew!' He chuckled.

Happiness welled up inside her. 'That's a good start, that they liked me.'

The train hissed to a halt and Charlie got in. He pulled down the window and leant out. 'You will write to me, won't you?'

'You know I will. It'll be good to get a letter actually from you, not just be passed the ones you send to Mrs Bygrove.'

'She passed them on to you?'

'I have them all, and I've read them over and over. It was a way to get close to you.'

'Aw, I'm touched.'

The guard walked down the platform, closing doors, peering up and down to make sure everyone had got on.

'Here, quick,' said Charlie. He put a hand around the back of her neck and kissed her. Both savoured the moment until the whistle blew.

Edie stepped back to watch the train start its slow chug out of the station. She waved. 'Bye bye, Charlie. I love you!'

'Now ya tell me!' he laughed. 'I love you, too. Take care.'

'And you,' she shouted. She blew him a kiss and he did likewise.

As the train left the station, Charlie pulled back and disappeared. Edie kept waving until the train was no longer in sight.

'Farewell, my love, take care,' she whispered. 'Until we meet again.'

A letter from Francesca

Thank you to all the readers who've sent lovely messages regarding my *Wartime in the Valleys* series. After setting a series in my mother's part of Wales, I decided to move down to the English south coast and set one where I was brought up.

I was born in Worthing, in West Sussex, but we moved to Littlehampton when I was three. My father had a seaside restaurant on Pier Road, a street my main character, Edie, walked down, the day she reached Littlehampton. That end of Pier Road, in 1914, with its row of cottages, looked quite different to how it does now. Those buildings were pulled down in the late 1920s and were rebuilt as they are today, consisting of restaurants and gift shops. The Harbour Tea Rooms occupied approximately the same space as my father's restaurant, which is now Osca's Fish and Chips.

The inspiration for the novel, however, came from some old photographs I happened upon, of the Beach Hotel from the early part of the twentieth century. I remember the hotel in my teens, standing as a grand edifice on South Terrace, overlooking the common and the beach. I never ventured inside, not having any reason to, but often wondered what it was like. In the late 1980s it was pulled down and replaced by a crescent of flats.

There's little evidence today, of what the interior of the hotel looked like during the early part of the twentieth century. The descriptions in the novel are mostly my own imagination, with a little help from the 1911 census, an interview with the owner from the 1950s and accounts of similar settings of the time.

I hope you've enjoyed your visit to the Beach Hotel and come to stay again when the second book in the series is published later in the year.

Best wishes

Francesca xx

Acknowledgments

A big thank you to Keshini Naidoo, at Hera Books for having faith in my new series, and to the editors whose editing skills I much appreciate.

Cheers to my friends who've been a great support network, particularly fellow authors Elaine Roberts and Angela Johnson. Thanks, as always, to the Romantic Novelists' Association, which has been instrumental in my writing journey.

And last, but not least, thank you to my children, Carmela, Peter, Giovanna and Jack for all their encouragement.